PRACTICE FOR ADVANCED MATHEMATICS



# PURE MATHEMATICS

K. M. MORELY

Hodder & Stoughton

A MEMBER OF THE HODDER HEADLINE GROUP

Orders: please contact Bookpoint Ltd, 39 Milton Park, Abingdon, Oxon OX14 4TD. Telephone: (44) 01235 400414, Fax: (44) 01235 400454. Lines are open from 9.00–6.00, Monday to Saturday, with a 24 hour message answering service. Email address: orders@bookpoint.co.uk

*British Library Cataloguing in Publication Data*
A catalogue record for this title is available from The British Library

ISBN 0 340 701 676

First published 1999

| | |
|---|---|
| Impression number | 10 9 8 7 6 5 4 3 2 1 |
| Year | 2004 2003 2002 2001 2000 1999 |




Cover photo from Tony Stone Images

Cover design by Liz Rowe.
Page design by Lynda King.
Illustrations by Jeff Edwards.

Typeset by Wearset, Boldon, Tyne and Wear.
Printed in Great Britain for Hodder & Stoughton Educational, a division of Hodder Headline Plc, 338 Euston Road, London NW1 3BH by Scotprint, Musselburgh, Scotland.

# INTRODUCTION

*Practice for Advanced Mathematics: Pure Mathematics* provides an extensive bank of graded practice questions for the aspiring AS or A level mathematics student.

It is not a teaching book and I am assuming that the book will be used to support taught lessons and also as an aid for both revision and consolidation. Each topic is introduced with a short statement of key points followed by some worked examples.

The exercises contain three types of questions. The **A** questions are fairly routine and the **B** questions are rather more demanding. At the end of each chapter is a set of **C** questions which are of A level standard; some are short, some are long and some are quite difficult. I hope that you find the questions useful and perhaps even enjoyable and entertaining.

I assume that you have the use of at least a scientific calculator but preferably a graphical calculator to help you answer the questions. Some answers are given in exact form, some are given to a required degree of accuracy and some are given to a sensible degree of accuracy.

The writing of this book has been a stimulating experience for both my colleague, Don Brownlow, and myself. It has been very much a team effort and many long evenings have been spent in argument and discussion. Without Don's help and support this book could not have been written and I am extremely grateful for his unstinting help and encouragement throughout.

K.M. Morley, March 1999

# CONTENTS

# Chapter 1

## BASIC ALGEBRA

## 1.1 Polynomials

### Key points

A **polynomial of degree 2** is a quadratic expression such as $2x^2 - 3x + 1$.
A **polynomial of degree 3** is a cubic expression such as $4x^3 + 7x^2 - 8x + 1$.
You need to be able to combine these expressions in various ways.

### Example 1

(a) Work out the brackets and simplify
$(x + 3)(2x - 5)^2$

(b) Simplify $\dfrac{x^3 - 16x}{x^2 + 4x}$

### Solution

(a) $(x + 3)(2x - 5)^2$
$\equiv (x + 3)(4x^2 - 20x + 25)$
$\equiv x(4x^2 - 20x + 25) + 3(4x^2 - 20x + 25)$
$\equiv 4x^3 - 20x^2 + 25x + 12x^2 - 60x + 75$
$\equiv 4x^3 - 8x^2 - 35x + 75$

Work out the second bracket

No further simplification is possible

(b) $\dfrac{x^3 - 16x}{x^2 + 4x} \equiv \dfrac{x(x^2 - 16)}{x(x + 4)}$

Look for factors

$\equiv \dfrac{x(x - 4)(x + 4)}{x(x + 4)}$

Look again

$\equiv \dfrac{x - 4}{1} \equiv x - 4$

### Example 2

(a) Find $\dfrac{1}{a} + \dfrac{1}{b}$ as a single fraction.

(b) Write $\dfrac{x}{x+3} - \dfrac{5}{x(x+1)}$ as a single fraction.

(c) Divide $x^3 + 4x^2 - 4x + 2$ by $(x + 2)$.

**Solution**

(a) $$\frac{1}{a} + \frac{1}{b} \equiv \frac{b}{ab} + \frac{a}{ab} \equiv \frac{b+a}{ab}$$

(b) $$\frac{x}{x+3} - \frac{5}{x(x+1)} \equiv \frac{x^2(x+1)}{x(x+3)(x+1)} - \frac{5(x+3)}{x(x+3)(x+1)}$$

$$\equiv \frac{x^2(x+1) - 5(x+3)}{x(x+3)(x+1)}$$

$$\equiv \frac{x^3 + x^2 - 5x - 15}{x(x+3)(x+1)}$$

(c)

$$\begin{array}{r}
x^2 + 2x - 8 \\
x + 2\,\overline{)\,x^3 + 4x^2 - 4x + 2} \\
x^3 + 2x^2 \qquad\qquad \\
\hline
2x^2 - 4x + 2 \\
2x^2 + 4x \qquad \\
\hline
-8x + 2 \\
-8x - 16 \\
\hline
18 \\
\hline
\end{array}$$

$x^2$ lots of $x + 2$

$2x$ lots of $x + 2$

$-8$ lots of $x + 2$

So $$\frac{x^3 + 4x^2 - 4x^2 + 2}{x+2} \equiv x^2 + 2x - 8 + \frac{18}{x+2}$$

An alternative, more direct method:

$x^3 + 4x^2 - 4x + 2$

Take out factors of $(x + 2)$ and see what you get

$\equiv x^2(x + 2) + 2x^2 - 4x + 2$

$\equiv x^2(x + 2) + 2x(x + 2) - 8x + 2$

$\equiv x^2(x + 2) + 2x(x + 2) - 8(x + 2) + 18$

Now if you divide by $(x + 2)$ you get

$$x^2 + 2x - 8 + \frac{18}{x+2}$$

## Exercise 1.1

In **A1** to **A6** expand and simplify, giving your answers in descending powers of $x$.

**A1** $(x+2)(2x^2-3x+4)$

**A2** $(2x-3)(x^3-2x-5)$

**A3** $(2x-3)^3$

**A4** $(x^2-3)(x^2-3x+2)$

**A5** $(x+1)(2x-3)(x-2)$

**A6** $(x-2)(x+1)^2(x+2)$

In **A7** to **A10** simplify

**A7** $(x^2+4x+3) \div (x-3)$

**A8** $(x^3-9x) \div (x-3)$

**A9** $\dfrac{x^2+6x+9}{x^2-9}$

**A10** $\dfrac{x^2-x-6}{4-x^2}$

Simplify the following:

**B1** $\dfrac{2}{3x-6} - \dfrac{3}{4x-8}$

**B2** $\dfrac{2}{x-3} - \dfrac{1}{2x^2-6x}$

**B3** $\dfrac{3}{x+2} + \dfrac{2}{x^2+4x+4}$

**B4** $\dfrac{2}{9-x^2} - \dfrac{1}{x^2+6x+9}$

**B5** $\dfrac{x+2}{x^2-3x+2} - \dfrac{x+1}{x^2+x-6}$

**B6** $\dfrac{x^2-4}{x^2-2x+1} \times \dfrac{x^2-x}{x^2-4x+4}$

**B7** $\dfrac{x^3-4x}{1-x^2} \div \dfrac{x^3+2x^2}{x^2+2x+1}$

**B8** $\dfrac{x^2(2x+5)-3x(2x+5)+4(2x+5)-3}{2x+5}$

**B9** $(x^3-3x^2-6x-9) \div (x-3)$

**B10** Divide $2x^3-3x^2+7$ by $(x-2)$

## 1.2 SURDS

### Key points

A **surd** is an expression of type $a + b\sqrt{c}$ where $c$ is not a perfect square.

The most useful fact about surds is

$$(a + b\sqrt{c})(a - b\sqrt{c}) \equiv a^2 - b^2c$$

So, for example $(2 + 3\sqrt{5})(2 - 3\sqrt{5}) = 4 - 45 = -41$

### Example 1

(a) Make the denominator into an integer for $\dfrac{2+\sqrt{3}}{5-3\sqrt{3}}$

(b) Simplify $\dfrac{4}{3 - 2\sqrt{2}} - \dfrac{3}{\sqrt{2} + 1}$

### Solution

(a) $(5 - 3\sqrt{3})(5 + 3\sqrt{3}) = 25 - 27 = -2$

Using the useful fact from Key points

$$\frac{2 + \sqrt{3}}{5 - 3\sqrt{3}} = \frac{2 + \sqrt{3}}{5 - 3\sqrt{3}} \times \frac{5 + 3\sqrt{3}}{5 + 3\sqrt{3}}$$

Multiplying top and bottom of a fraction by the same number doesn't change its value

$$= \frac{10 + 6\sqrt{3} + 5\sqrt{3} + 9}{-2}$$

$$= \frac{19 + 11\sqrt{3}}{-2}$$

An integer denominator

(b) $$\frac{4}{3 - 2\sqrt{2}} - \frac{3}{\sqrt{2} + 1}$$

**'Common denominator' method**

$$= \frac{4(\sqrt{2} + 1) - 3(3 - 2\sqrt{2})}{(3 - 2\sqrt{2})(\sqrt{2} + 1)}$$

$$= \frac{4\sqrt{2} + 4 - 9 + 6\sqrt{2}}{3\sqrt{2} + 3 - 4 - 2\sqrt{2}}$$

$$= \frac{10\sqrt{2} - 5}{-1 + \sqrt{2}}$$

$$= \frac{(10\sqrt{2} - 5)}{(-1 + \sqrt{2})} \times \frac{(-1 - \sqrt{2})}{(-1 - \sqrt{2})}$$

$$= \frac{-10\sqrt{2} - 20 + 5 + 5\sqrt{2}}{+1 - 2}$$

$$= \frac{-5\sqrt{2} - 15}{-1} = 5\sqrt{2} + 15$$

$$= 5(3 + \sqrt{2})$$

**'Make both denominators into integers' method**

$$= \frac{4(3 + 2\sqrt{2})}{(3 - 2\sqrt{2})(3 + 2\sqrt{2})} - \frac{3(\sqrt{2} - 1)}{(\sqrt{2} + 1)(\sqrt{2} - 1)}$$

$$= \frac{(12 + 8\sqrt{2})}{9 - 8} - \frac{(3\sqrt{2} - 3)}{2 - 1}$$

$$= (12 + 8\sqrt{2}) - (3\sqrt{2} - 3)$$

$$= 12 + 8\sqrt{2} - 3\sqrt{2} + 3$$

$$= 15 + 5\sqrt{2}$$

$$= 5(3 + \sqrt{2})$$

In this example, this method is quicker and easier

## Exercise 1.2

**A1** Simplify:

(a) $\sqrt{48}$

(b) $\sqrt{162}$

(c) $\sqrt{800}$

(d) $\sqrt{84}$

## Exercise 1.2 *continued*

**A2** Rationalise the denominator

(a) $\dfrac{1}{\sqrt{3}}$

(b) $\dfrac{2}{\sqrt{2}}$

(c) $\dfrac{5}{2\sqrt{2}}$

(d) $\dfrac{5}{5\sqrt{5}}$

**A3** Work out

(a) $(8 + 5\sqrt{3})(8 - 5\sqrt{3})$

(b) $(7 - \sqrt{2})(7 + \sqrt{2})$

**A4** Simplify

(a) $(2 + \sqrt{3})^2$

(b) $(6 - 5\sqrt{2})^2$

**A5** Work out $(4 - 3\sqrt{5})(7 - 8\sqrt{5})$

**B1** Simplify and rationalise the denominator

(a) $\dfrac{1}{2\sqrt{3}} - \dfrac{1}{\sqrt{3}}$

(b) $\dfrac{2}{\sqrt{5}} - \dfrac{3}{4\sqrt{5}}$

**B2** Make the denominator into an integer

(a) $\dfrac{2 + \sqrt{5}}{3 - 2\sqrt{5}}$

(b) $\dfrac{5 - 2\sqrt{7}}{4 - \sqrt{7}}$

**B3** If $\dfrac{1}{2\sqrt{20}} - \dfrac{1}{3\sqrt{5}} = k\sqrt{5}$ find the value of $k$.

**B4** Express $\dfrac{2 + \sqrt{2}}{(1 - \sqrt{2})(2 - \sqrt{2})}$ in the form $a + b\sqrt{2}$ here $a$ and $b$ are integers.

**B5** If $a = 1 - \sqrt{2}$, $b = 1 + \sqrt{2}$ and $\dfrac{1}{a} - \dfrac{1}{b} = p\sqrt{q}$ find the integer values of $p$ and $q$.

## 1.3 Quadratic equations

### Key points

If $(x - a)(x - b) = 0$, then $x = a$ or $x = b$.

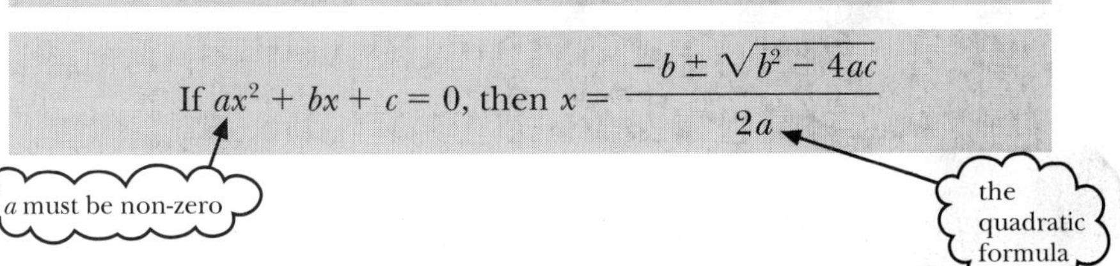


The main points to remember are

- Factorise if possible
- Completing the square may be convenient
- The formula will always work if $b^2 - 4ac \geq 0$

## Example 1

Solve where possible

(a) $x^2 - 5x = 0$ (b) $x^2 - 5 = 0$

(c) $x^2 - 4x - 396 = 0$ (d) $x^2 + 4 = 0$

### Solution

(a) $x^2 - 5x = 0$ ← Don't write $x^2 = 5x \Rightarrow x = 5$ or you miss a solution

$x(x - 5) = 0$

$x = 0,\ x = 5$

(b) $x^2 - 5 = 0$

$x^2 = 5$

$x = \pm\sqrt{5}$ ← Remember both square roots

(c) $x^2 - 4x - 396 = 0$

$x^2 - 4x + 4 = 400$

$(x - 2)^2 = 400$

$x - 2 = \pm 20$

$x = 22, -18$ ← You are expecting two roots

(d) $x^2 + 4 = 0$ ← no factorisation

$x^2 = -4$

which is impossible

so there are no real solutions.

## Example 2

If $m$ and $n$ are the roots of the quadratic equation $x^2 - 4x - 41 = 0$ and $m > n$ find

(a) the exact values of $m$ and $n$ (b) $m + n$

(c) $\frac{m}{n}$ in the form $p + q\sqrt{5}$ stating the exact values of $p$ and $q$

### Solution

(a) $x^2 - 4x - 41 = 0$

using the formula $a = 1$, $b = -4$, $c = -41$ →

$$x = \frac{4 \pm \sqrt{16 + 164}}{2}$$

$$x = \frac{4 \pm \sqrt{180}}{2}$$

$\sqrt{180} = \sqrt{36 \times 5} = 6\sqrt{5}$ →

$$x = \frac{4 \pm 6\sqrt{5}}{2} = 2 \pm 3\sqrt{5}$$

$m > n$ so $m = 2 + 3\sqrt{5}$ ← These are exact values

$n = 2 - 3\sqrt{5}$

Another way to do this question is to 'complete the square':

$$x^2 - 4x - 41 = 0$$

$$x^2 - 4x + 4 = 45$$

make the left hand side into a square

$$(x - 2)^2 = 45$$

$$x - 2 = \pm\sqrt{45}$$

$\sqrt{45} = \sqrt{9 \times 5} = 3\sqrt{5}$

$$x - 2 = \pm 3\sqrt{5}$$

$$x = 2 \pm 3\sqrt{5}$$

$m > n$ so $\quad m = 2 + 3\sqrt{5}$

and $\quad n = 2 - 3\sqrt{5}$

(b) $m + n = (2 + 3\sqrt{5}) + (2 - 3\sqrt{5}) = 4$

(c) $$\frac{m}{n} = \frac{2 + 3\sqrt{5}}{2 - 3\sqrt{5}} = \frac{(2 + 3\sqrt{5})(2 + 3\sqrt{5})}{(2 - 3\sqrt{5})(2 + 3\sqrt{5})}$$

multiply top and bottom by $2 + 3\sqrt{5}$

$$= \frac{4 + 12\sqrt{5} + 45}{4 - 45}$$

$$= \frac{49 + 12\sqrt{5}}{-41}$$

$$= \frac{-49}{41} - \frac{12}{41}\sqrt{5} \qquad \text{so } p = \frac{-49}{41} \text{ and } q = \frac{-12}{41}$$

## Exercise 1.3

**A1** Solve

(a) $x^2 = 4$

(b) $(x - 3)^2 = 4$

(c) $(5 - x)^2 = 4$

(d) $(x - 2)^2 = 0$

**A2** Solve

(a) $2x(x - 4) = 0$

(b) $3a(a - b) = 0$

**A3** Solve

(a) $x^2 = 3x$

(b) $x^2 + 7x = 0$

(c) $4x - x^2 = 0$

**A4** (a) Find $x$ if $(x - 2a)(2ax - 1) = 0$

(b) Find $y$ if $(3ay - 9)(ay - 7) = 0$

**A5** Solve

(a) $x^2 = 8$

(b) $(x + 1)^2 = 8$

(c) $(3 - x)^2 = 8$

**A6** Solve $2x^2 - 6x = x(x - 3)$

**A7** Solve where possible:

(a) $x^2 - 4x + 3 = 0$

(b) $x^2 - 4x + 4 = 0$

(c) $x^2 - 4x + 5 = 0$

**A8** Solve (a) $x^4 - 5x^2 + 4 = 0$
(Hint: let $x^2 = y$. This is a 'disguised' quadratic)
(b) $x + 6 = 5\sqrt{x}$ (Let $\sqrt{x} = z$)

**A9** Solve by 'completing the square'

(a) $x^2 + 4x = 1$

(b) $x^2 + 4x + 2 = 0$

(c) $x^2 + 4x - 896 = 0$

**A10** Find the value of $x$ if $(2x - 3)^2 = 4(x - 2)^2$

## Exercise 1.3 *continued*

**B1** Solve

(a) $(3x - 2)^2 = 16$

(b) $(2x - 3)^2 = 8$

**B2** Solve $x^2 - 6x - 9 = 0$

**B3** The area of a rectangle is 560 cm². The length of the rectangle is 8 cm greater than the breadth. Set up a quadratic equation for this situation and then find the dimensions of the rectangle.

**B4** Solve by factorisation:

(a) $2x^2 - 3x + 1 = 0$

(b) $2 + 9x + 4x^2 = 0$

(c) $x(5 - x) = 6$

**B5** *ABC* is a right angled isosceles triangle and $AC = 20$ cm. Find the exact length of *AB* by solving a quadratic equation.

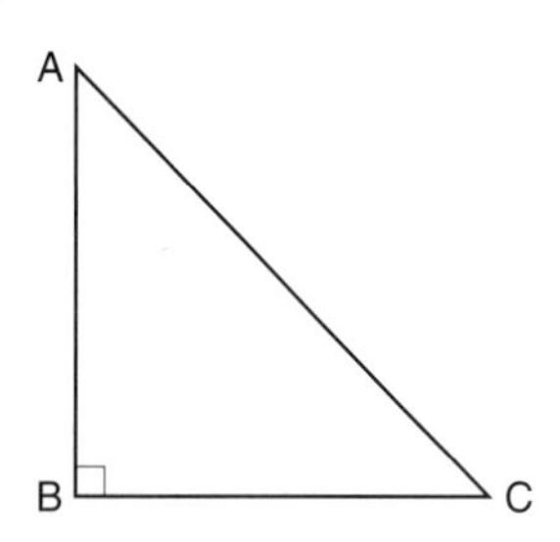


**B6** Solve by completing the square:

(a) $x^2 = 5x + 2$

(b) $2x^2 - 4x - 3 = 0$

**B7** Solve

(a) $x - 4 = \dfrac{5}{x}$

(b) $\dfrac{3x - 8}{x - 3} = x$

**B8** (a) If $2^x + \dfrac{3}{2^x} = 4$ find the two values of $2^x$.

Hint: another disguised quadratic

(b) Solve $\sqrt{x} + \dfrac{7}{\sqrt{x}} = 8$

**B9** Solve giving answers in surd form:

(a) $2x^2 - 3x - 4 = 0$

(b) $(2x + 1)(2x - 1) = 4x$

**B10** If $a = 2x - 5$, $b = 3x + 7$ solve to find $x$

(a) $\dfrac{1}{a^2} = \dfrac{1}{b^2}$

(b) $a^2 + b^2 = 74$

(c) $\dfrac{(a - b)^2}{(2a - b)^2} = 1$

## 1.4 Simultaneous equations

### Key points

You need to be confident with the algebraical manipulation for solving simultaneous equations. When two lines cross or when a line cuts a curve you need this process to find the co-ordinates of the points of intersection.

### Example 1

Solve the simultaneous linear equations:

$3x - 5y = 23$ ①

$2x + 3y = 9$ ②

elimination is easier here

You need to make the $x$ terms into $6x$ in both equations or the $y$ terms into $15y$ in both. Say you choose $y$:

① × 3 $\quad 9x - 15y = 69$

② × 5 $\quad 10x + 15y = 45$

Remember to multiply all three terms

Add

Add or subtract?

$$19x = 114$$
$$x = 6$$

Now substitute into the easier of ① or ②.

No particular difference here so choose ①.

When $x = 6$

$$\begin{aligned} 3(6) - 5y &= 23 \\ 18 - 5y &= 23 \\ 18 - 23 &= 5y \\ -5 &= 5y \\ -1 &= y \end{aligned}$$

Check in the other equation

LHS $= 2x + 3y = 12 - 3 = 9 =$ RHS

## Example 2

Find the co-ordinates of the points of intersection of the line $y = x + 3$ and the curve $xy = 4$.

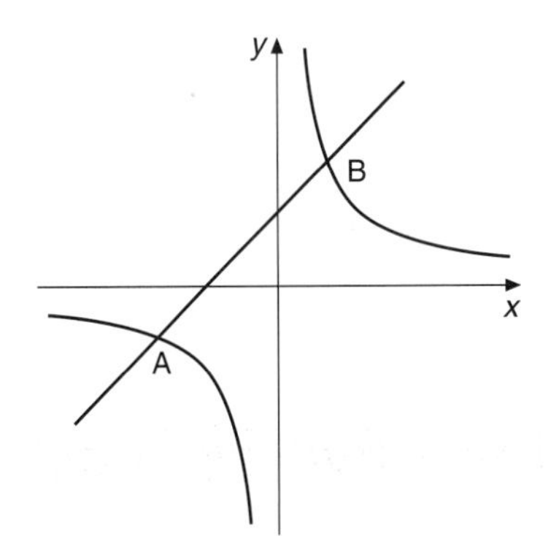


Substitute $y = x + 3$ into the equation of the curve

Generally substitute *from* the line *into* the curve

$$\begin{aligned} x(x + 3) &= 4 \\ x^2 + 3x - 4 &= 0 \\ (x + 4)(x - 1) &= 0 \end{aligned}$$

$x + 4 = 0 \qquad\qquad x - 1 = 0$

$x = -4 \qquad\qquad x = 1$

So $\quad y = x + 3 = -1 \qquad\qquad y = x + 3 = 4$

$A(-4, -1) \qquad\qquad B(1, 4)$

## Exercise 1.4

Solve the following equations for $x$ and $y$.

**A1** $y = 3x - 4$, $y = 2x - 7$

**A2** $y = 3x + 2$, $3x - 2y + 5 = 0$

**A3** $3x - y = 22$, $x + 2y = 12$

**A4** $x - y = 6$, $x + y = 12$

**A5** $2x + 5y = 2$, $3x - y = 20$

**A6** $4x - y + 7 = 0$, $2x - y + 3 = 0$

**A7** $5x + 4y = 2$, $2x - 3y = 4$

**A8** $x + 2y + 7 = 0$, $3x - y + 14 = 0$

**A9** $7x + 3y - 33 = 0$, $2y + 5x - 23 = 0$

**A10** $y = 2x - 3$, $\dfrac{4x - 2y}{x + y} = 1$

**B1** Find the coordinates of the points of intersection of the line $x + y = 4$ and the curve $y^2 = 2x$.

**B2** Where does the line $y = -4$ cut the parabola $y = (2 - x)(x + 1)$?

**B3** If $y = (x + 2)(x - 2)$ find the exact coordinates of the points of intersection with the line $y = 2$.

**B4** The lines $y = x + 3$ and $y + 2x = 3$ intersect at $A$. Find the coordinates of $A$. Find the finite area enclosed by the two lines and the $x$ axis. (A diagram could help your understanding.)

**B5** The line $y = 2x + 5$ intersects the circle $x^2 + y^2 = 10$ in two points. Find the coordinates of the points of intersection by solving the equations.

Solve the equations:

**B6** $2x^2 + y^2 = 19$
$2x - y = 5$

**B7** $x - 3y + 1 = 0$
$x^2 + y^2 + 2x - 4y = 5$

**B8** $y = (x + 1)(x - 3)$
$y = 9 - x$

**B9** $(x - 4)(y - 3) = 3$
$2x + y = 4$

**B10** $xy = 12$
$x^2 + y^2 = 25$

## 1.5 Indices and logarithms

### Key points

You need to understand the relationship between indices and logarithms and be able to use the laws of indices and logarithms.

If $a$ is a *positive* number and $x$ and $y$ are rational numbers then

| INDICES | | LOGARITHMS |
|---|---|---|
| $a^x = m$ | $\Leftrightarrow$ | $\log_a m = x$ |
| $a^x \times a^y = a^{x+y}$ | $\Leftrightarrow$ | $\log_a m + \log_a n = \log_a mn$ |
| $a^x \div a^y = a^{x-y}$ | $\Leftrightarrow$ | $\log_a m - \log_a n = \log_a \dfrac{m}{n}$ |
| $(a^x)^n = a^{xn}$ | $\Leftrightarrow$ | $\log_a m^n = n\log_a m$ |
| $a^0 = 1$ | $\Leftrightarrow$ | $\log_a 1 = 0$ |
| $a^1 = a$ | $\Leftrightarrow$ | $\log_a a = 1$ |

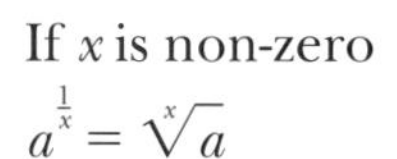


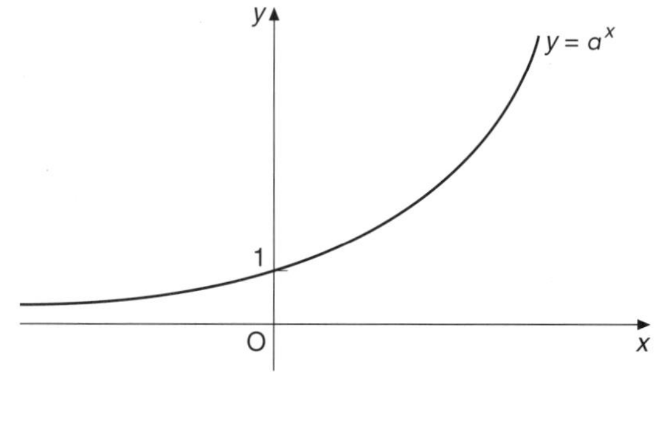


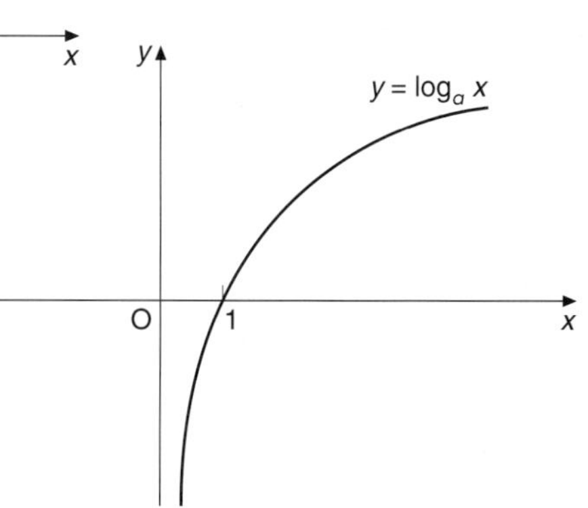


In particular **if $a = \mathrm{e}$**

$$\mathrm{e}^x = m \Leftrightarrow \log_{\mathrm{e}} m = x = \ln m$$

**if $a = 10$**

$$10^x = m \Leftrightarrow \log_{10} m = x = \log m$$

Remember $\ln m$ means $\log_{\mathrm{e}} m$
$\log m$ means $\log_{10} m$

You have the ln and log functions on your calculator and also the $\mathrm{e}^x$ and $10^x$ functions.

## Example 1

Solve $4^x - 13(2^x) + 40 = 0$ giving non-exact answers to 3 decimal places.

**Solution**

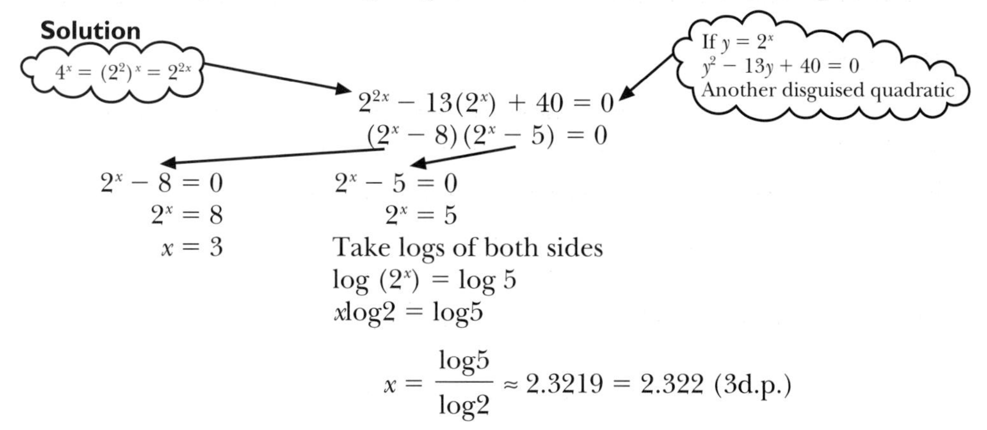

### Example 2

If $\ln x^3 - \ln xy^5 + 2\ln y = 0$, express $y$ in terms of $x$.

**Solution**

$$\begin{aligned} \ln x^3 - (\ln x + \ln y^5) + 2\ln y &= 0 \\ 3\ln x - \ln x - 5\ln y + 2\ln y &= 0 \\ 2\ln x - 3\ln y &= 0 \\ \ln x^2 - \ln y^3 &= 0 \\ \ln x^2 &= \ln y^3 \end{aligned}$$

$\ln AB = \ln A + \ln B$

So $y^3 = x^2$

$y = \sqrt[3]{x^2}$

So $y = x^{\frac{2}{3}}$ is the solution.

## Exercise 1.5

**A1** Write down the values of:

(a) $\log_3 81$ (b) $\log_2 32$ (c) $\log_2 \sqrt{2}$ (d) $\log_5 5$ (e) $\log_4 4^{\frac{1}{3}}$

**A2** Write the following in a form using logarithms

(a) $8^2 = 64$ (b) $16^{\frac{1}{2}} = 4$

(c) $7^0 = 1$ (d) $3^{-4} = \dfrac{1}{81}$

**A3** Write as a single logarithm

(a) $\log 2 - \log 8 + 2\log 3$

(b) $3\log 2 + \log 3^2$

**A4** Simplify

(a) $64^{-\frac{1}{2}}$ (b) $32^{\frac{3}{5}}$

(c) $27^{-\frac{2}{3}}$ (d) $\left(\dfrac{16}{81}\right)^{\frac{3}{4}}$

(e) $\left(\dfrac{3^3}{2^6}\right)^{-\frac{1}{3}}$

**A5** Find

(a) $\log_2 8$ (b) $\log_5 25$

(c) $\log_3\left(\dfrac{1}{9}\right)$ (d) $\log_{10}(0.00001)$

(e) $\log_4 8$

**A6** Write down the values of

(a) $\log_a a^2$ (b) $\log_b \sqrt{b}$

(c) $\log 1000$ (d) $\log_a 1$

**A7** Show that $4\log_3 6 - 3\log_3 2 = 4 + \log_3 2$

**A8** First write the equations in a form using logarithms and then find the value of $x$ to 2 decimal places.

(a) $e^x = 2$ (b) $e^{\ln x} = 3$

(c) $e^{2x} = 5$ (d) $10^x = 1240$

**A9** Solve $2^x = 9$ giving your answer to 3 significant figures.

**A10** Find $\log_3 16$ (to 3 sig figs)

(Hint: Let $\log_3 16 = x$ and then write in index form)

## Exercise 1.5 *continued*

**B1** Find the values of $a$ for which $\log_4 a^2 = 1$

**B2** Find the value of $a$ if

$$\frac{3}{2}\log a^3 - \log\sqrt{a} - 2\log a = 4$$

**B3** If $\log_6 5! = 2.672$ (3 d.p.) find $\log_6 6!$ to 3 d.p.

(Hint: Remember that $6! = 6 \times 5!$)

**B4** Simplify $\dfrac{x^{\frac{1}{2}} - x^{-\frac{3}{2}}}{x^{-\frac{1}{2}} + x^{-\frac{3}{2}}}$

(Hint: Multiply top and bottom by an appropriate power of $x$.)

**B5** Solve $2^{2x-3} = \dfrac{1}{16}$

**B6** Simplify
$2\log(x^2 - 4) - \log(x - 2) - 3\log(x + 2)$

**B7** Solve $5^{2x} - 7(5^x) + 10 = 0$

giving non-exact answers to 3 d.p.

**B8** Solve $9^x + 2(3^x) - 3 = 0$

**B9** Solve $3^{2x} - 4(3^{2+x}) + 243 = 0$

**B10** Show that $\log_y x = \dfrac{1}{\log_x y}$ and hence solve

$\log_3 x + 9\log_x 3 = 10.$

## 1.6 Partial fractions

### Key points

In 1.1 you added algebraical fractions together.

$$\text{i.e. } \frac{1}{x+5} + \frac{3}{2x+7} \equiv \frac{(2x+7)}{(x+5)(2x+7)} + \frac{3(x+5)}{(x+5)(2x+7)}$$

$$\equiv \frac{5x+22}{(x+5)(2x+7)}$$

Sometimes you need to work the other way around. You would start with $\dfrac{5x+22}{(x+5)(2x+7)}$ and establish that it is identical to $\dfrac{1}{x+5} + \dfrac{3}{2x+7}$

1) Linear denominators.

$$\frac{7x-5}{(x+4)(x-7)} \equiv \frac{A}{x+4} + \frac{B}{x-7}$$

$$\left(\text{in particular here } \frac{1}{x(x+1)} \equiv \frac{A}{x} + \frac{B}{x+1} \equiv \frac{1}{x} - \frac{1}{x+1} \text{ is useful}\right)$$

2) Linear and non-factorisable quadratic denominators.

$$\frac{2}{(x-1)(x^2+6x+1)} \equiv \frac{A}{(x-1)} + \frac{Bx+C}{x^2+6x+1}$$

linear numerator

3) Denominators with repeated factors.

$$\frac{3x + 1}{(x + 6)(x - 1)^2} \equiv \frac{A}{(x + 6)} + \frac{B}{(x - 1)} + \frac{C}{(x - 1)^2}$$

4) You must recognise that $\dfrac{x + 7}{x - 2} \equiv A + \dfrac{B}{x - 2}$

Hopefully the examiners will give you the identity and then it will be up to you to use your algebraical skills to find the values of the constants A, B, C. Sometimes you will use substitution, sometimes comparing coefficients and sometimes both.

## Example 1

(a) If $A(2x - 1) + B(x + 4) \equiv 14 - x$ find the values of A and B.

(b) Hence express $\dfrac{14 - x}{(x + 4)(2x - 1)}$ in partial fractions.

**Solution**

(a)
$$A(2x - 1) + B(x + 4) \equiv 14 - x$$
$$2Ax - A + Bx + 4B \equiv 14 - x$$
$$x(2A + B) + (4B - A) \equiv 14 - x$$

So $2A + B = -1$ ← comparing coefficients of $x$

$4B - A = 14$ ← comparing constants

Solve these simultaneous equations to get $A = -2$, $B = 3$.

(b) $$\frac{14 - x}{(x + 4)(2x - 1)} \equiv \frac{A}{x + 4} + \frac{B}{2x - 1}$$

Multiply both sides by $(x + 4)(2x - 1)$ to get

$14 - x \equiv A(2x - 1) + B(x + 4)$

You have solved this inequality in part (a) to get $A = -2$, $B = 3$ so

$$\frac{14 - x}{(x + 4)(2x - 1)} \equiv \frac{-2}{x + 4} + \frac{3}{2x - 1}$$

In the exam a quick check of $x = 0$ into both sides could reassure you.

left hand side $= \dfrac{14}{-4} = -3\frac{1}{2}$

right hand side $= -\frac{1}{2} + \dfrac{3}{-1}$

$= -\frac{1}{2} - 3 = -3\frac{1}{2}$

## Example 2

Write $\dfrac{11x - 18}{(3 - x)^2(2x - 1)}$ as the sum of three partial fractions.

### Solution

$$\frac{11x - 18}{(3 - x)^2(2x - 1)} \equiv \frac{A}{3 - x} + \frac{B}{(3 - x)^2} + \frac{C}{2x - 1}$$

multiply by $(3 - x)^2(2x - 1)$

$$11x - 18 \equiv A(3 - x)(2x - 1) + B(2x - 1) + C(3 - x)^2$$

An identity is true for all $x$

Let $x = 3$

$$\begin{aligned} 33 - 18 &= B(6 - 1) \\ 15 &= 5B \\ 3 &= B \end{aligned}$$

Let $x = \frac{1}{2}$

$$\begin{aligned} 5\tfrac{1}{2} - 18 &= C(2\tfrac{1}{2})^2 \\ -12\tfrac{1}{2} &= 6\tfrac{1}{4}C \\ -2 &= C \end{aligned}$$

Let $x = 0$

$$\begin{aligned} -18 &= -3A - B + 9C \\ -18 &= -3A - 3 - 18 \\ 3 &= -3A \\ -1 &= A \end{aligned}$$

So $\dfrac{11x - 18}{(3 - x)^2(2x - 1)} \equiv \dfrac{-1}{3 - x} + \dfrac{5}{(3 - x)^2} - \dfrac{2}{2x - 1}$

## Exercise 1.6

**A1** Find A, B, C if $Ax^2 + Bx + C$ is

(a) $\equiv 3x^2 - 7x - 2$

(b) $\equiv 6x^2 + 9$

(c) $\equiv 3x$

(d) $\equiv 3(x + 2) - x(x + 5)$

(e) $\equiv 2x(x + 7) - 3(x - 3) - 9$

In questions **A2–A5** find the values of A and B.

**A2** (a) $\dfrac{11 + 7x}{(1 + x)(2 + x)} \equiv \dfrac{A}{1 + x} + \dfrac{B}{2 + x}$

(b) $\dfrac{2(4x - 1)}{1 - x^2} \equiv \dfrac{A}{1 - x} + \dfrac{B}{1 + x}$

**A3** (a) $\dfrac{x + 3}{x - 2} \equiv A + \dfrac{B}{x - 2}$

(b) $\dfrac{5x + 1}{x - 3} \equiv A + \dfrac{B}{x - 3}$

**A4** $\dfrac{21x + 3}{x(x + 3)} \equiv \dfrac{A}{x} + \dfrac{B}{x + 3}$

**A5** $\dfrac{x^2 + x + 9}{x^2 + 5x + 4} \equiv A + \dfrac{B}{x + 1} + \dfrac{C}{x + 4}$

Express in partial fractions

**A6** $\dfrac{x + 8}{(x + 2)(x - 1)}$

**A7** $\dfrac{7}{(4x - 1)(2x + 3)}$

## Exercise 1.6 *continued*

**A8** $\dfrac{19 - x}{(5 - 2x)(3 + x)}$

**A9** $\dfrac{5x - 1}{x^2 - 1}$

**A10** $\dfrac{x^2 + 14x - 8}{x(x + 2)(x - 2)}$

**B1** (a) If $(A - 2B)x^2 + (B + C)x + A \equiv x^2 + 6x + 3$ find A, B, C.
(b) If $(A + B + C)x^2 + (A - B + C)x + 2A + 3B \equiv 3x^2 + 7x + 4$ find A, B, C.

**B2** If $\dfrac{3}{2(x + 1)} - \dfrac{4}{(2x + 3)} + 2 \equiv \dfrac{Ax^2 + Bx + C}{2(x + 1)(2x + 3)}$ find A, B, C.

**B3** If $px^2 + (p - 2q)x + rp \equiv ax^2 + bx + c$ find $p$, $q$ and $r$ in terms of $a$, $b$ and $c$.

**B4** If $\dfrac{6x^2 - x + 3}{x(x + 6)^2} \equiv \dfrac{A}{x} + \dfrac{B}{x + 6} + \dfrac{C}{(x + 6)^2}$ find A, B, and C.

**B5** If $\dfrac{4x^2 + 5x - 2}{(2x + 3)(x^2 + x + 1)} \equiv \dfrac{A}{2x + 3} + \dfrac{Bx + C}{x^2 + x + 1}$ find A, B, and C.

Express in partial fractions.

**B6** $\dfrac{5}{(x^2 + 1)(2 - x)}$

**B7** $\dfrac{4x^2 - 6x + 3}{(x^2 + 2x - 1)(x - 2)}$

**B8** $\dfrac{2x^2 + 6x + 7}{(x - 2)(x^2 + 2x + 1)}$

**B9** $\dfrac{6x^2 + 5x + 3}{x^2(x + 1)}$

**B10** $\dfrac{3x^2 + 2x - 3}{x^2 - 1}$

## Chapter 1: A level questions

**C1** (a) Solve $8^{x-2} = 2^{x+2}$
(b) Solve the equation $3^{2x+1} - 28(3^x) + 9 = 0$

**C2** (a) If $\log x + \log y = 2$ show that $xy = 100$ and then solve the simultaneous equations

$$\log x + \log y = 2$$
$$2x + y = 54$$

(b) If $2\log_2 y = 4 - \log_2 x$ find $y$ in terms of $x$.
Find the value of $y$ when $x = 2y$.

**C3** (a) Solve the equation $9^x - 3^x - 72 = 0$
(b) Find the value of $x$, correct to 3 significant figures for which $5^{2x} + 5^x = 20$.

**C4** (a) Simplify (i) $\log_a 1$ (ii) $\log_a a$ (iii) $\log_a a^2$ (iv) $\log_a\left(\dfrac{1}{a}\right)$
(b) If the base of the logarithm is 10 find $x$ if

(i) $\log 2x + \log\left(\dfrac{3x - 5}{4}\right) = 0$

(ii) $\log(x + 2) + \log(3x - 7) = 1$

(iii) $\log(x^2 + 6x + 9) = 2$

## Chapter 1: A level questions *continued*

**C5** Given that $P(x) \equiv x^3 + 4x^2 + 4x$ and $Q(x) \equiv x^4 - 4x^2$ factorise $P(x)$ and $Q(x)$ completely.

(a) Simplify $\dfrac{Q(x)}{P(x)}$ and then obtain $\dfrac{Q(x)}{P(x)}$ in the form $Ax + B + \dfrac{C}{x+2}$ where A, B, C are to be found.

(b) If $R(x) \equiv 3xP(x) - Q(x)$ then write $R(x)$ in fully factorised form and solve the equation $R(x) = 0$.

**C6** Show that $P(x) \equiv x^4 - 5x^3 + 5x^2 + 5x - 6$ is divisible by $x^2 - 5x + 6$. Hence find the four linear factors of $P(x)$ and solve $P(x) = 0$.

**C7** If $\dfrac{Ax^2 + \sqrt{x}(Bx + C) + D}{2\sqrt{x}(x^2 - 1)} \equiv \dfrac{2}{(x+1)} + \dfrac{3}{2(x-1)} + \dfrac{5}{\sqrt{x}}$ find A, B, C and D and verify that $A - B - 7C + D = 0$.

**C8** Triangle ABC is right angled at B. The hypotenuse is 8 cm longer than the side BC and the other side is 1 cm shorter than BC. Find the lengths of the sides of the triangle and also its area.

**C9** A ball is thrown vertically upwards from a point O with speed 20 $ms^{-1}$. The height $h$ metres above O after $t$ seconds is given by $h = 20t - 5t^2$.

(a) By completing the square find the greatest height reached.

(b) Find how long the ball is at least 15 metres above O.

(c) Find how long the ball takes to return to O.

**C10** Find the solutions $x_1$ and $x_2$ of the equation $x^2 - 4x - 1 = 0$ in the form $a + b\sqrt{c}$ where $a$, $b$, $c$ are integers. Obtain the exact values of

(a) $x_1 + x_2$

(b) $x_1x_2$

(c) $\dfrac{1}{x_1} + \dfrac{1}{x_2}$

(d) $x_1^2 + x_2^2$

# Chapter 2

## GRAPH SKETCHING

### 2.1 Linear graphs, simple factorised quadratic and cubic graphs

#### Key points

**Linear Graphs**
In general, linear equations are of the type

$$ax + by + c = 0$$

and they represent a straight line.

- If $a = 0$ the line is parallel to the $x$ axis
- If $b = 0$ the line is parallel to the $y$ axis
- If $c = 0$ the line passes through $(0,0)$

Hints for sketching:

1. Find the points of intersection with the axes
2. Join up the points and make the line longer if it is helpful to do so.

#### Example 1

Sketch the graph of $3x + 5y - 10 = 0$
and find the finite area between the line and the axes.

**Solution**

When $x = 0$, $0 + 5y - 10 = 0$

$$y = 2$$

$\therefore$ $(0,2)$ is the intersection with the $y$ axis.
When $y = 0$ $3x + 0 - 10 = 0$

$$x = \frac{10}{3}$$

$\therefore \left(\frac{10}{3},0\right)$ is the intersection with the $x$ axis.

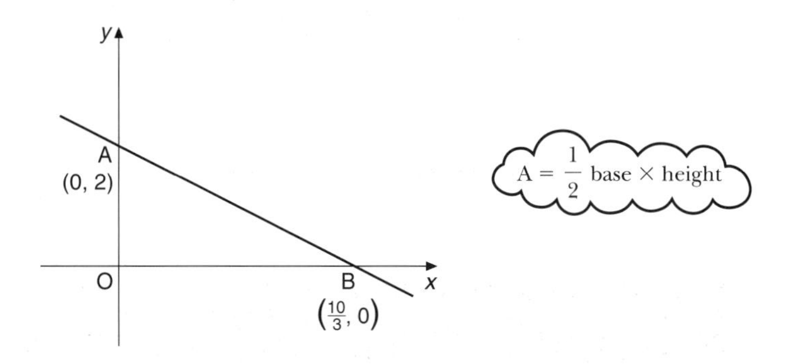


$$\text{Area AOB} = \frac{1}{2}\left(\frac{10}{3}\right) \times 2 = \frac{10}{3} \text{ square units.}$$

## Key points

**Factorisable quadratics**

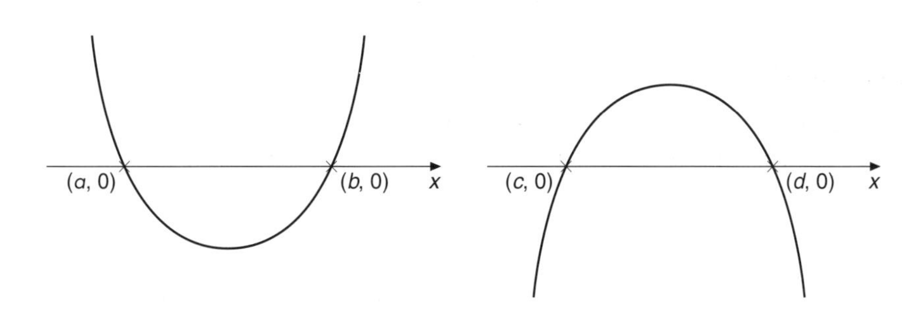

Coefficient of $x^2$ is $+1$

Coefficient of $x^2$ is $-1$

Hints for sketching:

1. Find the zeros
2. Check if the coefficient of $x^2$ is positive or negative to determine the 'way up'
3. Dot in the line of symmetry
4. Find the coordinates of the turning point
5. Find the $y$ intercept
6. Sketch the curve.

**Factorisable cubics (three linear factors)**

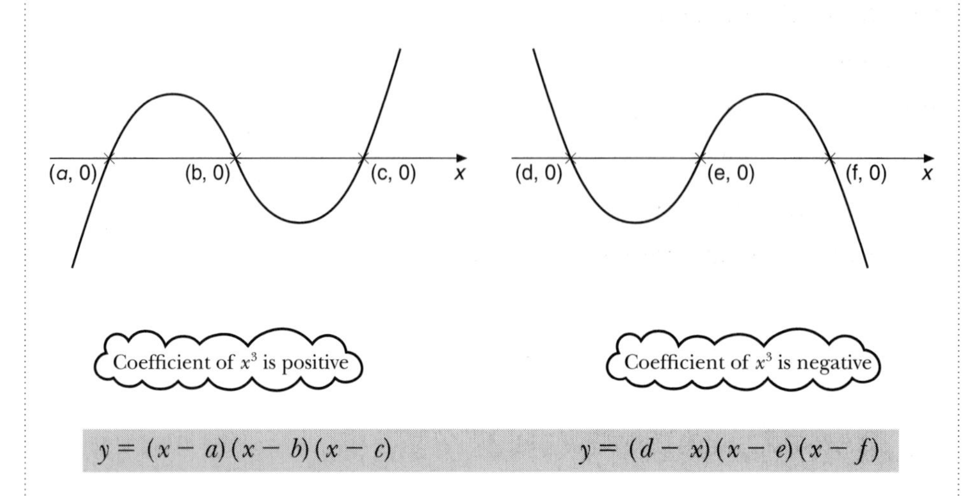


Hints for sketching:

1. Find the zeros
2. Check the coefficient of $x^3$ to determine the 'way up'
3. Find the $y$ intercept
4. Sketch the curve.

## Example 2

Sketch $y = (5 - x)(x + 1)$ and mark the coordinates of the turning point and where the graph cuts the axes.

**Solution**

When $y = 0$

$$0 = (5 - x)(x + 1)$$

$$5 - x = 0 \quad \text{or} \quad x + 1 = 0$$

$$5 = x \qquad\qquad x = -1$$

Zeros at $x = 5$, $x = -1$

The coefficient of $x^2$ is negative.

When $x = 0$ $y = (5 - 0)(0 + 1) = 5$

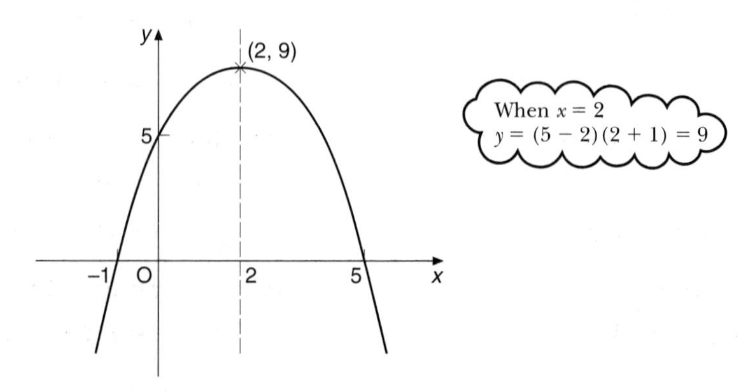

## Example 3

Sketch $y = x(x-3)(x+5)$

**Solution**

When $0 = x(x-3)(5+x)$

Zeros at $x = 0 \quad x = 3 \quad x = -5$

The coefficient of $x^3$ is positive.

When $x = 0$ the y intercept is zero here.

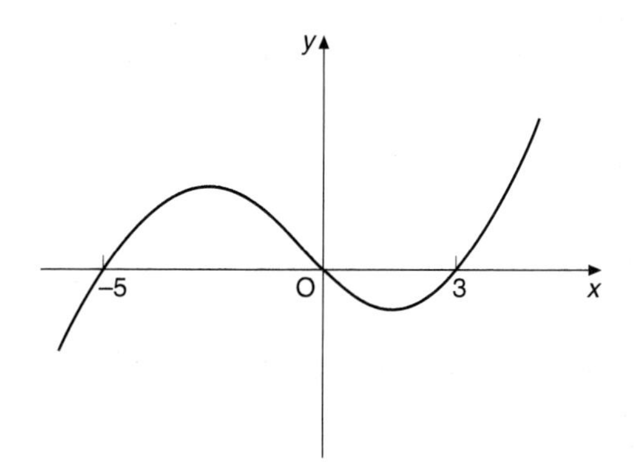


## Exercise 2.1

Sketch the following linear graphs.

**A1** (a) $y = 3x - 2$

(b) $y + 4x = 6$

(c) $3y - 4x + 12 = 0$

(d) $\dfrac{x}{2} + \dfrac{y}{3} = 1$

**A2** (a) $y = 3(x - 2)$

(b) $x + y = 7$

(c) $2x + 5y + 10 = 0$

Sketch the following quadratic graphs.

**A3** (a) $y = (x+3)(x-3)$

(b) $y = (x-1)(x-5)$

(c) $y = (x-4)(x+5)$

**A4** (a) $y = (2x-1)(x+3)$

(b) $y = (4-x)(1-x)$

(c) $y = (x+2)(5-x)$

(d) $y = (2x+5)^2$

**A5** Sketch

(a) $y = (x+1)^2$

(b) $y = (2x-3)^2$

(c) $y = (4x-1)^2$

**A6** Sketch

(a) $y = x^2 - x + 6$

(b) $y = x^2 - 6x + 9$

Sketch the following cubic graphs.

**A7** (a) $y = (x+3)(x-1)(x-4)$

(b) $y = 9x - x^3$

(c) $y = (x-1)(x-3)^2$

**A8** (a) $y = x^3 - 4x^2 + 4x$

(b) $y = x(2-x)(x+3)$

## Exercise 2.1 *continued*

Sketch the following.

**A9** (a) $y = 9 - 4x^2$

(b) $24 + 8y + 3x = 0$

(c) $y = 3x^2 - 6x$

(d) $y = (4 - x)(3 + 2x)(5 + x)$

**A10** Give possible equations for the following.

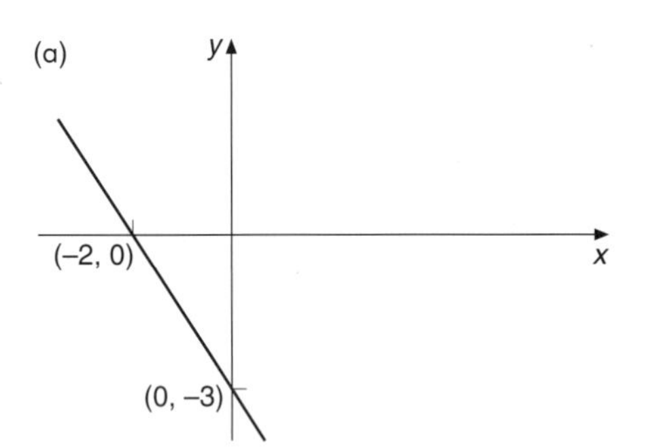


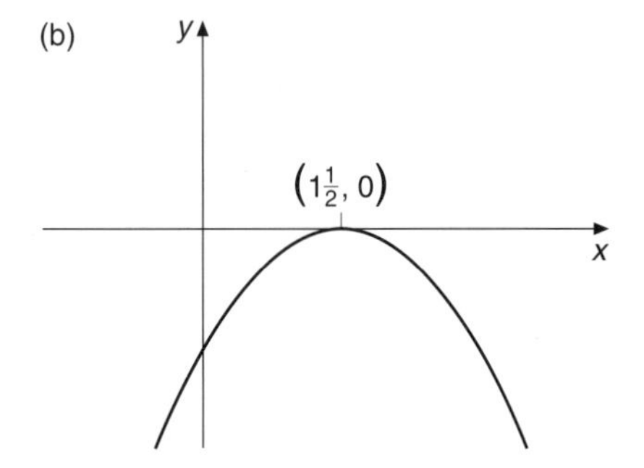


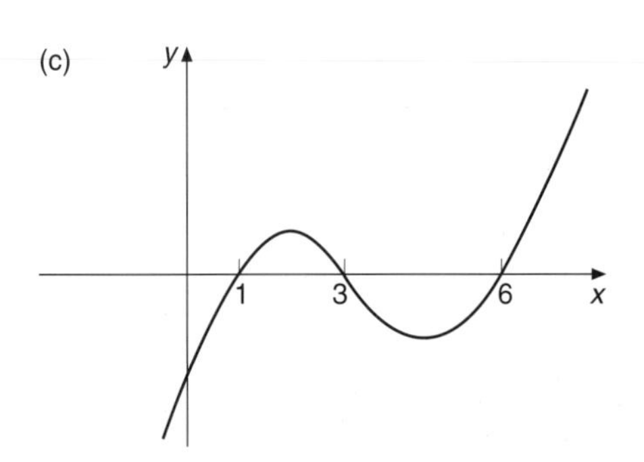


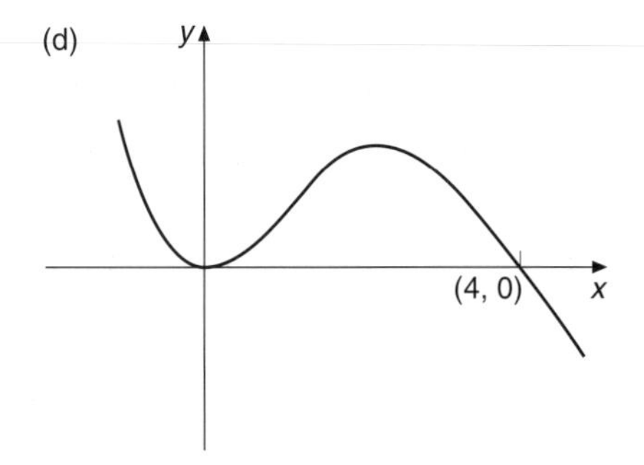


## 2.2 Simple inequalities

### Key points

> means 'is greater than'

### Example 1

Solve the inequality $2x - 5 < 7x + 2$.

**Solution**

We will be much safer if we collect the $x$ terms on the side where the coefficient of $x$ is the largest. Here $7x$ is the larger of the two $x$ terms.

So we get $-2 - 5 < 7x - 2x$

Collect the $x$ terms on the right hand side

$-7 < 5x$

$\frac{-7}{5} < x$ so $x > \frac{-7}{5}$

If you divide or multiply both sides of an inequality by a negative number then the inequality sign changes.

Here are some examples of more difficult inequalities.

## Example 2

Solve $|x| > 2$

**Solution**

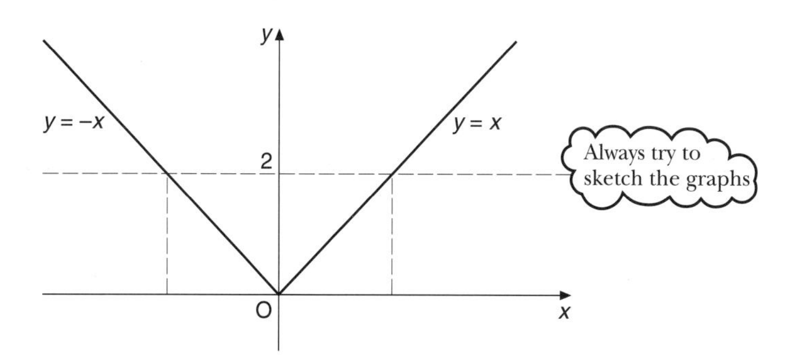


We want to find the parts of the modulus graph which are 'above' $y = 2$.

The points of intersection needed are $y = 2$, with $y = x$ and $y = 2$ with $y = -x$.

These are (2,2) and (−2,−2) respectively.

So for $|x| > 2$

$x > 2$ or $x < -2$.

## Example 3

Solve $x^2 > 4$

**Solution**

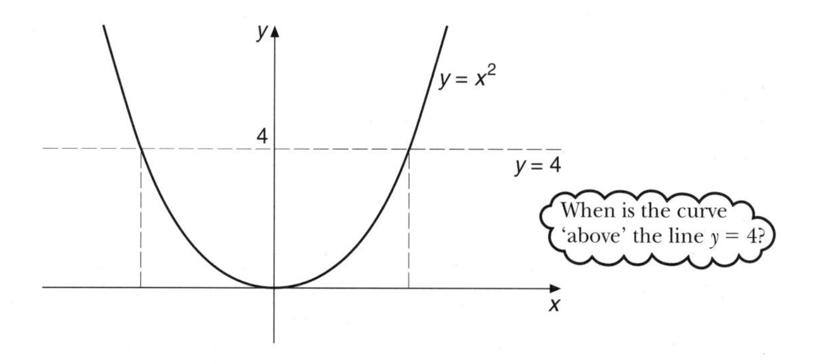


We need to find where $y = 4$ cuts the parabola $y = x^2$. We have

$4 = x^2$

$\pm 2 = x$ ← two roots

So $x^2 > 4$ when $x > 2$

and when $x < -2$.

## Example 4

Solve the inequality $(x + 2)(x - 4) \leq 0$

$\leq$ means less than or equal to

**Solution**

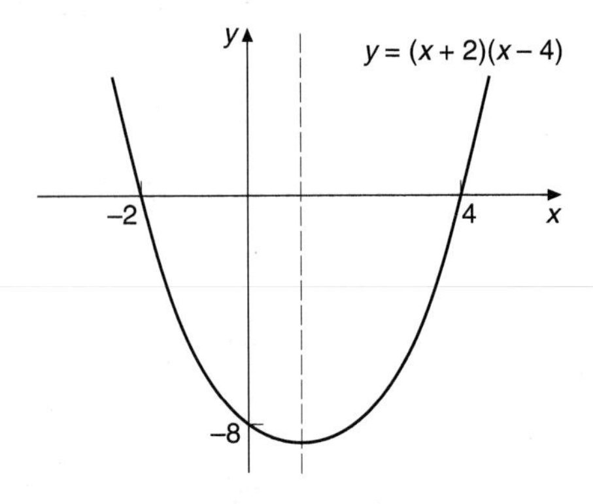


$y = (x - 2)(x - 4)$ zeros at $-2, 4$

We need the values of $x$ when $y \leq 0$
(i.e. the values of $x$ when the curve is *on* or below the $x$ axis)
so $-2 \leq x \leq 4$.

## Example 5

For which ranges of $x$ does the inequality $(x + 1)(x - 1)(x - 4) > 0$ hold?

**Solution**

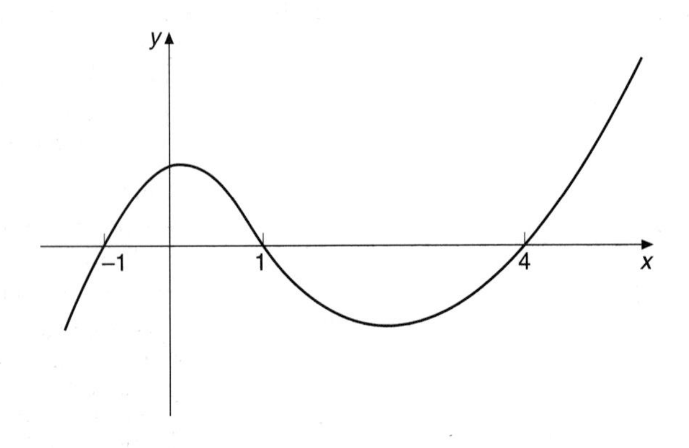

$y = (x + 1)(x - 1)(x - 4)$ has zeros at $x = -1$, $x = 1$, $x = 4$.

The coefficient of $x^3$ is positive so we know which 'way up' it is.

Here we need the values of $x$ when the curve is above the $x$ axis.

So $-1 < x < 1$ and $x > 4$.

## Exercise 2.2

Solve the inequalities:

**A1** (a) $2x < 5$

(b) $2x + 1 < 5$

(c) $3x + 4 < 5$

**A2** (a) $-7x < 14$

(b) $16 < -8x$

(c) $-2x > -4$

**A3** (a) $3(x - 1) < 2$

(b) $4(x + 1) - (x - 5) < 0$

(c) $2(x + 1) - 3(2x + 1) < 0$

**A4** $(x - 1)(x + 4) < 0$ [draw a simple sketch of $y = (x - 1)(x + 4)$]

**A5** (a) $(2x + 1)(4 - x) < 0$

(b) $3x^2 + 4x + 1 < 0$

(c) $x^2 + 3x > 0$

(d) $x^2 < 64$

(e) $(x - 3)^2 \leq 100$

(f) $(x - 3)^2 \leq 18$

**A6** $5(3x - 2) - 2(4x - 3) < 10$.

**A7** $\dfrac{x + 2}{3} - \dfrac{2x - 3}{4} \geq \dfrac{1}{2}$

**A8** (a) $x^2 < 9$

(b) $x^2 \geq 9x$

**A9** $(3x + 2)(3 - 2x) \leq 0$

**A10** $(x - 3)(2x - 1)(x + 1) > 0$

Solve the inequalities:

**B1** (a) $|x + 4| < 5$

(b) $|2x - 1| < 3$

(c) $|2x - 1| < x$

*Remember $|x| < 7$ means $-7 < x < 7$*

**B2** (a) $2(x^2 - 18) < 21x$

(b) $\dfrac{x^2 - 3x}{4} \leq 1$

(c) $x \geq 5$ and $(x + 1)(x - 9) < 0$

*Factorise the quadratic or get the zeros from the calculator then draw the simple sketch*

**B3** $3x^2 + 10x - 8 > 0$

**B4** $15 + 11x < 12x^2$

**B5** $(x - 3)(2x - 1)^2 \geq 0$

**B6** $12x - 3x^3 \leq 0$

**B7** $13x^2 + 5x > 6x^3$

**B8** The length of a field is 15 metres more than twice its width and it has an area of at least 500 m$^2$. Find the possible values of the width.

(Think about the possible domain for $x$)

**B9** The area of a right angled isosceles triangle has *not* to exceed 50 cm$^2$. Find the possible values for (a) the lengths of the shorter sides and (b) the perimeter.

**B10** (a) Express $x^2 - 8x - 4$ in completed square form.
Hence find exact solutions to the equation $x^2 - 8x - 4 = 0$ and then solve $x^2 - 8x - 4 < 0$.

(b) Sketch $y = (x^2 - 8x - 4)(x + 10)$ showing the zeros in their exact form and hence solve the inequality $(x^2 - 8x - 4)(x + 1) \leq 0$

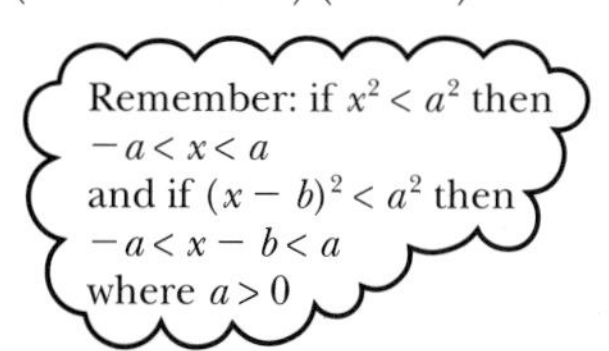

## 2.3 Simple transformations

### Key points

Ideas about simple transformations are shown in the following diagrams.

**A** (a)

Graph of $y = |x|$

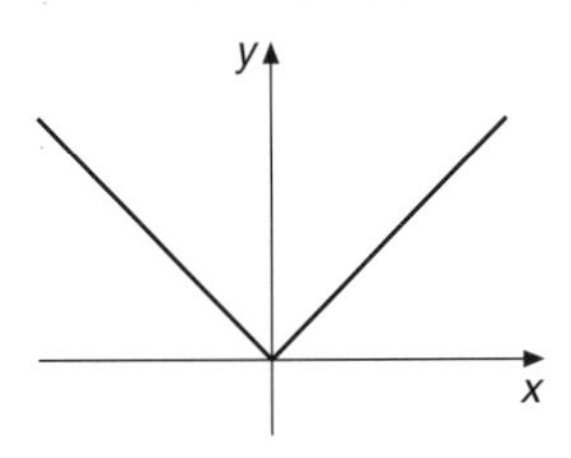


(b)

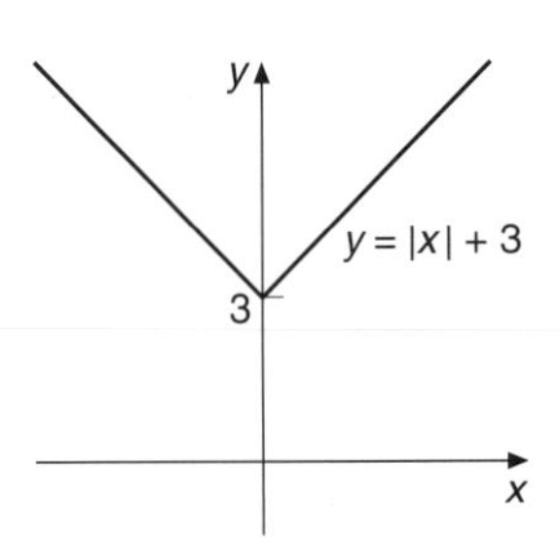


translation vector $\begin{pmatrix} 0 \\ 3 \end{pmatrix}$ 'move 3 units upwards'

(c)

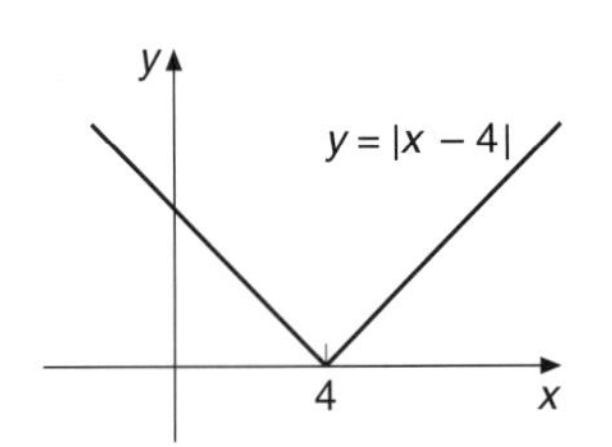


translation vector $\begin{pmatrix} 4 \\ 0 \end{pmatrix}$ 'move 4 units to the right'

(d)

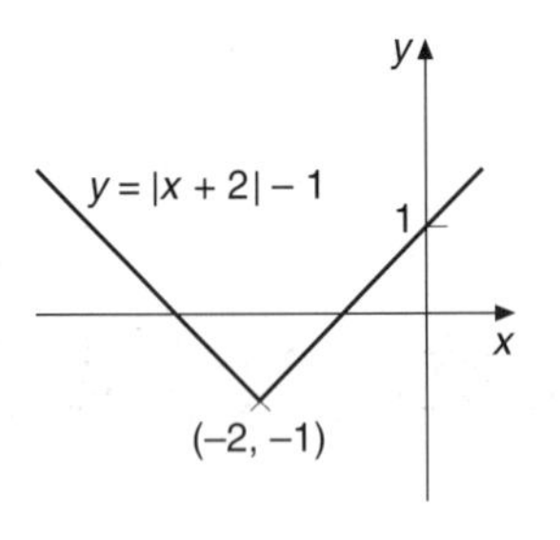


translation vector $\begin{pmatrix} -2 \\ -1 \end{pmatrix}$ 'move 2 to the left and 1 down in either order'

(e)

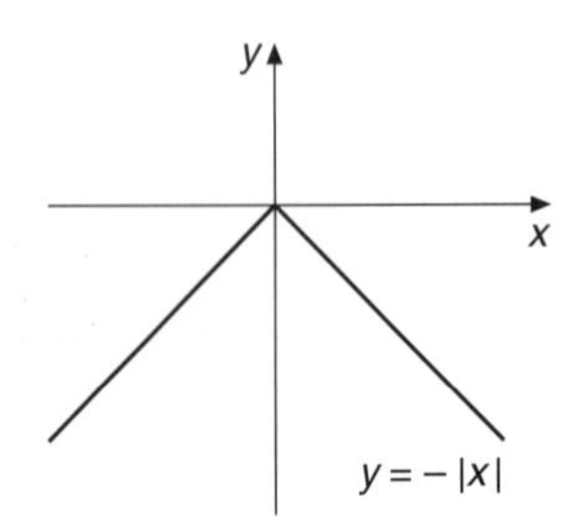


reflect in the $x$ axis

**B** (a)

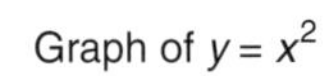


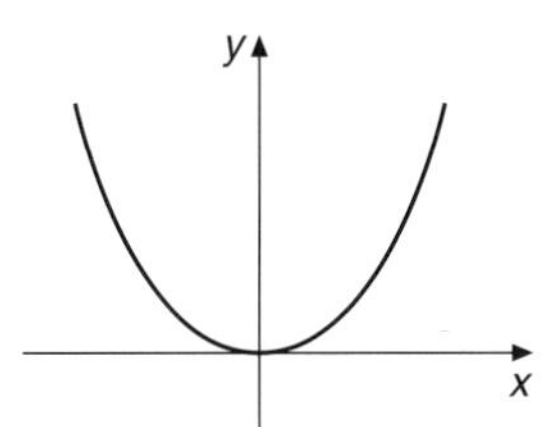


(b)

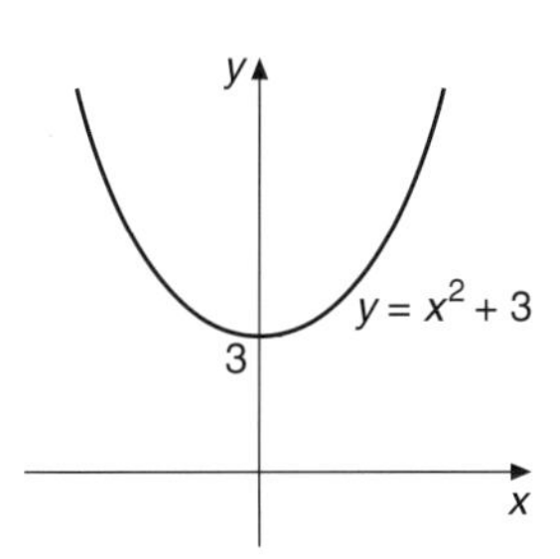


translation vector $\begin{pmatrix} 0 \\ 3 \end{pmatrix}$ 'move 3 units upwards'

(c)

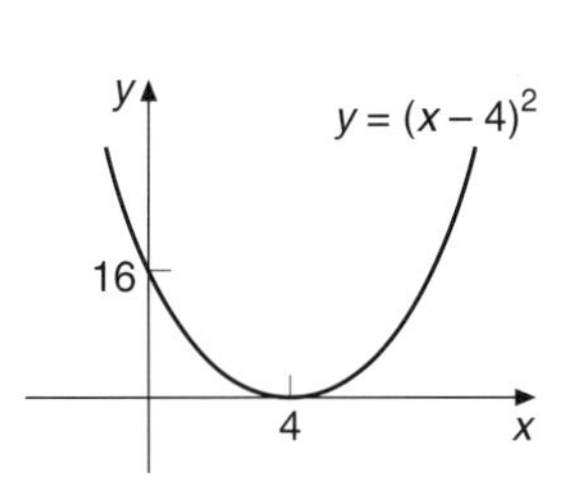


translation vector $\begin{pmatrix} 4 \\ 0 \end{pmatrix}$ 'move 4 units to the right'

(d)

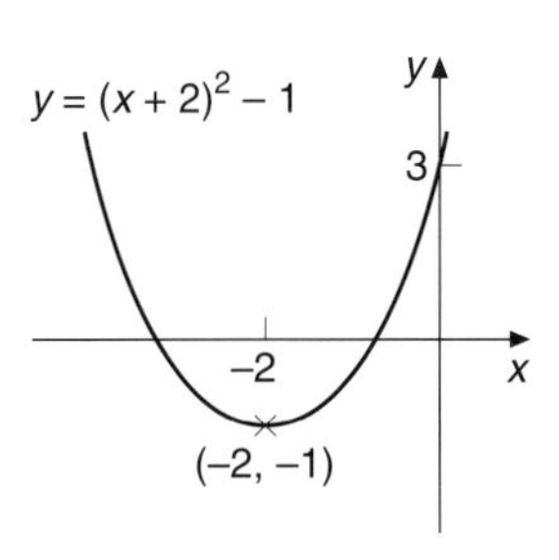


translation vector $\begin{pmatrix} -2 \\ -1 \end{pmatrix}$ 'move 2 to the left and 1 down in either order'

(e)

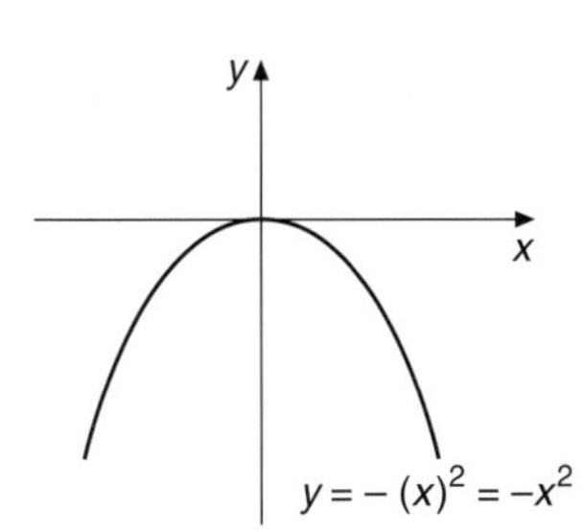


reflect in the $x$ axis

## Exercise 2.3

Suggest equations for the following

**A1** (a)

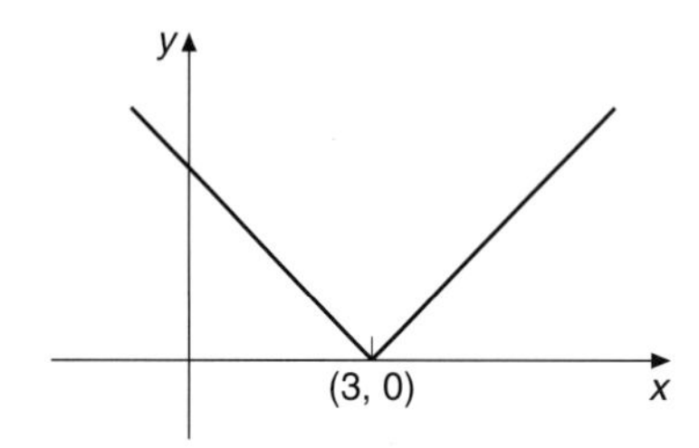


(b)

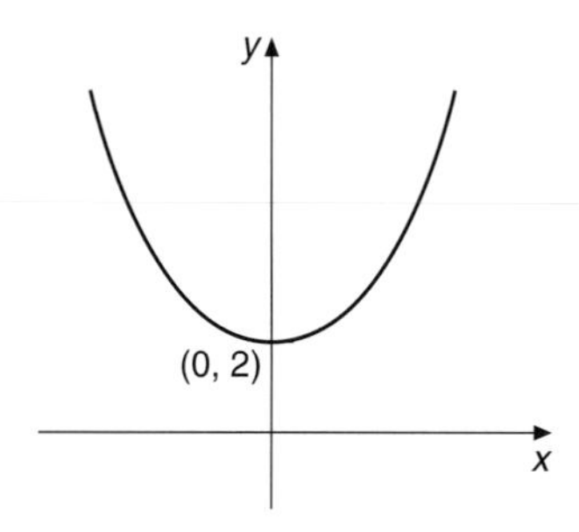


(c)

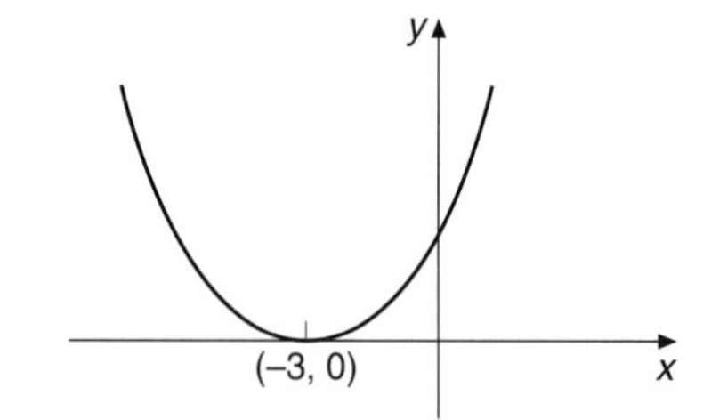

(d)

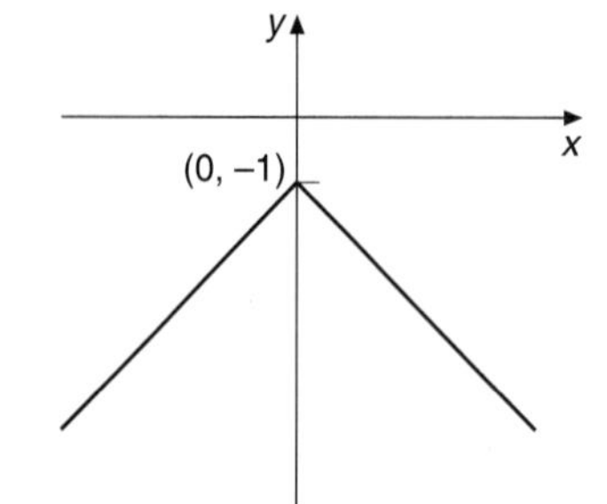

**A2**

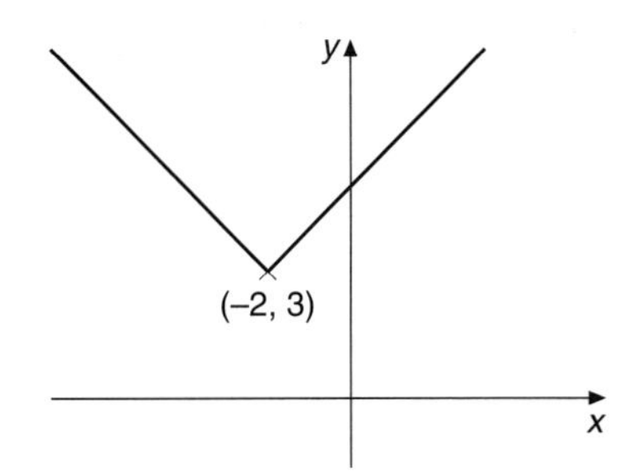


**A3**

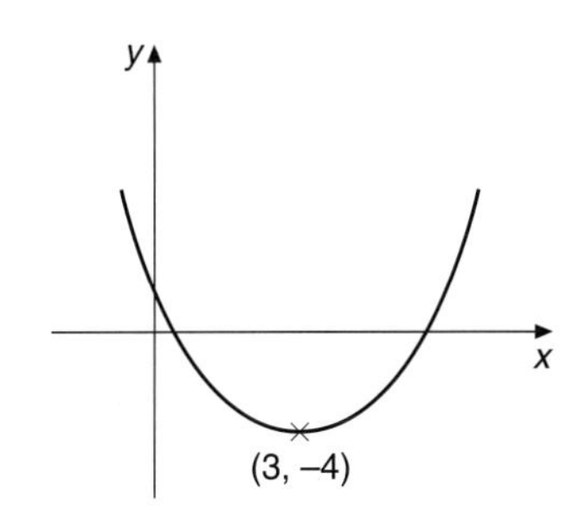


**A4**

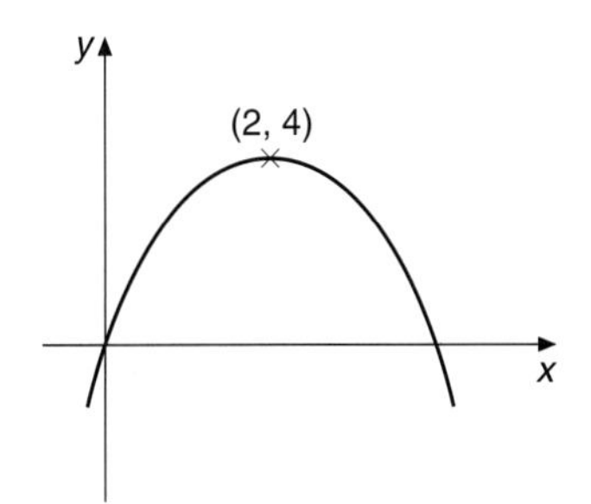


**A5**

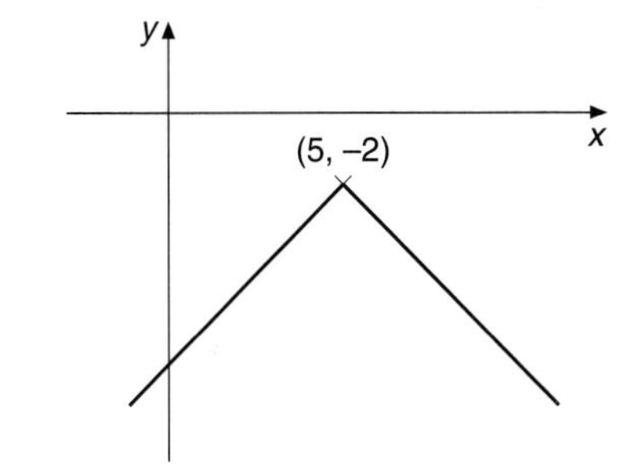

Sketch the following graphs:

**B1** $y = |x + 3| - 4$

**B2** $y = (x - 2)^2 + 5$

**B3** $y = 3 - |x - 2|$

**B4** $y = (x + 3)^2 - 4$

**B5** $y = 9 - (x - 3)^2$

Sketch:

**B6** $y = x^2 + 4x + 8$

**B7** $y = x^2 - 2x - 7$

**B8** $y = 6 - 3x - x^2$

**B9** $y = 8 + 6x - x^2$

**B10** $y = (x - 3)(x - 1) + 2$

## 2.4 The general quadratic function

### Key points

$$y = ax^2 + bx + c$$

is the equation for the general **quadratic function**.

It can also be written as

$$y = p(x + q)^2 + r$$

- If $a > 0$

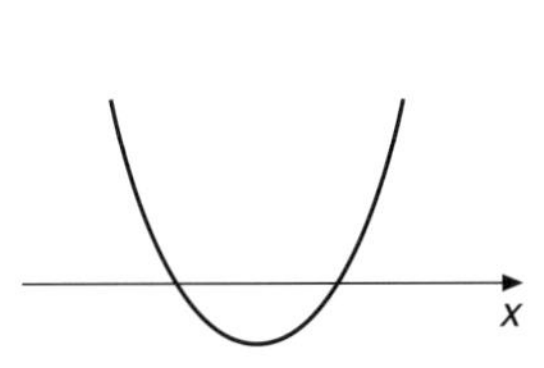

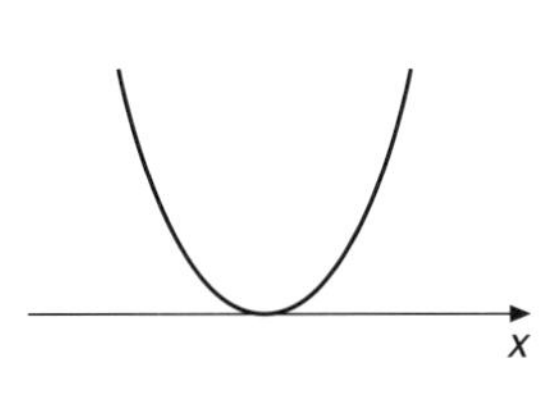

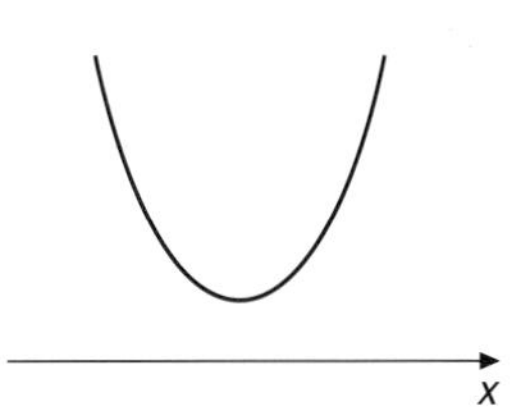


$b^2 - 4ac > 0$ $\quad$ $b^2 - 4ac = 0$ $\quad$ $b^2 - 4ac < 0$

- If $a < 0$

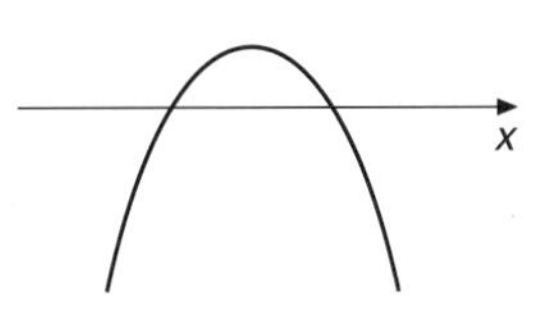

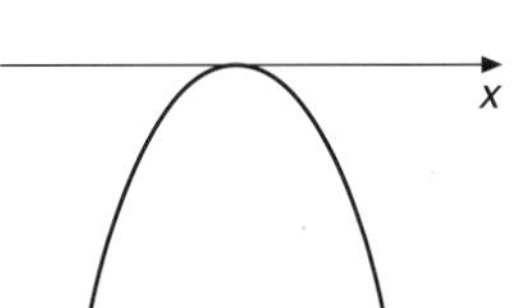

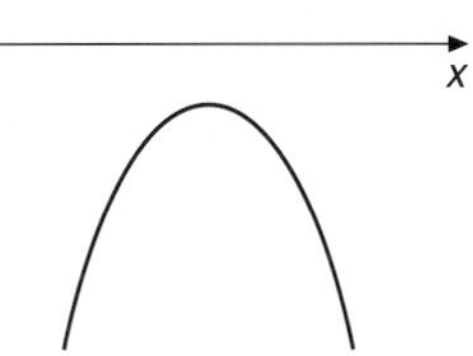


Two real roots $\quad$ Two equal roots $\quad$ No real roots

Consider $y = x^2$ and $y = 2x^2$

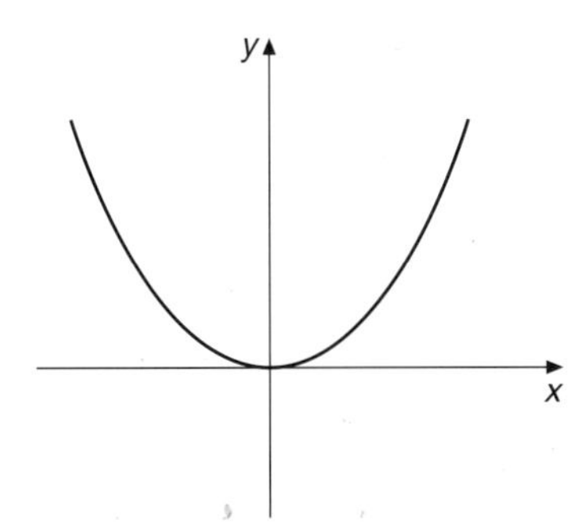

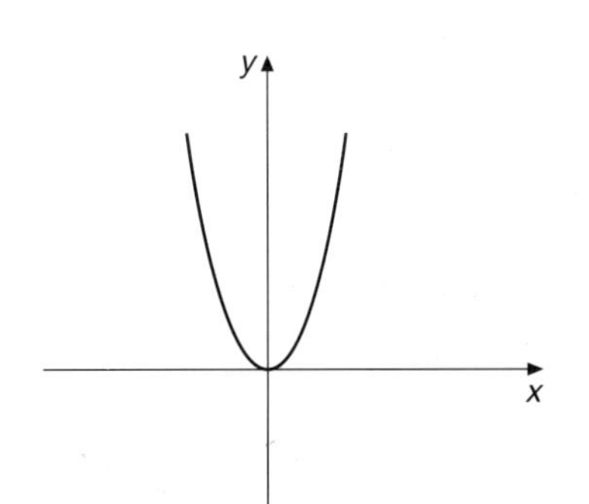

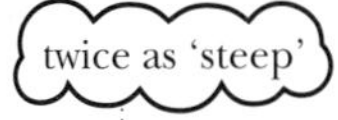


- $y = kx^2$ implies a 'stretch' scale factor $k$ parallel to the $y$ axis
- $y = p(x + q)^2 + r$ is $y = x^2$ translated $\begin{pmatrix} -q \\ 0 \end{pmatrix}$, stretched scale factor $p$ parallel to the $y$ axis and then translated $\begin{pmatrix} 0 \\ r \end{pmatrix}$

## Example

(a) Sketch $y = 2(x - 3)^2 + 4$ describing the series of transformations from $y = x^2$.

(b) If $y = 3x^2 - 6x - 8$ can be written in the form $y = k(x + a)^2 + b$ find $k$, $a$ and $b$.

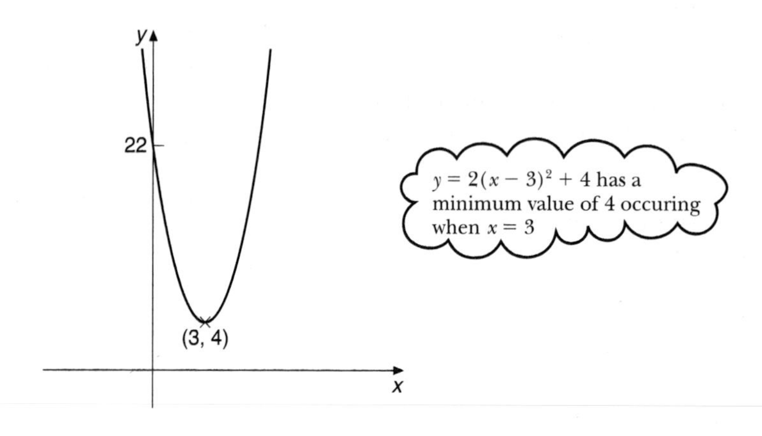


### Solution

(a) Translate $\begin{pmatrix} 3 \\ 0 \end{pmatrix}$, scale factor 2 parallel to the $y$ axis then translate $\begin{pmatrix} 0 \\ 4 \end{pmatrix}$.

(b) *Method 1* Complete the square

$$y = 3\left(x^2 - 2x - \frac{8}{3}\right)$$

$$= 3\left[(x - 1)^2 - \frac{11}{3}\right]$$

$$= 3(x - 1)^2 - 11$$

So $k = 3$, $a = -1$, $b = -11$.

*Method 2* Multiply out and compare coefficients.

$$3x^2 - 6x - 8 \equiv kx^2 + 2kax + ka^2 + b$$

Comparing $x^2$ terms $3 = k$

Comparing $x$ terms $-6 = 2ka$

so $-6 = 6a$

$-1 = a$

Comparing constants $-8 = ka^2 + b$

$-8 = 3(-1)^2 + b$

$-8 = 3 + b$

$-11 = b$

## Exercise 2.4

**A1** Write out the following in the form $y = a(x + b)^2 + c$ and state the values of $a$, $b$ and $c$.

(a) $y = x^2 + 6x - 2$

(b) $y = 2x^2 + 8x - 1$

(c) $y = 3x^2 + 6x + 5$

**A2** Write down the minimum values of $y$ in **A1** and the values of $x$ when this minimum occurs.

**A3** Write down the necessary transformations to change $y = x^2$ into

(a) $y = 2(x + 1)^2 - 5$

(b) $y = \frac{1}{2}(x + 1)^2 - 5$

(c) $y = -2(x + 1)^2 - 5$

**A4** State the maximum or minimum value of $y$ and the corresponding value of $x$ when

(a) $y = (x - 3)^2 + 8$

(b) $y = 2(x - 3)^2 + 8$

(c) $y = 5 - 3(x - 4)^2$

**A5** Find the minimum value of $5x^2 - 20x - 8$

Sketch the following graphs showing the coordinates of the vertex and the intersection with the $y$ axis.

**B1** $y = 2x^2 - 12x + 11$ (Hint: you can write this in the form $y = a(x - b)^2 + c$)

**B2** $y = \frac{1}{3}(x^2 - 2x + 1)$ (Hint: factorise the expression and then sketch)

**B3** Sketch $y = 4 - x^2$ and $y = 8 - 2x^2$ on the same axes

**B4** Sketch $y = 4(2 - x)(x + 3)$ and $y = (2 - x)(x + 3)$ on the same axes

**B5** $y = 3 + \frac{4x - x^2}{2}$ (Hint: sketch $y = 4x - x^2$ first)

## Chapter 2: A level questions

**C1** Sketch the graph of $y = 3x^2 + 10x - 8$ and use it to solve the inequality $(3x - 2)(x + 4) < 0$.

**C2** Express $3x + 2x^2 - x^3$ as a product of three factors.

Sketch the graph of $y = 3x + 2x^2 - x^3$ and use it to find the set of values of $x$ for which $x^3 \geq 2x^2 + 3x$.

**C3** (a) Express $x^2 - 6x + 2$ in the form $(x - a)^2 - b$ where $a$ and $b$ are positive integers.

(b) Write down the exact solutions of the equation $x^2 - 6x + 2 = 0$.

(c) Sketch the graph of $y = (x + 2)(x^2 - 6x + 2)$ marking the exact points of intersection with the $x$ and $y$ axes.

(d) Use your graph to help you solve the inequality $(x + 2)(x^2 - 6x + 2) < 0$.

**C4** On the same grid sketch the graphs of $y = |x - 5|$ and $y = |x| + 2$.

Calculate the coordinates of the point of intersection of the graphs and find the set of values of $x$ for which $|x - 5| - |x| \geq 2$.

**C5** Write $2x^2 + 4x - 1$ in the form $a(x + b)^2 + c$ and state the values of $a$, $b$ and $c$. Describe the series of simple transformations necessary to transform the graph of $y = x^2$ into the graph of $y = 2x^2 + 4x - 1$.

## Chapter 2: A level questions *continued*

Sketch the graph marking in the coordinates of the turning point, the intercept with the $y$ axis and the equation of the line of symmetry.

**C6** The following diagram, not to scale, represents a rectangular sheep pen constructed from 100 metres of fencing forming three of its sides. The fourth side is an existing wall. If the length of each of the equal pieces of fencing is $x$ metres show that $y = 100x - 2x^2$ if $y$ m$^2$ is the area of the pen. Sketch the graph of $y$ against $x$ and hence find the dimensions of the sheep pen when its area is a maximum.

x m

y m$^2$

x m

**C7**

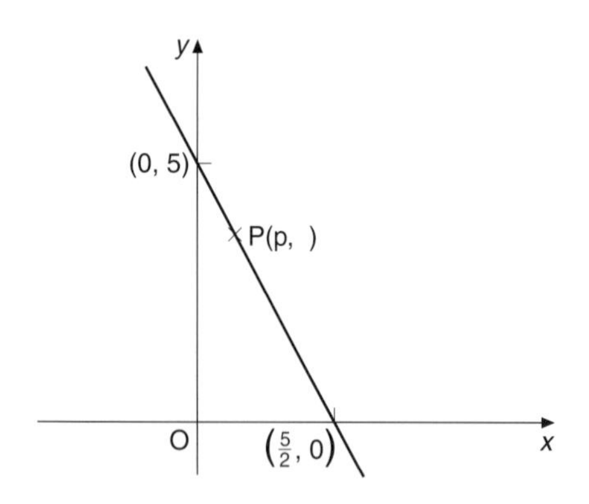


The above diagram is a sketch (not to scale) of the line $y + 2x = 5$. $O$ is the origin and $P$ is a point on the line whose $x$ coordinates is $p$ where

$$0 \leq p \leq 2\frac{1}{2}.$$

Show that the $y$ coordinate of $P$ is $5 - 2p$. Use Pythagoras' Theorem to find $OP^2$ in terms of $p$.

Show that $OP^2 = kz$ where $k$ is a value to be found and $z = p^2 - 4p + 5$.

By writing $z$ in the form $(p - a)^2 + b$ state the smallest value of $z$ and hence the shortest possible distance $OP$.

**C8** Calculate the coordinates of the points of intersection of the graphs $y = 6x - x^2$ and $y = x^2 - 4x$. Sketch the two graphs on the same diagram (you do not have to use the same scales on the two axes). Write down the coordinates of the maximum point $A$ and the minimum point $B$. Lines parallel to the $x$ axis are drawn through $A$ and $B$ to meet lines drawn parallel to the $y$ axis through the points of intersection. Find the area of the rectangle formed by these lines.

**C9** On the same axes sketch the graphs of $y = |2x - 3|$ and $y = x + 1$.

Find the points of intersection of the graphs and then use your diagram to find the set of values of $x$ which satisfy the inequality $|2x - 3| < x + 1$.

**C10**

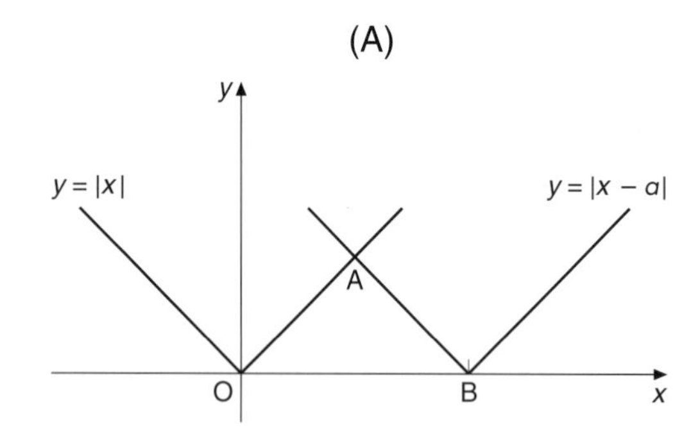


The diagram A shows sketches of the graphs $y = |x|$ and $y = |x - a|$, intersecting at $A$. Find the area of triangle $OAB$.

## Chapter 2: A level questions *continued*

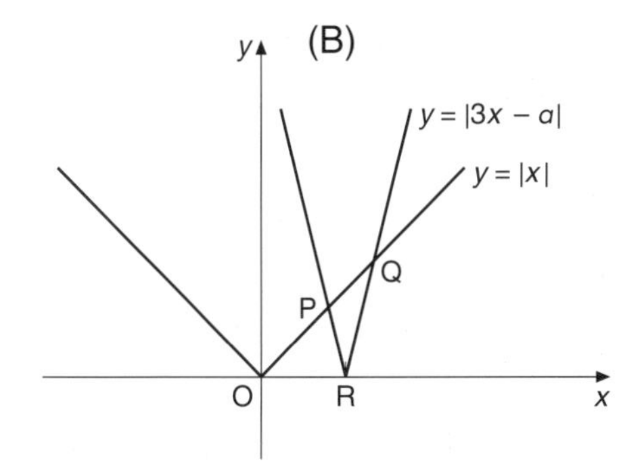


The diagram B shows sketches of the graphs $y = |x|$ and $y = |3x - a|$, intersecting at $P$ and $Q$. Obtain the coordinates of $P$, $Q$ and $R$ and hence show that Area $OAB$ : Area $OQR$ : Area $OPR = 6 : 2 : 1$.

# Chapter 3

## SEQUENCES AND SERIES

### 3.1 Sequences

#### Key points

**We define $t_r$ as the $r^{\text{th}}$ term of a sequence.**

If $t_r = (3r - 5)$ is the $r^{\text{th}}$ term of a sequence we can write
$t_1 = 3(1) - 5 = -2$, $t_2 = 3(2) - 5 = 1$, $t_3 = 3(3) - 5 = 4$,
$t_4 = 3(4) - 5 = 7$, $t_n = 3n - 5$, $t_a = 3a - 5$ etc.

So we form the sequence $-2, 1, 4, 7 \ldots$ where $t_r = 3r - 5$.

There are four types of sequence we need to recognise

- Convergent

  $1, \frac{1}{2}, \frac{1}{3}, \frac{1}{4}, \frac{1}{5}, \ldots$ where $t_r = \frac{1}{r}$

  The terms get closer and closer to a fixed number called 'the limit'

- Divergent

  $6, 12, 18, 24, \ldots$ where $t_r = 6r$

  $-6, -12, -18, -24, \ldots$ where $t_r = -6r$

- Oscillating

  $-2, 4, -8, 16, \ldots$ where $t_r = (-2)^r$

- Periodic

  $0, 2, 0, 2, 0, 2, 0 \ldots$ where $t_r = 1 + (-1)^r$

#### Example 1

Write down the first 4 terms generated by

(a) $t_r = 3r - 1$

(b) $t_r = 4r^2 - 3$

**Solution**

(a) $t_r = 3r - 1$
$t_1 = 3 - 1 = 2$
$t_2 = 6 - 1 = 5$
$t_3 = 9 - 1 = 8$
$t_4 = 12 - 1 = 11$
The sequence is 2, 5, 8, 11, . . .

This is an arithmetic sequence

(b) $t_1 = 4(1)^2 - 3 = 4 - 3 = 1$
$t_2 = 4(2)^2 - 3 = 16 - 3 = 13$
$t_3 = 4(3^2) - 3 = 36 - 3 = 33$
$t_4 = 4(4)^2 - 3 = 64 - 3 = 61$
The sequence is 1, 13, 33, 61, . . .

## Example 2

(a) Write down the first 4 terms of the sequence if $t_r = 2r + \frac{(-1)^r}{r}$

(b) If $t_{n+1} = 4 - t_n$ and $t_1 = 4$ write out the sequence and state the nature of the sequence.

**Solution**

(a) $t_1 = 2 + \frac{(-1)}{1} = 2 - 1 = 1$ $\qquad t_3 = 6 + \frac{(-1)^3}{3} = 6 - \frac{1}{3} = 5\frac{2}{3}$

$t_2 = 4 + \frac{(-1)^2}{2} = 4 + \frac{1}{2} = 4\frac{1}{2}$ $\qquad t_4 = 8 + \frac{(-1)^4}{4} = 8 + \frac{1}{4} = 8\frac{1}{4}$

The sequence is 1, $4\frac{1}{2}$, $5\frac{2}{3}$, $8\frac{1}{4}$, . . .

(b) When $n = 1$ $t_2 = 4 - t_1 = 4 - 4 = 0$
When $n = 2$ $t_3 = 4 - t_2 = 4 - 0 = 4$
When $n = 3$ $t_4 = 4 - t_3 = 4 - 4 = 0$
So 4, 0, 4, 0, . . . is a periodic sequence.

## Exercise 3.1

Generate the first 4 terms of the sequence if

**A1** $t_r = r^2$

**A2** $t_r = 2r - 5$

**A3** $t_r = r^3$

**A4** $t_r = \frac{1}{r+1}$

**A5** $t_r = \frac{(-1)^r}{r^2}$

**A6** State the nature of the sequences in **A1–A5**.

**A7–A10**: Find the 4th, the 9th and 10th terms of the following sequences.

**A7** $t_r = 10 - 2r$

## Exercise 3.1 *continued*

**A8** $t_r = (2r+1)(r+2)$

**A9** $t_r = r + \frac{2}{r}$

**A10** (a) $t_r = (-1)^r$

(b) $t_r = (-1)^{r+1}$

Find the first 4 terms of the following sequences and state the nature of each.

**B1** $t_{n+1} = \frac{1}{2}t_n$ and $t_1 = 4$

**B2** $t_{n+1} = t_n^2 - 1$ and $t_1 = 2$

**B3** $t_{n+1} = 4 - t_n^2$ and $t_1 = 0$

**B4** $t_r = \frac{(-1)^r}{2^r}$

**B5** $t_{n+2} = 2t_{n+1} - 3t_n$ and $t_1 = 0$, $t_2 = 3$

**B6** $t_r = 1 + (-1)^r$

**B7** $t_r = 3r^2 - 2^r$

**B8** $t_r = r - |3 - r|$

**B9** $t_r = r - |4 - r|$

**B10** $t_r = 2^r + (-2)^r$

## 3.2 The sigma notation

### Key points

$$\sum_{r=1}^{n} t_r = t_1 + t_2 + t_3 + t_4 + \ldots + t_n$$

### Example 1

(a) Work out $\sum_{r=3}^{7}(2r+1)$

(b) Write $3 + 7 + 11 + 15 + 19$ using the sigma notation.

**Solution**

(a) $\sum_{r=3}^{7}(2r+1) = 7 + 9 + 11 + 13 + 15 = 55$

$\uparrow$ $r=3$, $\uparrow$ $r=4$, $\uparrow$ $r=5$, $\uparrow$ $r=6$, $\uparrow$ $r=7$

(b) $3 + 7 + 11 + 15 + 19$

$t_r = 4r - 1$ so $\sum_{r=1}^{5}(4r-1)$

## Exercise 3.2

**A1** Find the numerical value of

(a) $\sum_{r=1}^{5}(r+3)$

(b) $\sum_{r=1}^{5}(2r+3)$

**A2** Write in $\sum$ notation

(a) $1+4+9+16+25+36$

(b) $25+36+49+64$

(c) $100+121+144$

**A3** Express the following in terms of $a$.

(a) $\sum_{r=1}^{4}(ar+1)$

(b) $\sum_{r=0}^{6}(ra^2+3)$

(c) $\sum_{r=1}^{5}(ar+ar^2)$

**A4** Write in $\sum$ notation

(a) $8+9+10+11+12$

(b) $50+49+48+\ldots+9+8$

(c) $2+4+6+8+\ldots+50$

**A5** Find the value of

(a) $\sum_{3}^{9}(1-3r)$

(b) $\sum_{1}^{5}(r^2-r^3)$

Write the first four terms and the last terms of the series

**B1** (a) $\sum_{p=6}^{50}\frac{2(p-3)}{p}$

(b) $\sum_{r=4}^{r=10}\frac{1}{(r-3)^2}$

**B2** (a) $\sum_{r=0}^{17}\left(\frac{1}{2}\right)^r$

(b) $\sum_{q=1}^{6}(0.1)^q$

**B3** $\sum_{p=-2}^{10}2p^3$

**B4** $\sum_{r=0}^{10}(-1)^r r$

**B5** $\sum_{r=1}^{20}(-1)^{r+1}(r^2+1)$

## 3.3 The arithmetic series

### Key points

- A **series** is the **sum** of a sequence, for example, $1+2+3+4+5$.
- In an **arithmetic series**, a fixed number $d$ is **added** to a term to get the next term of the series.
- $S_n=\sum_{r=1}^{n}[a+(r-1)d]=a+(a+d)+(a+2d)+\ldots+[a+(n-1)d]$

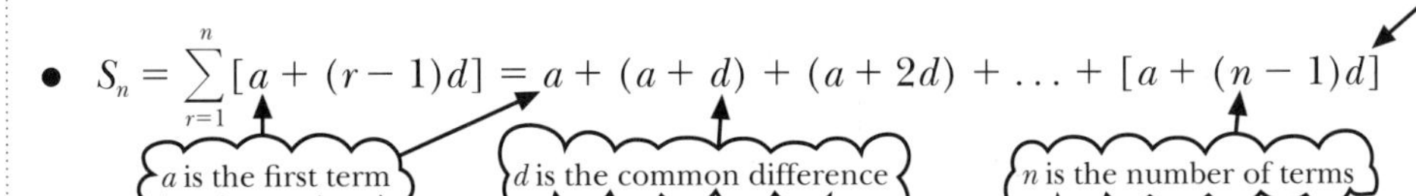


- $S_n=\frac{n}{2}[2a+(n-1)d]=\frac{n}{2}$ [first term + last term]

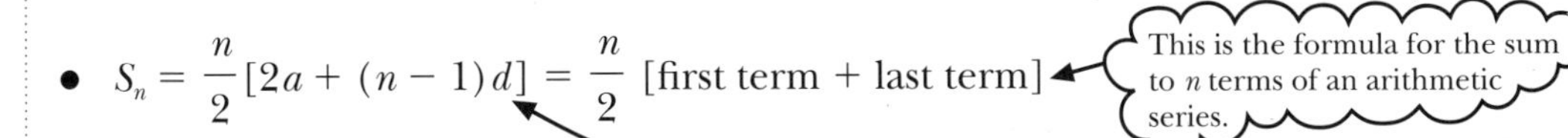

## Example 1

Show that the sum of $1 + 3 + 5 + \ldots + (2n - 1)$ is always a perfect square.

**Solution**

This is an arithmetic series with $a = 1$, $d = 2$ and it has $n$ terms.

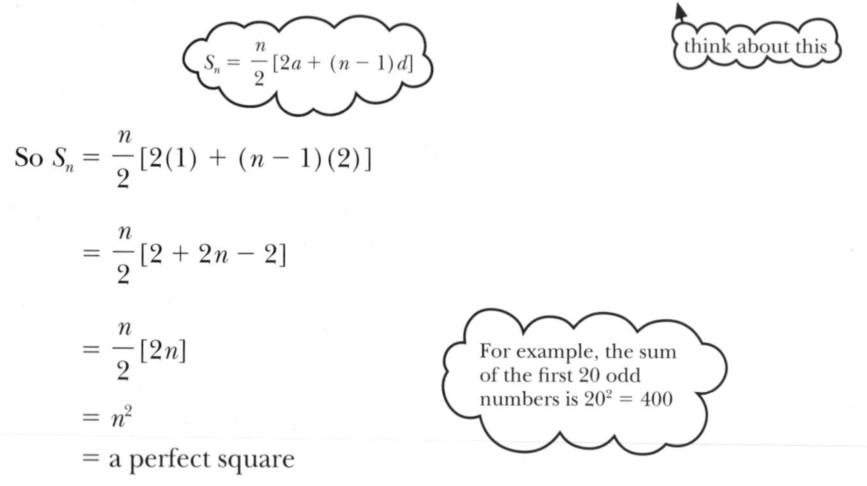


$$\text{So } S_n = \frac{n}{2}[2(1) + (n-1)(2)]$$

$$= \frac{n}{2}[2 + 2n - 2]$$

$$= \frac{n}{2}[2n]$$

$$= n^2$$

= a perfect square

## Example 2

Find the value of $\sum_{r=1}^{20} \log 3^r$

**Solution**

$$\sum_{r=1}^{20} \log 3^r = \log 3 + \log 3^2 + \log 3^3 + \ldots + \log 3^{20}$$

$$= \log 3 + 2\log 3 + 3\log 3 + \ldots + 20\log 3$$ ← This is an arithmetic series

$a = \log 3$, $d = \log 3$, $n = 20$

$$S_n = \frac{n}{2}[2a + (n-1)d]$$

$$S_{20} = \frac{20}{2}[2\log 3 + 19\log 3]$$

$$= 10[21\log 3]$$

$$= 210\log 3$$

An alternative, more direct method:

$\log 3 + 2\log 3 + 3\log 3 + \ldots 20\log 3$

$= \log 3(1 + 2 + 3 + \ldots 20)$ ← This is an arithmetic series

$$= \log 3\left(\frac{20}{2}[2 + 19]\right)$$

$= \log 3(210)$

$= 210\log 3.$

## Exercise 3.3

**A1** Find the $14^{th}$ term (i.e. $a + 13d$) of the following arithmetic **sequences**

(a) $2, 5, 8, \ldots$

(b) $7, 5, 3, \ldots$

(c) $6, 13, 20, \ldots$

(d) $-5, -9, -13, \ldots$

**A2** Find the sum of the first 14 terms $\left(\text{i.e. } S_{14} = \frac{14}{2}(2a + 13d)\right)$ of the arithmetic **series**

(a) $2 + 5 + 8 + \ldots$

(b) $7 + 5 + 3 + \ldots$

(c) $6 + 13 + 20 + \ldots$

(d) $-5 - 9 - 13 - \ldots$

**A3** Find the number of terms of the arithmetic series

(a) $10 + 14 + 18 + \ldots + 50$

(b) $10 + 7 + 4 + \ldots - 50$

**A4** Find the sum of the first 60 odd integers.

**A5** Find the sum of the first 60 even integers.

In **A6**, **A7** and **A8** find the sum of the arithmetic series.

**A6** (a) $3 + 8 + 13 + \ldots$ to 20 terms

(b) $13 + 9 + 5 + \ldots$ to 16 terms

**A7** (a) $3 + 5 + 7 + \ldots + 37$

(b) $68 + 63 + 58 + \ldots + 18$

**A8** (a) $-17 - 14 - 11 - \ldots$ from the $5^{th}$ term to the $15^{th}$ term inclusive

(b) All the terms less than 100 in $2 + 12 + 22 + \ldots$

**A9** Evaluate

(a) $\sum_{r=1}^{10}(3r - 2)$

(b) $\sum_{r=11}^{40}(28 - r)$

**A10** Find the sum of all the even numbers between 11 and 111.

**B1** The sum of the first 6 terms of an arithmetic series is $-3$ and the sixth term is $-8$. Find the first term, the common difference, the fiftieth term and the sum of the first 50 terms of the series.

**B2** The first term of an arithmetic series is 30 and $S_4 = 84$. Find the common difference and the number of terms needed for the sum to be zero.

**B3** Find the sum of the first thousand positive integers.

**B4** How many terms of the arithmetic series $3a + 5a + 7a + 9a + \ldots$ must be taken for the sum to be $624a$?

**B5** The first and last terms of an arithmetic series are $-2$ and 47 and the sum of all the terms is $2227\frac{1}{2}$.

Find

(a) the number of terms

(b) the common difference

(c) the middle term.

**B6** Find the sum of all odd multiples of 3 between 1 and 101.

**B7** Find $n$ such that $\sum_{r=1}^{n}(2r + 5) = 520$.

**B8** The sum of the first $n$ term of series is $2n^2 + 5n$.

Obtain the first 4 terms of the series.

**B9** The sum of 3 consecutive terms of an arithmetic series is 30 and their product is 510. Find the numbers.

**B10** If the sum of the first 5 terms of an arithmetic series is double its $9^{th}$ term, show that its first term is double its common difference.

## 3.4 The geometric series

### Key points

- In a **geometric series**, each term is **multiplied** by a fixed number, $r$, to get the next term of the series.

- $S_n = \sum_{p=1}^{n} ar^{p-1} = a + ar + ar^2 + \ldots + ar^{n-1}$

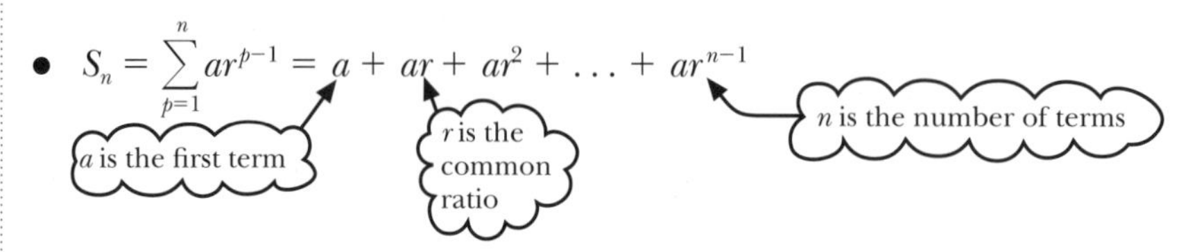


- $S_n = \dfrac{a(1 - r^n)}{1 - r}$

- $S_\infty = \dfrac{a}{1 - r}$ (for $|r| < 1$ ← a convergent series)

- If $|r| > 1$ then the series is divergent and **no sum to infinity exists.**

### Example 1

(a) Find the sum to infinity of the geometric series generated by the recurring decimal $0.\dot{3}\dot{7}$.

(b) The second term of a geometric series is $-6$ and the fifth term is $20\frac{1}{4}$. Find the common ratio.

#### Solution

(a) $0.\dot{3}\dot{7} = 0.37373737\ldots$

$$= \frac{37}{10^2} + \frac{37}{10^4} + \frac{37}{10^6} + \ldots$$

This is a geometric series with

$$a = \frac{37}{10^2}, \; r = \frac{1}{10^2}$$

($-1 < r < 1$)

$$\text{So } S_\infty = \frac{a}{1 - r} = \frac{\frac{37}{100}}{1 - \frac{1}{100}} = \frac{\frac{37}{100}}{\frac{99}{100}} = \frac{37}{99}$$

(b) second term $ar = -6$

$$\text{fifth term } ar^4 = 20\frac{1}{4}$$

$$\text{So } (ar)r^3 = \frac{81}{4}$$

$$-6r^3 = \frac{81}{4}$$

$$r^3 = -\frac{81}{24} = -\frac{27}{8}$$

$$r = -\frac{3}{2}.$$

## Example 2

A sum of £500 is invested on 1 January in each of four successive years. The investment earns compound interest at 5% per annum. Find the total amount in the bank at the end of the fourth year.

### Solution

The first investment amounts to $500\ (1{\cdot}05)^4$ after 4 years
The second investment amounts to $500\ (1{\cdot}05)^3$ after 3 years
The third investment amounts to $500\ (1{\cdot}05)^2$ after 2 years
The fourth investment amounts to $500\ (1{\cdot}05)$ after 1 year.

Either calculate the four separate amounts and add them together or treat the terms as a geometric series.

$$\text{Total amount} = 500(1{\cdot}05 + 1{\cdot}05^2 + 1{\cdot}05^3 + 1{\cdot}05^4)$$

This is a geometric series with $a = 1{\cdot}05$ and $r = 1{\cdot}05$

$$= 500\left[\frac{1{\cdot}05(1 - 1{\cdot}05^4)}{1 - 1{\cdot}05}\right]$$

$$= 2262{\cdot}82 \text{ (2 d.p.)}$$

$\therefore$ The amount in the bank is £2262·82

## Exercise 3.4

**A1** Find the 20th term (i.e. $ar^{19}$) of the following geometric sequences, leaving your answers in index notation.

(a) $2, 1, \frac{1}{2}, \ldots$

(b) $5, 20, 80, \ldots$

(c) $-3, -6, -12, \ldots$

(iv) $3, -1, \frac{1}{3}, \ldots$

## Exercise 3.4 *continued*

**A2** Find the sum of the first 20 terms of the geometric series

$$\left(S_{20} = \frac{a(1-r^{20})}{1-r}\right)$$

(a) $2 + 1 + \frac{1}{2} + \ldots$

(b) $5 + 20 + 80 + \ldots$

(c) $-3 - 6 - 12 - \ldots$

(iv) $3 - 1 + \frac{1}{3} - \ldots$

**A3** Find the sum of the following geometric series

(a) $\frac{1}{2} + 1 + 2 + \ldots + 128$

(b) $4000 + 800 + \ldots + 2{\cdot}56 \times 10^{-6}$

Find the sum of the geometric series in questions **A4–A7**

**A4** (a) $2 + 4 + 8 + \ldots$ to 10 terms

(b) $1 - 2 + 4 - \ldots$ to 9 terms

**A5** (a) $3 - 1 + \frac{1}{3} - \ldots$ to 8 terms

(b) $8 + 2 + \frac{1}{2} + \ldots$ to 7 terms

**A6** (a) $\frac{1}{8} + \frac{1}{2} + \ldots + 32$

(b) $81 - 27 + \ldots + \frac{1}{81}$

**A7** (a) $8 + 4 + 2 + \ldots + \frac{1}{64}$

(b) $9 - 6 + 4 - \ldots - \frac{128}{243}$

**A8** Find the value of $\sum_{r=1}^{8} 3(2^r)$.

**A9** The sum of the first three positive terms of a geometric series is 560.

If the first term is 80 find the common ratio.

**A10** Find the 12<sup></sup>th term and the sum of the first ten terms of the geometric series

$$36 - 12 + 4 - \frac{4}{3} + \ldots$$

**B1** Find $\sum_{1}^{\infty} \frac{1}{2^r}$

**B2** If $S_n = \sum_{r=1}^{n} 2(-3)^n$ find $S_1$, $S_2$, $S_3$, $S_4$, and $S_n$.

**B3** How many terms of the series $2 + 4 + 8 + 16 + \ldots$ must be taken for the sum to equal $(2^n - 2)$?

**B4** A man invests £2,000 annually and the investment earns compound interest at 7% per annum. How much money will be in his account immediately after his 8th investment?

**B5** A ball is dropped vertically from a height of $d$ metres and rebounds to a height of $\frac{2d}{3}$ metres. By modelling the ball as a particle, find the height of the 6th bounce and the total distance travelled by the ball to the top of the 6th bounce.

**B6** The 6th term of a geometric series is $-96$ and its 3rd term is 12. Find the sum of its first 6 terms.

**B7** In a geometric series the sum of all the terms except for the first three is $\frac{1}{8}$ of the sum to infinity. Find the common ratio.

**B8** Given that $4x + 1$, $6x - 1$ and $9x - 5$ are consecutive terms of a geometric series, find these numbers and also the common ratio of the series.

**B9** In a geometric series the sum to infinity is 81 and the sum of the first 4 terms is 80. Find the first 4 terms of the series. Is your answer unique?

**B10** Find $n$ if $\sum_{r=1}^{n} \left(-\frac{1}{2}\right)^{r-1} = \frac{85}{128}$.

## 3.5 The binomial series

### Key points

- $(1+x)^n = 1 + nx + \frac{n(n-1)}{2!}x^2 + \frac{n(n-1)(n-2)}{3!}x^3 + \ldots + x^n$
- $(a+b)^n = a^n + \binom{n}{1}a^{n-1}b + \binom{n}{2}a^{n-2}b^2 + \ldots + b^n$
- $\binom{n}{r} = \frac{n!}{r!(n-r)!}$

$n$ is a positive integer

### Example 1

Write down the first 4 terms of

(a) $(1-2x)^{10}$

(b) $(2+px)^7$

**Solution**

(a) $(1-2x)^{10} = 1 + 10(-2x) + \frac{10 \times 9}{2!}(-2x)^2 + \frac{10 \times 9 \times 8}{3!}(-2x)^3 + \ldots$

$= 1 - 20x + 180x^2 - 960x^3 + \ldots$

(b) $(2+px)^7 = 2^7 + \binom{7}{1}2^6(px) + \binom{7}{2}2^5(px)^2 + \binom{7}{3}2^4(px)^3 + \ldots$

$= 2^7 + 7px(2^6) + 21p^2x^2(2^5) + 35p^3x^3(2^4) + \ldots$

$= 128 + 448px + 672p^2x^2 + 560p^3x^3 + \ldots$

### Example 2

Find the coefficient of the term in $x^6$ in the expansion of $(2+3x)(3-2x)^8$.

**Solution**

$(2+3x)(3-2x)^8$

$= 2(3-2x)^8 \quad + \quad 3x(3-2x)^8$

Now you work out the term in $x^6$ from each of these

the term in $x^6$ is $2\binom{8}{6}3^2(-2x)^6 = 32256x^6$

the term in $x^6$ is $3x\binom{8}{5}(3^3)(-2x)^5 = -145152x^6$

Add together giving $-112896x^6$

So the coefficient of $x^6$ is $-112896$.

## Exercise 3.5

**A1** Expand

(a) $(1-x)^4$

(b) $(1+x)^6$

**A2** Expand

(a) $(1-3x)^5$

(b) $(2-x)^4$

**A3** Write down, and simplify, the first 4 terms in the expansion of

(a) $(1+2x)^8$

(b) $(1-3x)^{10}$

(c) $(2+3x)^9$

**A4** Write down the first four terms and the last term of

(a) $(1+5x)^{20}$

(b) $(1-5x)^{20}$

(c) $(2+x)^{10}$

**A5** Expand

(a) $\left(1-\frac{x}{2}\right)^4$

(b) $(1-px)^4$

**A6** Expand $(p+qx)^5$

In **A7–A9** find the first three terms in the expansion

$a + bx + cx^2$

**A7** $(3+4x)(1-2x)^6$

**A8** $(2-3x)(2+5x)^5$

**A9** $(1-2x)(1-4x)^4$

**A10** (No calculator)

Find $(2.0001)^8$ correct to 10 decimal places.

**B1** Write down and simplify the middle term of

(a) $(1+2x)^8$

(b) $\left(x+\frac{1}{x}\right)^{10}$

(c) $\left(3p+\frac{1}{p}\right)^6$

**B2** Find the coefficient of the term in $x^3$ for $(1-4x)^9$.

**B3** If $a = 1+\sqrt{2}$ and $b = 2-\sqrt{2}$ find

(a) $a^4$

(b) $(b-a)^3$

(c) $\left(\frac{b}{a}\right)^3$

**B4** If $a = (1-x)$ and $b = (1+x)$ find

(a) $a^5 - b^5$

(b) $a^5b^5$ (Hint $a^5b^5 = (ab)^5$)

**B5** Write down the expansion of $(4+x)^5$. Hence find the exact value of $(3.99)^5$.

**B6** Find the term in $x^6$ in the expansion of $(1+2x)(2+3x)^6$.

**B7** Find the term in $x^5$ in the expansion of $(2-3x)(3+2x)^8$.

**B8** Obtain the coefficient of

(a) $x^5$ in $(2x-5)^9$

(b) $x^6$ in $(3x-4)^8$ leaving your answers as products of prime factors.

**B9** Find the ratio of the coefficients of $x^6$ and $x^7$ in the expansion of $(2+5x)^{11}$.

**B10** Expand and simplify $(1+2x)^8 - (1-2x)^8$.

## Chapter 3: A level questions

**C1** The twelfth term of an arithmetic series is 47 and the sum of the first twelve terms is 300. Show that the seventh term is the cube of the first term.

**C2** Write out the first five terms of the series $\sum_{1}^{100} 3r$. How many terms are needed for the sum to exceed 3000?

**C3** For the series $x + x^3 + x^5 + x^7 + \ldots$ ($|x| \neq 1$) write down the $n^{\text{th}}$ term and find $S_n$, the sum of the first $n$ terms. If $x = \frac{1}{4}$ show that as $n \to \infty$ then the series converges to $\frac{4}{15}$.

**C4** A mother and father celebrate the birth of a new baby girl, and each guesses how many months it will be before the baby is twice as long as she measured at birth. The father guesses 18 months and the mother 30 months. If the baby's length increases by 3% each month then by how many months does

(a) the father underestimate

(b) the mother overestimate?

(Give your answer to 1 decimal place.) Whose guess is best?

**C5** A pie chart is cut into ten sectors whose areas form an arithmetic series. The first sector represents the mass of the baby at birth and they continue until it has trebled that mass (so the area of the largest sector is three times that of the smallest sector).

Find the angle between the straight edges of the smallest sector giving your answer to the nearest degree.

**C6** In the expansion of the expression $(2 - x)(a + bx)^{10}$ the coefficient of $x^7$ is zero. Find, in its simplest form, the ratio $a : b$.

**C7** Find $n$ if

(a) $\sum_{r=1}^{n} (2r + 3) = 480$

(b) $\sum_{r=1}^{n} \left(\frac{1}{2}\right)^{r-1} = \frac{511}{256}$

**C8** The sequence $t_1, t_2, t_3, \ldots$ is such that $t_{r+1} = -\frac{t_r}{2}$. If $t_1 = 8$, find

(a) $t_5$ and $t_6$

(b) $t_{r+2} : t_r$

(c) $\sum_{r=1}^{\infty} t_r$

**C9** In a simple model of a 10 year savings plan £600 is invested in the account at the beginning of each 'year' (1 April) and interest of 7% is calculated at the end of that 'year' (31 March) and added to the account. Show that the £600 invested at the beginning has become £600 $(1.07)^{10}$ at the end of 10 years and that the final £600 invested has become £642. Find the total in the account at the end of the plan.

**C10** Use the expansion of $(1 + x)^5$ to find the exact value of $(1.001)^5$.

**C11** The first term of a geometric series is 9 and the sum to infinity is 10. Find the common ratio and the sum of the first 5 terms. Find also, in its simplest form, the ratio of the fifth term to the sum of all terms after the fifth term.

# Chapter 4

## TRIGONOMETRY I

### 4.1 Bearings, sine & cosine rule, area of a triangle

**Key points**

Your formula sheet helps you here.

The sine rule $\dfrac{a}{\sin A} = \dfrac{b}{\sin B} = \dfrac{c}{\sin C}$

The cosine rule $a^2 = b^2 + c^2 - 2bc\cos A$

$$\cos A = \frac{b^2 + c^2 - a^2}{2bc}$$

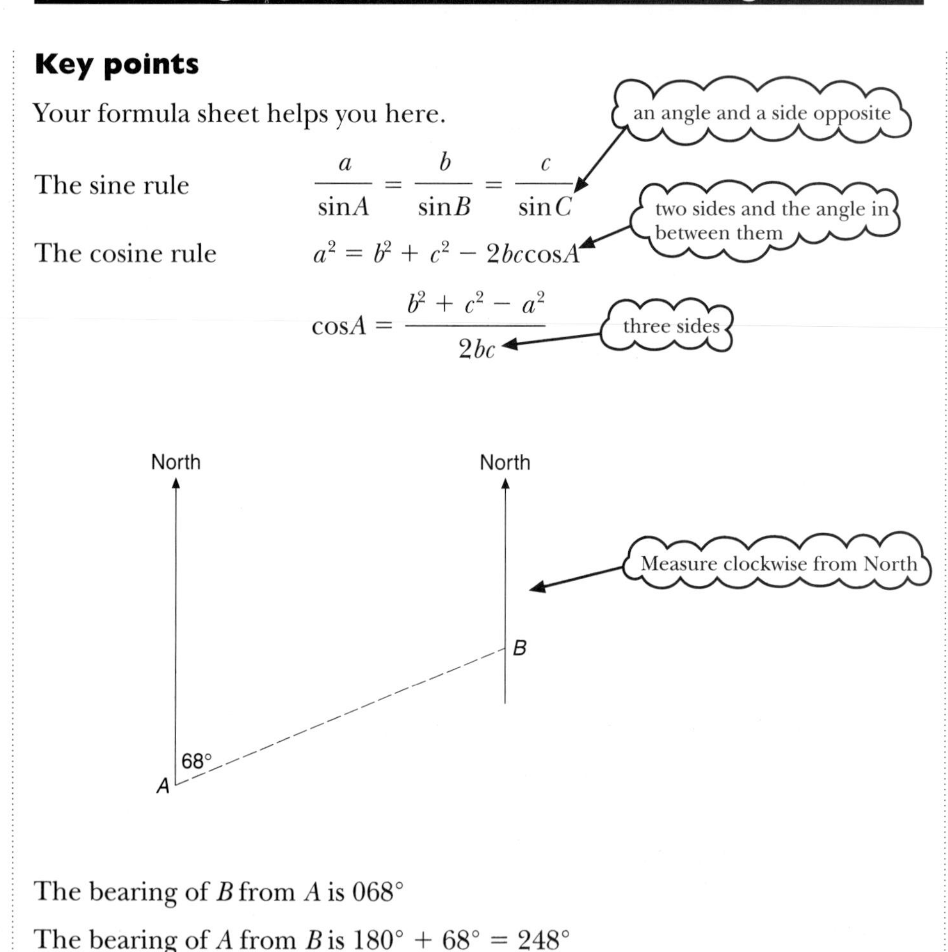


The bearing of $B$ from $A$ is 068°

The bearing of $A$ from $B$ is $180° + 68° = 248°$

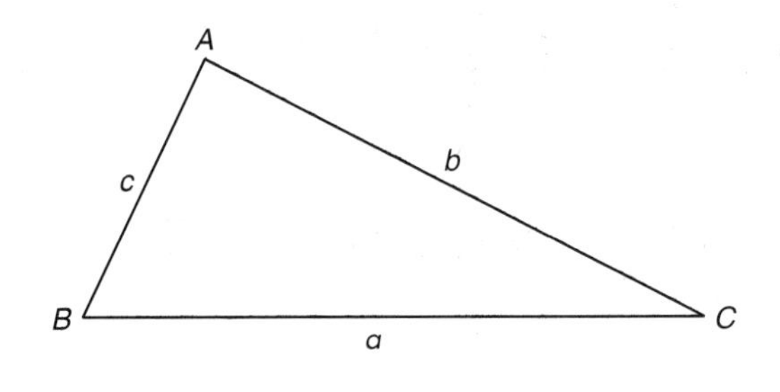


The area is $\frac{1}{2}ab\sin C$ ← or $\frac{1}{2}bc\sin A$ or $\frac{1}{2}ac\sin B$

## Example 1

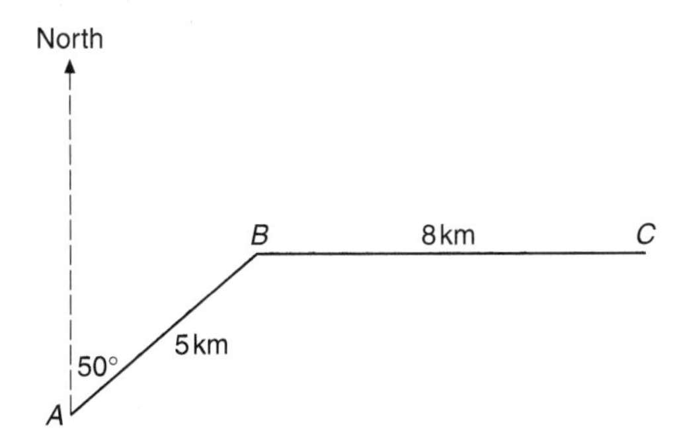


$B$ is on a bearing 050° from $A$ and $C$ is due east of $B$.

Find the distance and bearing of $C$ from $A$.

**Solution**

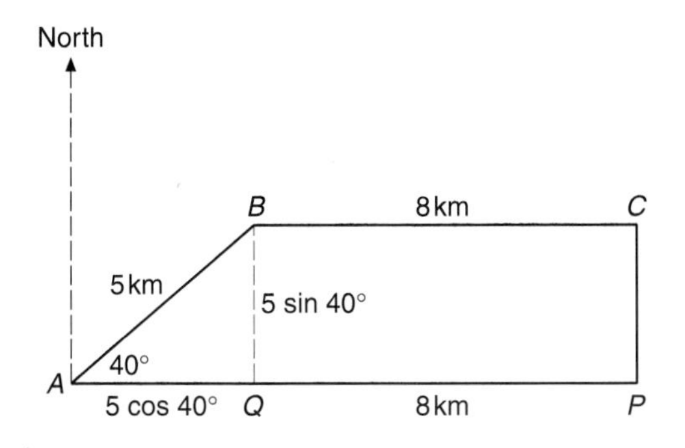


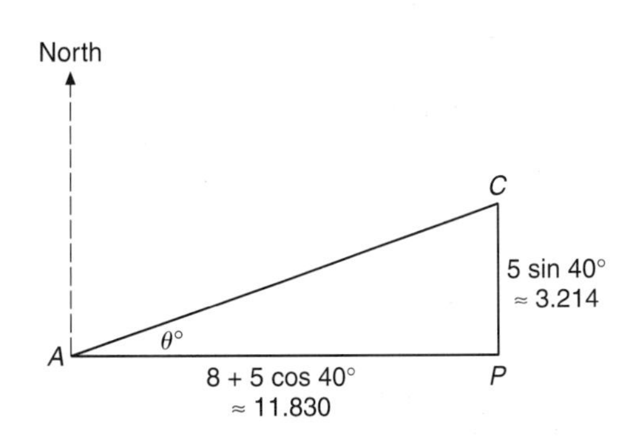

Pythagoras' Theorem gives $AC = 12.26$ (2 d.p.)

$\tan\theta° \approx \dfrac{3.214}{11.830} \Rightarrow \theta = 15°$ (to the nearest degree)

So $C$ is 12.26 km from $A$ on a bearing 075°. ← $90 - \theta$

## Example 2

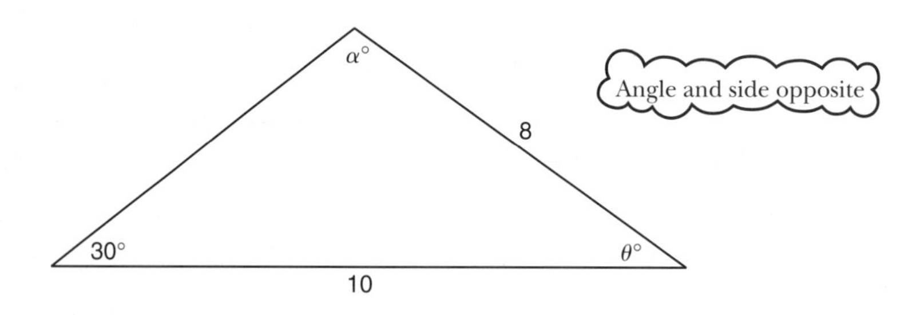


Find the possible values for $\theta$ and the corresponding areas of the triangles

**Solution**

Use the Sine Rule to get $\dfrac{10}{\sin\alpha°} = \dfrac{8}{\sin 30°}$

which is $\dfrac{\sin\alpha°}{10} = \dfrac{\sin 30°}{8}$

so $\sin\alpha° = \dfrac{10\sin 30°}{8} = 0.625$

Your calculator gives $\alpha = 38.7$

$\sin(180 - \theta)° = \sin\theta°$

So another possible value is $180° - 38.7° = 141.3°$

Our triangle is still possible so either

$\alpha = 38.7$ or $\alpha = 141.3$

$\theta = 180 - 30 - 38.7$ or $\theta = 180 - 30 - 141.3$

$= 111.3$ $\theta = 8.7$

The corresponding areas using $\dfrac{1}{2}ab\sin C$ are

$\dfrac{1}{2}(8)(10)\sin 111.3°$ or $\dfrac{1}{2}(8)(10)\sin 8.7°$

$\approx 37.3$ $\approx 6.1$

## Exercise 4.1

In your answers, give lengths and areas correct to 2 decimal places, angles correct to 1 decimal place.

In **A1–A4** find the distance and bearing of $C$ from $A$.

**A1** $C$ is 8 km due west of $B$ and $B$ is 5 km due north of $A$.

**A2** $C$ is 4 km due north of $B$ and $A$ is 5 km due east of $B$.

**A3** $B$ is 20 km on a bearing of 052° from $A$. $C$ is 10 km due south of $B$.

**A4** $B$ is 8 km from $A$ on a bearing of 147° from $A$. $B$ is 10 km due west of $C$.

**A5** Find the area of triangle $XYZ$ if $\hat{X} = 90°$, $\hat{Z} = 35°$ and $YZ = 20$ cm.

**A6** Find the area of the triangle with sides of length 17 mm, 17 mm, and 16 mm.

In **A7–A10** find the length or angle asked for in the triangle $ABC$.

In each case find the area of the triangle.

**A7** $B = 32.4°$, $a = 12.2$ cm, $c = 8.7$ cm. Find $b$.

**A8** $c = 3.8$ cm, $B = 63°$, $A = 56°$. Find $a$.

**A9** $a = 11$ cm, $b = 7$ cm, $c = 6$ cm. Find $A$.

**A10** $c = 5.4$ cm, $B = 38.7°$, $C = 51.3°$. Find $A$.

**B1** Find the area of a parallelogram with sides of lengths 5 cm and 7 cm, and an angle of 143°.

**B2** A rectangle has diagonal length 10 cm and one side has length 4 cm.

Find its perimeter and its area.

**B3** A triangle $ABC$ whose area is 10.5 $cm^2$ has $a = 6$ cm and $b = 7$ cm. Find angle $C$.

**B4** Find the length of a side of a regular hexagon whose area is 48 $cm^2$.

**B5** Isosceles triangles $ABC$, $PQR$ each have area 40 $cm^2$ and

$AB = AC = PQ = PR = 10$ cm.

Given that $QR > BC$ find the difference in the perimeters of the triangles.

**B6** $R$ is 11 km from $Q$ on a bearing of 252°. $P$ is 8 km from $Q$ on a bearing of 303°.

Find the distance and bearing of $P$ from $R$.

**B7** $B$ is 6 km due north of $A$, $C$ is 7 km due east of $B$ and $D$ is 10 km from $C$ on a bearing of 150°.

Find distance and bearing of $D$ from $A$.

**B8** Triangle $XYZ$ has $XY = 4$ cm, $YZ = 3$ cm and $ZX = 2$ cm. Find angles $X$, $Y$ and $Z$.

**B9** In triangle $ABC$, $c = 10$ cm, $a = 11$ cm and $\hat{A} = 25°$. Find $C$, $b$ and the area of the triangle.

**B10** The triangle $PQR$ has $PQ = 10$ cm, $QR = 7$ cm and $Q\hat{P}R = 30°$. Show that two triangles can be drawn and calculate the possible lengths of $PR$. Show that the difference between these lengths is $4\sqrt{6}$ cm.

## 4.2 Application of trigonometry in 2D and 3D

### Key points

You need to know:

- the distance between two points $(a, b, c)$ and $(p, q, r)$ in three dimensions is

$$\sqrt{(p-a)^2 + (q-b)^2 + (r-c)^2}$$

- $\theta$ is the angle between $AP$ and the plane.

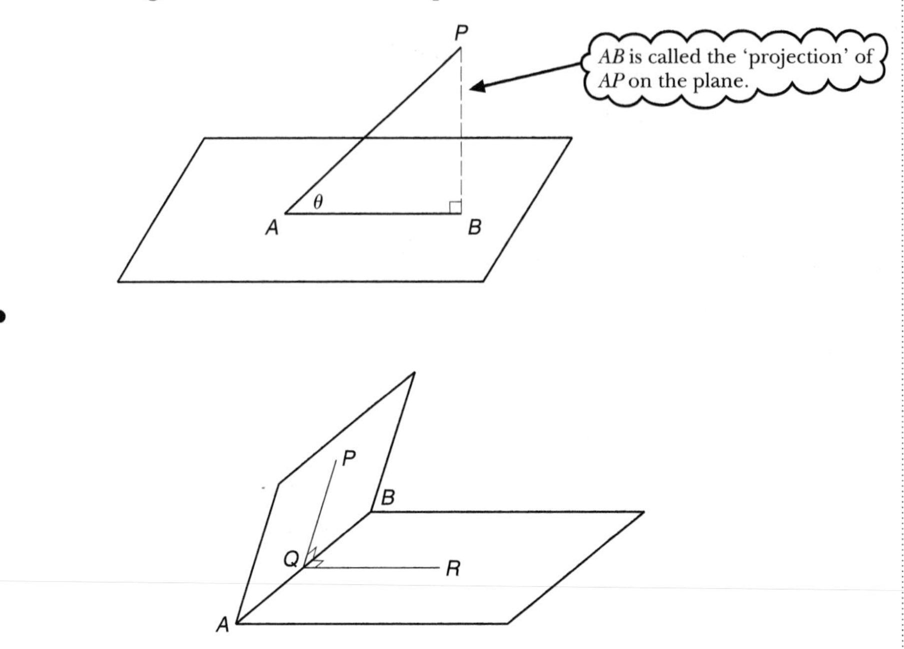


If $PQ$ meets $AB$ at 90°, $QR$ meets $AB$ at 90° then $\angle PQR$ is the angle between the planes.

## Example I

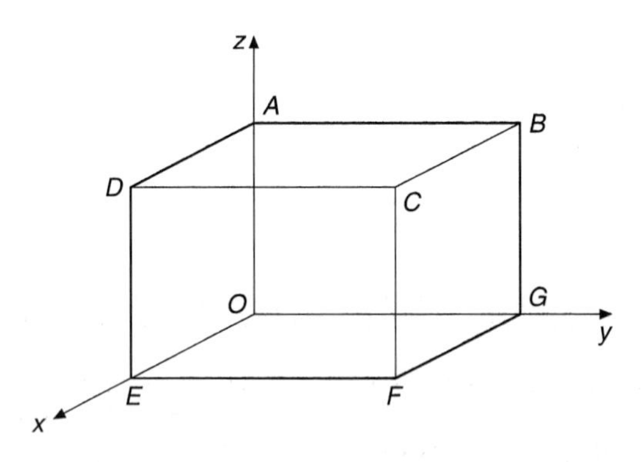


The diagram shows a rectangular block with $O(0,0,0)$ and $C(3,8,4)$.

Find the length $BE$ and the exact angle between $BE$ and the plane $EFGO$.

**Solution**

We need $\angle BEG$ ($EG$ is the projection of $EB$ on the plane $EFGO$).

The coordinates of $C$ give the dimensions of the box, so we can find the coordinates of $E$ and $B$.

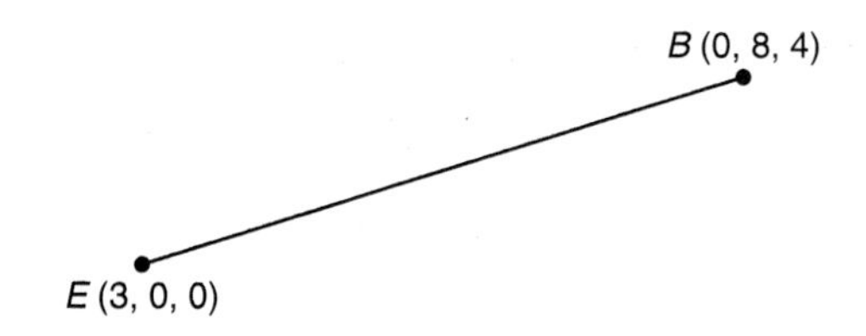


$$\text{So } EB^2 = (3-0)^2 + (0-8)^2 + (0-4)^2$$
$$= 9 + 64 + 16 = 89$$
$$EB = \sqrt{89}$$

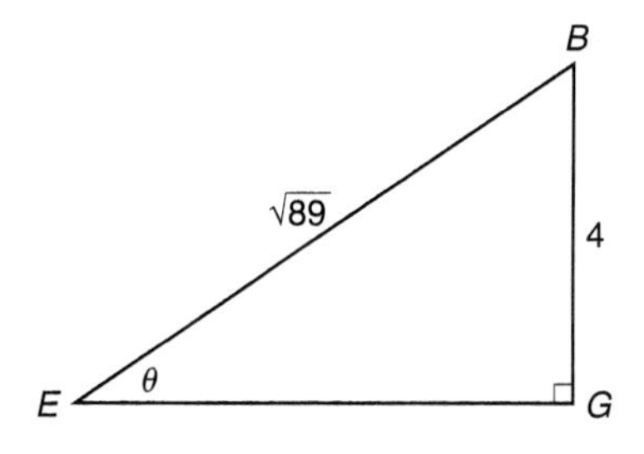


In $\Delta BEG$

$$\sin\theta = \frac{4}{\sqrt{89}}$$

$$\theta = \sin^{-1}\left(\frac{4}{\sqrt{89}}\right)$$

## Exercise 4.2

Give answers to a reasonable degree of accuracy.

**A1** Jean is standing on the edge of a cliff. Her eye is 40 metres above sea level. She observes a boat sailing directly towards her, at an angle of depression of 13°. Two minutes later the angle of depression has increased to 33°. Find the average speed of the boat. How much longer will it take the boat to reach the foot of the cliff (assumed vertical) at the same average speed?

**A2** *ABCD* is a horizontal square of side 4 metres. A point *E* is 3 metres vertically above *D*. What is the angle of elevation of:

(a) *E* from *A*

(b) *E* from *B*

(c) *E* from the mid point of *AC*.

**A3** Points *A*, *B* and *C* lie, in that order, on a horizontal line and the point *D* is vertically above *C*. $AB = 20$ cm. The angles of elevation of *D* from *A* and *B* are 18° and 27° respectively. Calculate the distance *CD*.

## Exercise 4.2 *continued*

**A4** A pyramid has its square base of side 8 cm placed on a horizontal surface and its vertex is 10 cm vertically above the centre of its base. Find:

(a) the angle between a slant edge and the base.

(b) the angle between a slant face and the base.

**A5**

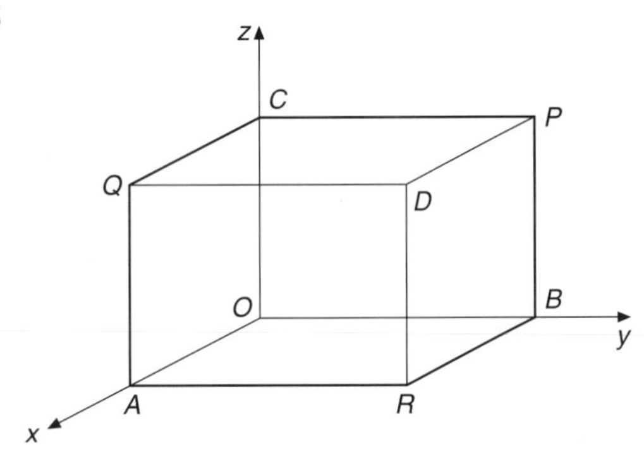


The diagram represents a rectangular box (cuboid), with $OA = 3$ cm, $OB = 6$ cm and $OC = 2$ cm.

Find the angle which the diagonal $OD$ makes with:

(a) $OA$ (b) $OB$ (c) $OC$

**B1** Find the angle which the diagonal of a cube makes with one of its faces.

**B2** A plane roof is a rectangle 10 metres by 4 metres with the 10 m edges horizontal. The roof is inclined at 25° to the horizontal. Find the angle between a diagonal of the roof and the horizontal.

**B3** A right pyramid has a rectangular base $ABCD$ with $AB = 2a$ and $BC = 2b$, where $a \neq b$. O is the centre of the base, $V$ is the vertex of the pyramid and $OV = h$. Find expressions for the angles made with $ABCD$ by:

(a) the edge $VB$

(b) the plane $VAB$

(c) the plane $VBC$.

**B4** A door is a rectangle $ABCD$ with $AB = 75$ cm and $BC = 2$ metres. It is hinged to the doorframe along the vertical line $BC$. From its closed position it is opened through an angle of 60°. Find the angle between the diagonal of the door, $BD$, in its initial and final positions.

**B5** Points $A$, $B$, $C$ have coordinates (4,0,0) (0,4,0) and (0,0,3) respectively. $O$ is the origin. Find the angle between the planes $AOB$ and $ACB$.

## 4.3 Radians, arc length, sector of a circle

### Key points

- In any circle
  Arc length $= r\theta$

  Area of sector $= \dfrac{1}{2}r^2\theta$

  $\theta$ measured in RADIANS

  $2\pi$ radians $= 180°$

-

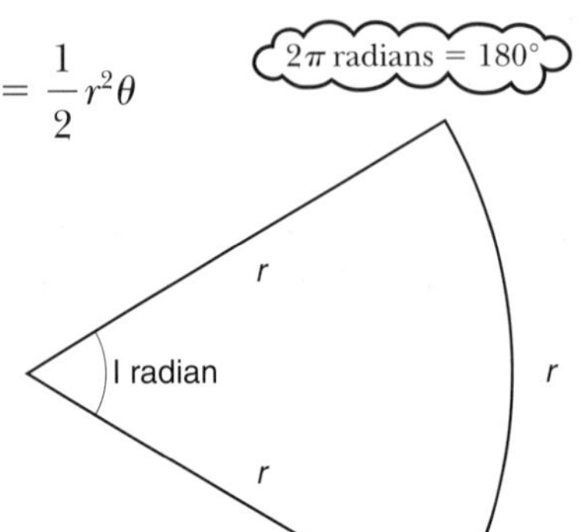


For 1 radian arc length = radius

## Example 1

The shaded area in the diagram is called the minor segment. Find the area of this segment, given that $O$ is the centre of the circle.

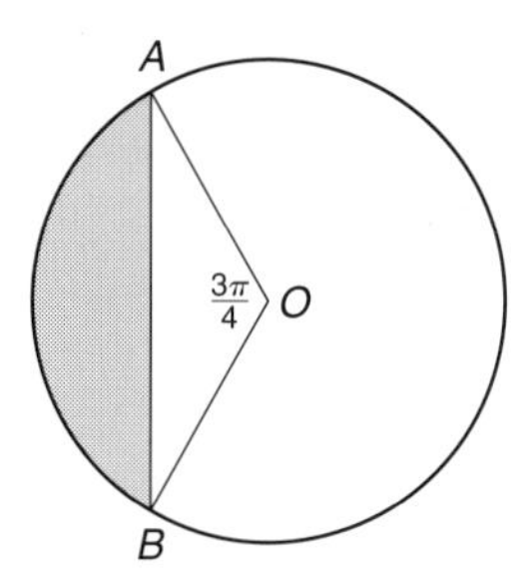


### Solution

You have to find the area of sector $AOB$ and subtract the area of $\Delta AOB$. This leaves the minor segment.

$$\text{Area of sector } AOB = \frac{1}{2}r^2\theta = \frac{1}{2}(6^2)\frac{3\pi}{4} = \frac{27\pi}{2} \text{ cm}^2$$

$$\text{Area of } \Delta AOB = \frac{1}{2}ab\sin\hat{O}$$

Using "$\frac{1}{2}ab\sin C$"

$$= \frac{1}{2}(6)(6)\sin\frac{3\pi}{4}$$

$$= \frac{18}{\sqrt{2}}$$

$$= 9\sqrt{2} \text{ cm}^2$$

So the area required

$$= \left(\frac{27\pi}{2} - 9\sqrt{2}\right)$$

this is the exact value

$$= 29.7 \text{ (1 d.p.)}$$

## Example 2

If the area of sector $AOB$ is 48 cm$^2$ and the length of the minor arc $AB$ is 12 cm, find the angle of the sector and also the length of the major arc $AB$.

### Solution

$$\text{Area} = \frac{1}{2}r^2\theta = 48$$

$$r^2\theta = 96$$

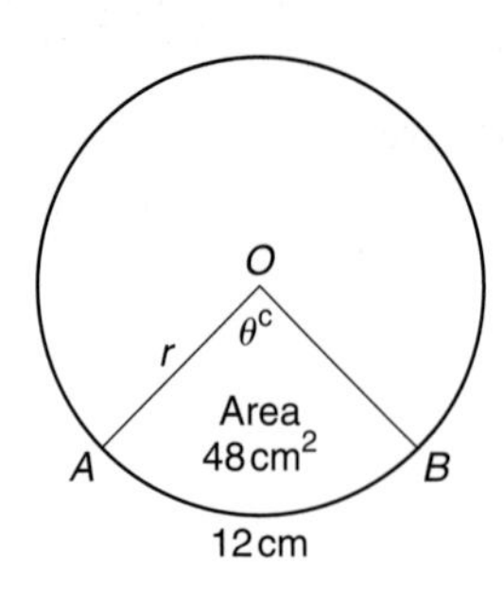


Arc length $r\theta = 12$

$$r^2\theta = r(r\theta) = 96$$

You now have to find a relationship between $r^2\theta$ and $r\theta$.

Hence $r(12) = 96$

So $r = 8$

So $8\theta = 12$

Going back to $r\theta = 12$

$$\theta = \frac{12}{8} = \frac{3}{2}$$

$\therefore$ Angle of sector $AOB$ is $1.5^c$.

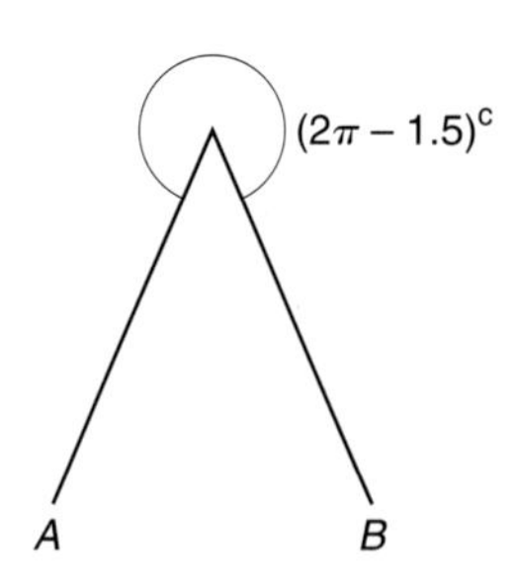


$$\begin{aligned} \text{Major arc } AB &= 8(2\pi - 1.5) \\ &= 16\pi - 12 \\ &= 38.27 \text{ cm (2 d.p.)} \end{aligned}$$

arc length $= r\theta$

## Exercise 4.3

Give answers to a reasonable degree of accuracy.

**A1** Change 30°, 720°, 150°, 45°, 18° into radians (exact).

**A2** Find the area and arc length of the following sectors:

(a)

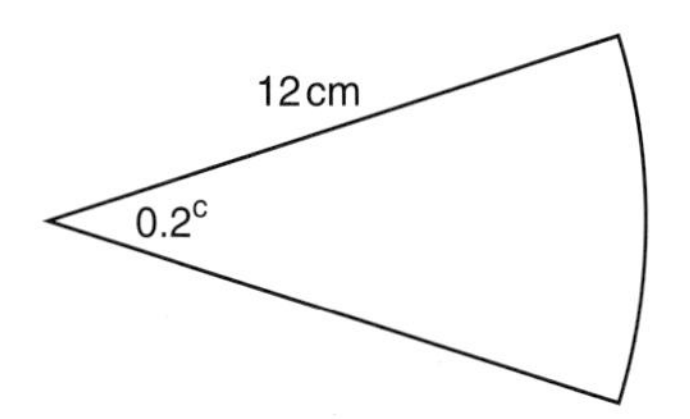


(b)

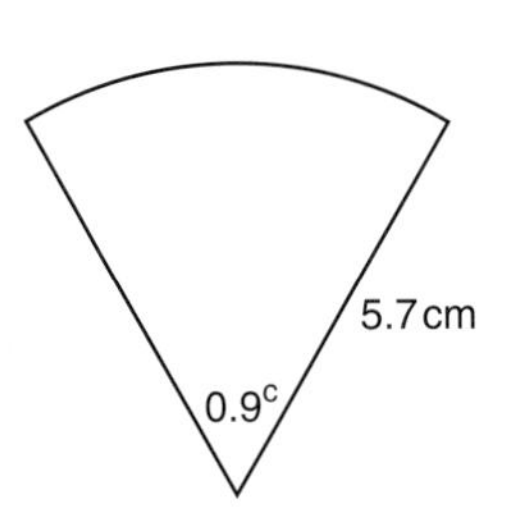


(c)

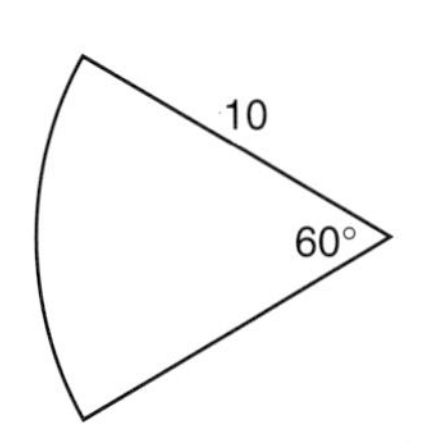


**A3** The areas of the following are 100 cm$^2$. Find the angle of the sector in *radians* and hence the arc length of the sector.

(a)

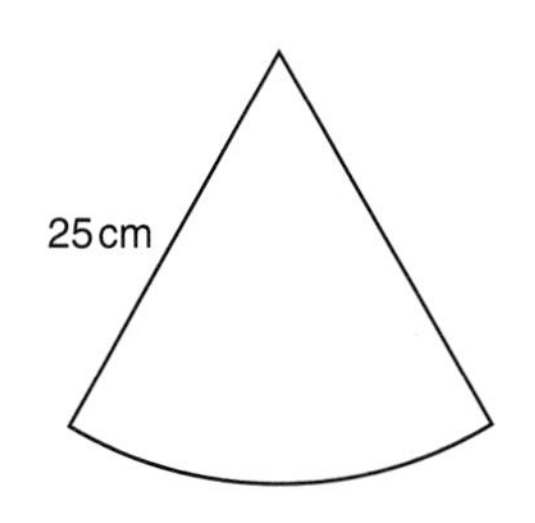


(b)

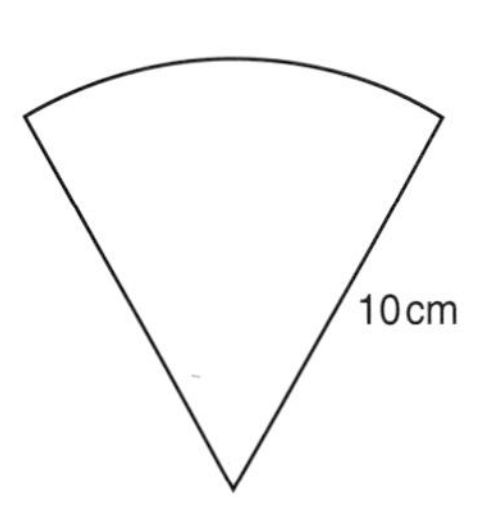


**A4**

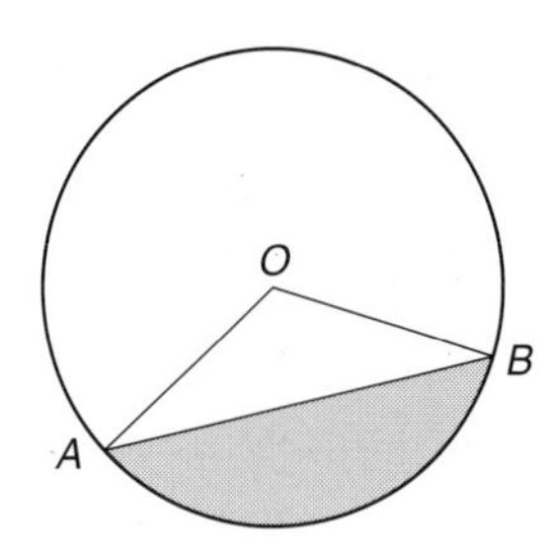


Find the shaded area if the radius of the circle is 4 cm and $\angle AOB = 1.5$ radians.

$\left(\text{Remember that the area of triangle is } \frac{1}{2}ab\sin\hat{C}\right)$

**A5**

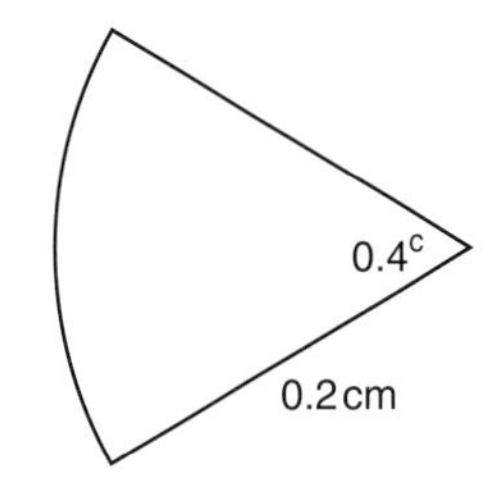


Find the area and the perimeter of the sector of the circle.

In questions **A6–A9**, $O$ is the centre of a circle with radius $R$ and points $A$ and $B$ lie on its circumference.

**A6** $A\hat{O}B = 108°$, $R = 8$ cm.

Find the length of

(a) the minor arc $AB$

(b) the major arc $AB$

(c) the length of the perimeter of the minor segment formed by $AB$.

## Exercise 4.3 *continued*

**A7** $A\hat{O}B = 2.4^c$, $R = 10$ cm.

Find the length of

(a) the minor arc $AB$

(b) the major arc $AB$

(c) the length of the perimeter of the minor segment formed by $AB$.

**A8** $A\hat{O}B = 81°$, $R = 7.8$ cm.

Find the areas of

(a) the minor sector $AOB$

(b) the major sector $AOB$

(c) the minor segment cut off by $AB$.

**A9** $A\hat{O}B = 1.23^c$, $R = 4.3$ cm.

Find the areas of

(a) the minor sector $AOB$

(b) the major sector $AOB$

(c) the major segment cut off by $AB$.

**A10** In the diagram $0 < \theta < \dfrac{\pi}{2}$, $AT$ is the tangent at $A$ to the circle centre $O$. Angle $AOB = \theta^c$.

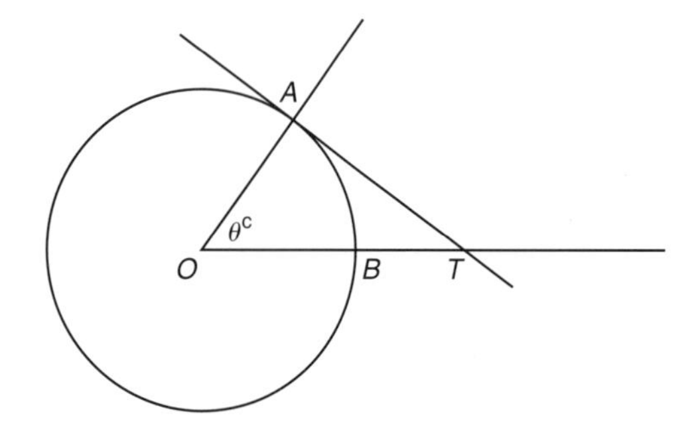


By comparing the areas of triangle $AOB$, sector $AOB$ and triangle $OAT$ show that $\sin\theta < \theta < \tan\theta$.

**B1**

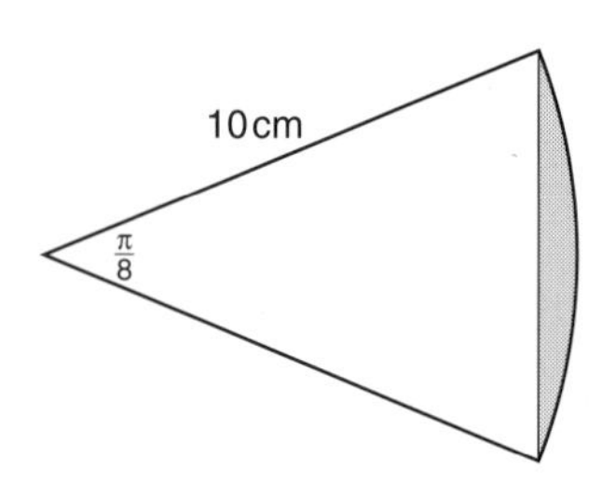


Find the shaded area.

**B2** The arc length of a sector is 30 cm, and the area is 600 cm$^2$. Form two equations involving $r$ and $\theta$ and solve them simultaneously to find $r$ and $\theta$.

**B3** The number of square metres in a sector of a circle is six times the number of metres in the arc length. Find the radius of the circle and the exact angle of the sector when the area is $12\pi$ m$^2$.

**B4**

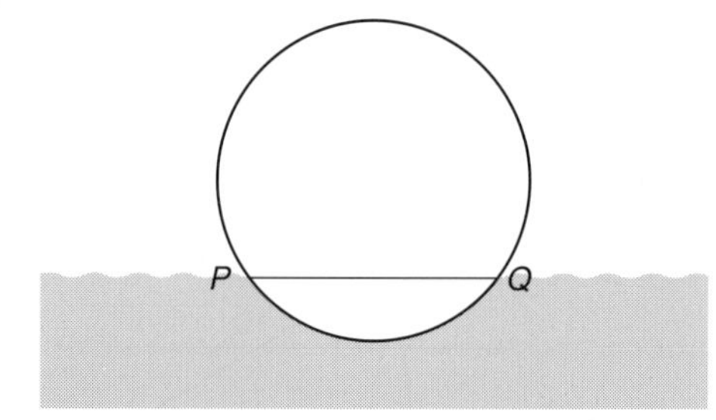


A cylindrical oil drum of length 1 metre and diameter 56 cm is floating in a river.

If $PQ$ is 40 cm find the volume of the drum which lies above the surface of the water.

**B5** A swing ball completes 10 full circles in 8 seconds. How fast is the ball moving if it maintains the same angular speed? Show that it will take $\dfrac{0.32}{\pi}$ seconds to travel 120 cm if the string is 1.5 metres long.

## Exercise 4.3 *continued*

**B6** $A$ and $B$ are points on the circumference of a circle centre $O$, radius $r$.

(a) If the length of the arc $AB$ is $\frac{3r}{2}$ find, in terms of $r$, the area of the minor segment formed by $AB$.

(b) Repeat (i) if instead the length of the chord $AB$ is $\frac{3r}{2}$.

**B7**

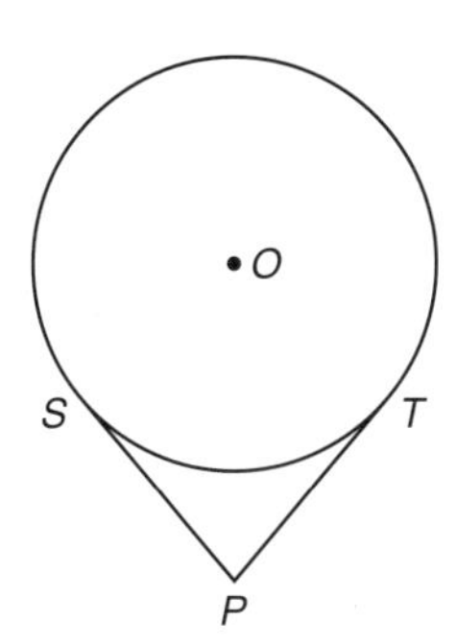


From a point $P$, 10 cm from the centre $O$ of a circle of radius 7 cm, tangents are drawn to touch the circle at $S$ and $T$. Calculate:

(a) the length of the perimeter of the region bounded by $PS$, $PT$ and the major arc $ST$.

(b) the area of this region.

**B8**

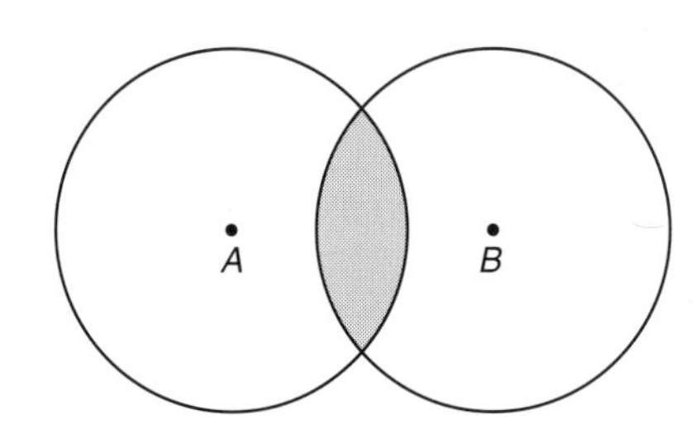


Two circles, each of radius 5 cm have centres $A$ and $B$, situated 8 cm apart. Find the area common to the two circles (shaded in diagram) and the length of the boundary of this area.

**B9**

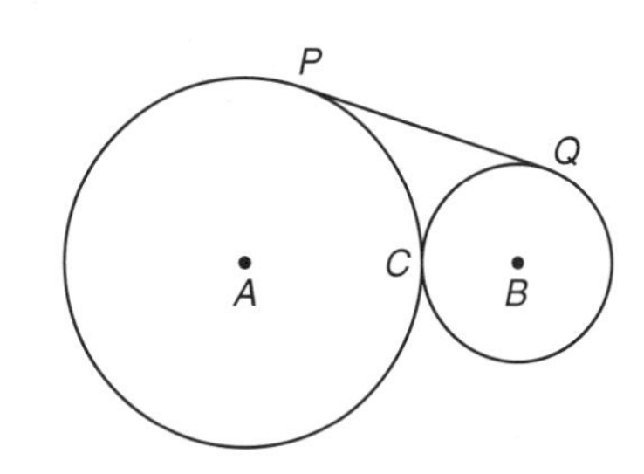


The diagram shows two circles with centres $A$ and $B$. They have radii 3 cm and 2 cm respectively and touch externally at $C$. $PQ$ is a common tangent to the circles.

Find the area of the region bounded by $PQ$, and arc $QC$ and the arc $CP$.

Also find the perimeter of this region.

**B10**

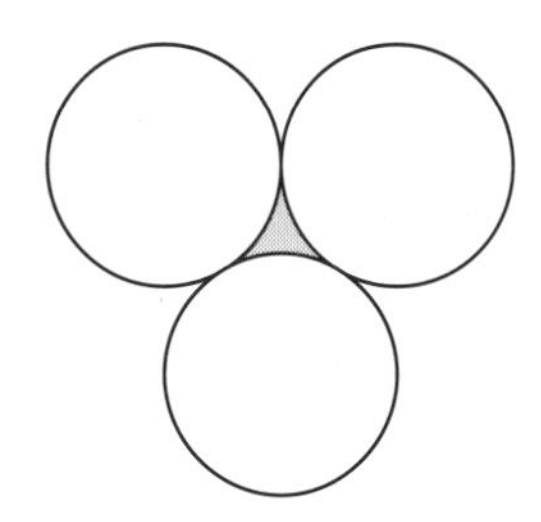

The diagram represents three identical coins, each with radius $r$ placed on a horizontal surface such that each coin touches the other two. Find, in terms of $r$, the area of the surface visible 'inside' the coins (shaded in the diagram).

You can find the exact answer if you use $\sin 60° = \frac{\sqrt{3}}{2}$.

**[Diagrams are not to scale]**

## 4.4 Simple trigonometric equations

### Key points

- Remember that $\sin(180 - \theta)^\circ = \sin\theta^\circ$
  $\cos(180 - \theta)^\circ = -\cos\theta^\circ$
  $\tan(180 - \theta)^\circ = -\tan\theta^\circ$

For example, $\sin 35^\circ = \sin 145^\circ$

- and that $\cos\theta^\circ = \cos(-\theta)^\circ$
  $\sin\theta^\circ = -\sin(-\theta)^\circ$
  $\tan\theta^\circ = -\tan(-\theta)^\circ$

For example, $\cos 40^\circ = \cos(-40)^\circ$

- The graphs of the three trig functions, sine, cosine, tangent will often make your understanding clearer when you are solving easy trig equations.

  The ideas and methods are usually the same so study the examples carefully (as always!)

- You should try to remember these exact values because questions can ask for answers in 'exact form'.

| $\theta$ | $0^\circ$ | $30^\circ$ | $45^\circ$ | $60^\circ$ | $90^\circ$ |
|---|---|---|---|---|---|
| $\sin\theta$ | 0 | $\frac{1}{2}$ | $\frac{1}{\sqrt{2}}$ | $\frac{\sqrt{3}}{2}$ | 1 |
| $\cos\theta$ | 1 | $\frac{\sqrt{3}}{2}$ | $\frac{1}{\sqrt{2}}$ | $\frac{1}{2}$ | 0 |
| $\tan\theta$ | 0 | $\frac{1}{\sqrt{3}}$ | 1 | $\sqrt{3}$ | not defined |
| $\theta$ | $0^c$ | $\frac{\pi^c}{6}$ | $\frac{\pi^c}{4}$ | $\frac{\pi^c}{3}$ | $\frac{\pi^c}{2}$ |

### Example 1

Solve $3\cos\theta^\circ\sin\theta^\circ = 2\sin\theta^\circ$ for $-180 \leq \theta < 180$ giving non exact answers to 1 decimal place.

**Solution**

collect the terms on one side

$$3\cos\theta^\circ\sin\theta^\circ - 2\sin\theta^\circ = 0$$

$$\sin\theta^\circ(3\cos\theta^\circ - 2) = 0$$

Take out the common factor

$\sin\theta^\circ = 0$ or $\cos\theta^\circ = \frac{2}{3}$

$\theta = 0, -180$ $\qquad$ $\theta = \pm 48.2$

(you can't have $180^\circ$ in this domain for $\theta$)

Always check the domain

## Example 2

Solve $\sin\left(x - \frac{\pi}{4}\right) = \frac{7}{10}$ for $-2\pi < x < 2\pi$ giving answers to 2 decimal places.

Answer must in RADIANS

**Solution**

Let $X = x - \frac{\pi}{4}$ so $\sin X = \frac{7}{10}$.

This makes the question look 'friendlier'

$-2\pi < x < 2\pi$ so $-2\pi - \frac{\pi}{4} < x - \frac{\pi}{4} < 2\pi - \frac{\pi}{4}$

Now your calculator gives $X \approx 0.775$ (radians remember).

This is just *one* of many possible solutions.

A picture always helps so sketch $y = \sin X$ for $-2\pi - \frac{\pi}{4} < X < 2\pi - \frac{\pi}{4}$

i.e. $-\frac{9\pi}{4} < X < \frac{7\pi}{4}$

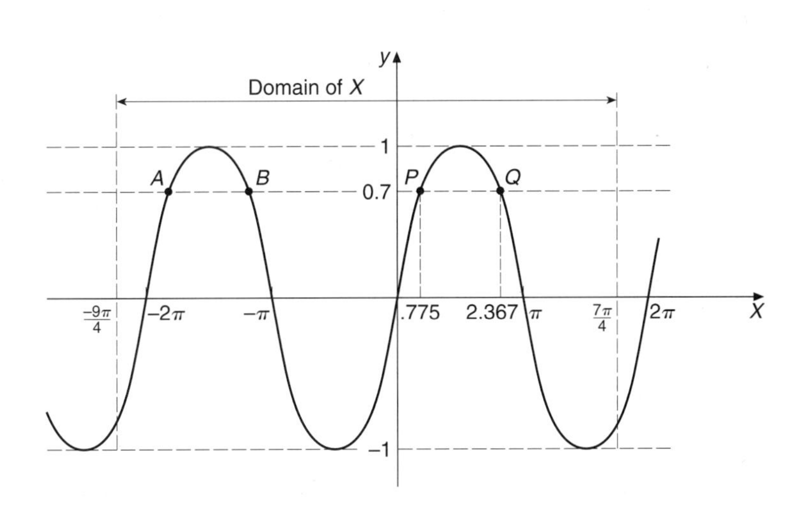


From the graph there are four points of intersection of the line $y = 0.7$ and the curve in the domain of $X$.

At $P$ $\quad X = 0.775$ radians

At $Q$ $\quad X = \pi - 0.775$ radians

$= 3.142 - 0.775$

$= 2.367$ radians.

At $A$ $\quad X = 0.775 - 2\pi = -5.509$

At $B$ $\quad X = 2.367 - 2\pi = -3.917$

So looking at the original equation now $X = x - \frac{\pi}{4} \approx 0.775, 2.367, -5.509,$
$-3.917$

but $x = X + \frac{\pi}{4}$

$\therefore x = 1.56, 3.15, -4.72, -3.13$ (correct to 2 d.p.)

## Exercise 4.4

Give your answers to 1 decimal place unless your answer can be written in an exact form.

**A1** Solve, if possible, for $-180 < \theta < 180$:

(a) $4\sin\theta° = 3$

(b) $3\cos\theta° = -2$

(c) $\tan\theta° = 2$

(d) $\cos\theta° = 2$

**A2** Given that $-360 \le \theta \le 360$, find $\theta$ if:

(a) $\sin\theta° = 0$

(b) $\cos\theta° = 0$

(c) $\tan\theta° = 0$

**A3** If $(\sin\theta° - 1)(2\sin\theta° - 1) = 0$ find the six values of $\theta$ in the domain $-360 < \theta < 360$

**A4** If $-2\pi \le x \le 2\pi$ solve:

(a) $\sin x = 1$

(b) $\cos x = -1$

(c) $\tan x = 1$

**A5** If $\sin^2\theta° = \frac{1}{16}$ find the four values of $\theta$ if $0 < \theta < 360$

**A6** If $|\theta| \le 360$ find $\theta$ when:

(a) $\sin\theta° = -\frac{\sqrt{3}}{2}$

(b) $\cos\theta° = \frac{\sqrt{2}}{2}$

(c) $\tan\theta° = -\frac{1}{\sqrt{3}}$

**A7** Solve $\sin\theta°(\cos\theta° - 1) = 0$ for $-360 < \theta \le 360$

**A8** For $|x| \le 2\pi$ find $x$ if:

(a) $\tan x = \sqrt{3}$

(b) $\sin x = \sin\frac{2\pi}{5}$

**A9** Solve $\cos\theta° = \frac{1}{\cos\theta°}$ for $0 < \theta < 360$

**A10** (a) Given that the angle $A$ is acute and $\cos A = \frac{12}{13}$ find the exact values of $\sin A$ and $\tan A$.

(b) Given that the angle $B$ is obtuse and $\sin B = \frac{8}{17}$ find the exact values of $\cos B$ and $\tan B$.

Give exact answers where possible, but for non-exact give the answers in degrees to 1 decimal place and the answers in radians to 2 decimal places.

**B1** Solve

(a) $\sin X = 0.5 \quad 0 < X < 2\pi$

(b) $\sin\left(x - \frac{\pi}{2}\right) = 0.5 \qquad \frac{\pi}{2} < x < \frac{5\pi}{2}$

**B2** For $-180 \le \theta \le 180$ solve

(a) $\sin 3\theta° = 1$

(b) $\cos 2\theta° = 0$

(c) $\tan\left(\frac{\theta}{2}\right)° = -1$

## Exercise 4.4 *continued*

**B3** Solve

(a) $\cos X = -1 \quad 0 < X < 2\pi$

(b) $\cos\left(x + \frac{\pi}{3}\right) = -1 \qquad -\frac{\pi}{3} < x < \frac{5\pi}{3}$

**B4** For $|x| \leq \pi$ solve

(a) $\sin 2x = -\frac{\sqrt{3}}{2}$

(b) $\cos\left(\frac{3x}{2}\right) = -\frac{1}{2}$

(c) $\tan\left(\frac{4x}{3}\right) = -\sqrt{3}$

**B5** Solve

(a) $\tan X^\circ = 1, \quad 0 < X < 360$

(b) $\tan\,(x - 20)^\circ = 1, \quad 20 < x < 380$

**B6** If $0 \leq x \leq 2\pi$ solve:

(a) $4\sin^2 x = 1$

(b) $\cos^2(2x) = \frac{3}{4}$

(c) $\tan^2\left(\frac{x}{3}\right) = 1$

**B7** Solve

(a) $\sin(\theta + 10)^\circ = \frac{1}{2}$

(b) $\cos(2\theta + 60)^\circ = -\frac{1}{2}$

for $-180 < \theta < 180$.

**B8** Solve for $|\theta| < 180$

(a) $5\sin(2\theta - 23)^\circ = -2$

(b) $4\cos(3\theta + 57)^\circ = 3$

**B9** Solve $\sin(x - 0.14) = 0.8$ for $-\pi < x < \pi$

**B10** Solve $2\cos\left(2x + \frac{\pi}{3}\right) = 1$ for $-\frac{\pi}{2} < x < \frac{\pi}{2}$ giving exact answers.

## Chapter 4: A level questions

**C1** A fishing boat sails from Whitby for 25 km on a bearing of 050° and then changes direction and sails on a bearing of 140° for another 25 km. Find the distance and bearing of the fishing boat from Whitby.

**C2**

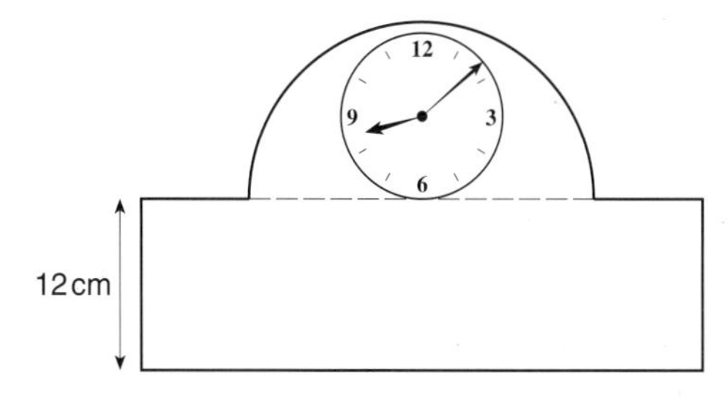


The diagram represents a clock resting on a mantlepiece. The diameter of the clock face is 10 cm and the tip of the minute hand reaches its circumference. An insect rests at the tip of the minute hand.

(a) How far above the mantlepiece is the insect at 0810 hours?

(b) How far does the insect travel in the next 25 minutes?

(c) What time will it be when the insect has travelled approximately 100 centimetres?

**C3** Sketch the graph of $y = \cos x$ for $0 \leq x \leq 2\pi$.

## Chapter 4: A level questions *continued*

Hence find the set of values of $x$ in $0 \leq x \leq 2\pi$ for which $2|\cos x| \leq 1$.

**C4** Three netball posts are placed on a large area of tarmac for a class of girls to practice passing and shooting. The posts are placed on points $A$, $B$ and $C$ such that $AB = 40$ m, $BC = 50$ m and $CA = 60$ m. Show that $\cos C = \frac{3}{4}$.

By finding the value of $\sin C$ in surd form find the exact area of tarmac enclosed by triangle $ABC$.

**C5** Show that if $\theta$ is acute and $\tan\theta = \frac{4}{3}$ then $\sin\theta = \frac{4}{5}$ and $\cos\theta = \frac{3}{5}$.

In triangle $ABC$, $c = 10$, $b = 9$, $a = x$ and $B = \theta$. Use the cosine rule with $b^2$ as subject to show that $x^2 - 12x + 19 = 0$ and confirm that $6 + \sqrt{17}$ is the larger of the two possible lengths of $BC$.

Find the area of the triangle $ABC$.

**C6**

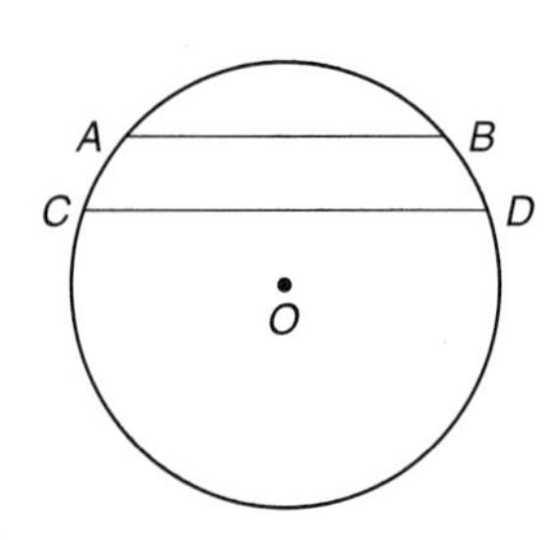


In the diagram (not to scale) $AB$ and $CD$ are parallel chords of a circle centre $O$, radius $r$. Angle $AOB$ is $\frac{\pi}{2}$ radians and angle $COD$ is $\left(\frac{\pi}{2} + 2\theta\right)$ radians $\left(0 < \theta < \frac{\pi}{4}\right)$.

(a) Write down the area of triangle $AOB$

(b) Show that the area of triangle $COD$ may be written as $\frac{1}{2}r^2\cos 2\theta$

(c) Find the areas of the sectors $AOB$ and $BOD$

(d) Show that the area of the part of the circle between $AB$ and $CD$ is $\frac{1}{2}r^2(1 + 2\theta - \cos 2\theta)$ and find this area when $\theta = \frac{\pi}{12}$ leaving your answer in terms of $\pi$.

**C7** Triangle $AOB$ has angle $OAB = \alpha$ and angle $OBA = \beta$. It lies in a horizontal plane with lines $AB$ and $BQ$ of equal lengths drawn vertically upwards. The angles of elevation of $P$ and $Q$ from $O$ are $\theta$ and $\varnothing$ respectively.

With the help of the sine rule show that $\sin\alpha\tan\varnothing = \sin\beta\tan\theta$

Now, given that $\alpha = 60°$, $\beta = 30°$, $\theta = 45°$ find $\varnothing$.

**C8**

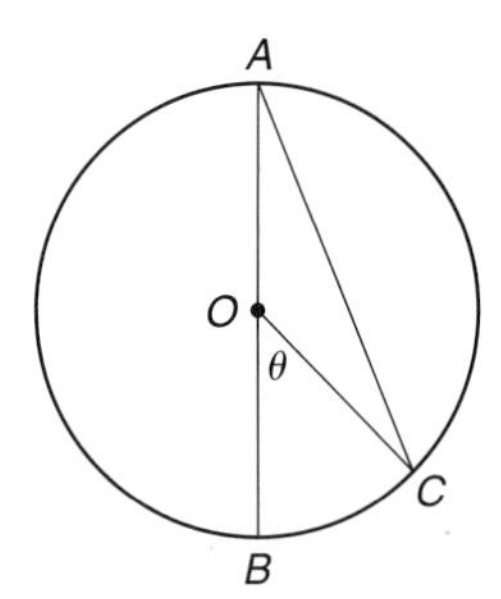


$AB$ is a diameter of a circle centre $O$. $C$ is a point on the circumference such that $\angle BOC = \theta$

(a) Use the cosine rule in $\Delta AOC$ to show that $AC = r\sqrt{2}\,(1 + \cos\theta)^{\frac{1}{2}}$.

(b) Show that the area of triangle $BOC$ is the same as the area of triangle $AOC$.

(c) Find $\theta$ when $AC = r\sqrt{3}$

**C9** A big wheel at a fairground has a diameter of 10 metres and a seat in the lowest position is 1 metre above the ground.

## Chapter 4: A level questions *continued*

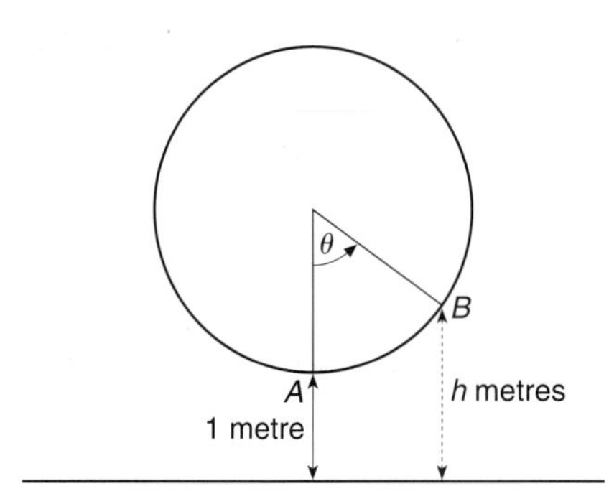


The diagram represents a model of the situation.

(a) Find an expression for $h$, the height in metres above the ground, when the seat has turned through $\theta°$.

(b) Find $\theta$ when $h = 3.5$, $h = 6$ and $h = 11$.

(c) Find the distance travelled by a chair when it turns through angles of 100° and 450°.

**C10** If the height of the tide is $y$ metres at $t$ hours after midnight where

$y = 6 + 3\sin\dfrac{\pi t}{6}$ find at what times over the next 12 hours the height of the tide is

(a) 9 metres

(b) 6 metres

(c) 3 metres

(d) 7.5 metres

Sketch the graph of $y$ over this 12 hour period.

# Chapter 5

## TRIGONOMETRY 2

### 5.1 Definition of tanx and the introduction of secx, cosecx, cotx and their graphs

#### Key points

We define

$$\tan x = \frac{\sin x}{\cos x}$$

$$\sec x = \frac{1}{\cos x}$$

$$\operatorname{cosec} x = \frac{1}{\sin x}$$

$$\cot x = \frac{1}{\tan x} = \frac{\cos x}{\sin x}$$

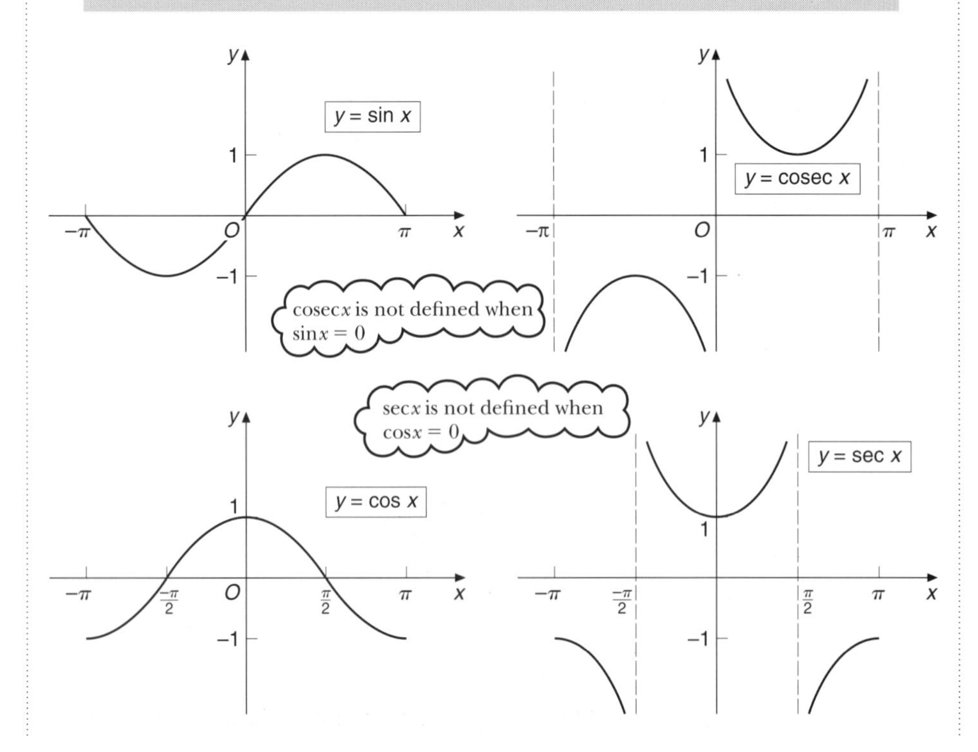

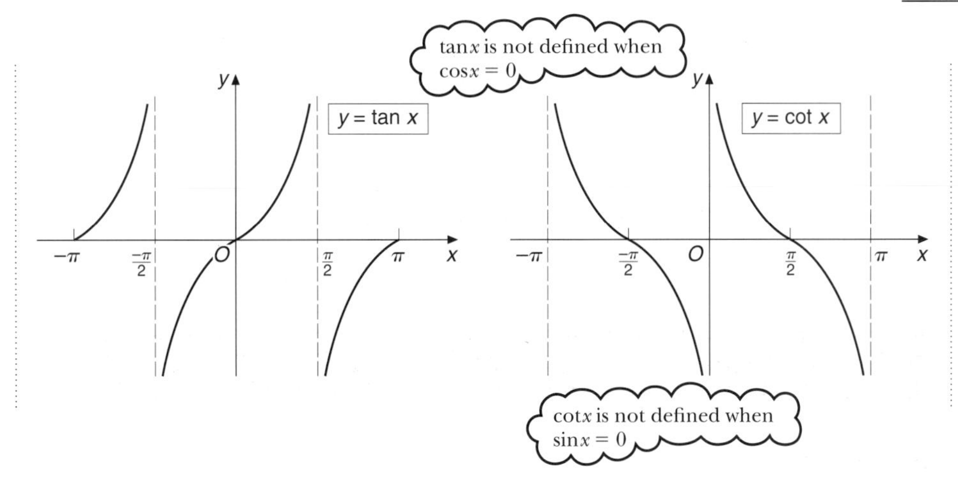


## Example 1

Solve $\sec\theta = \sqrt{2}$ for $0° < \theta < 180°$

**Solution**

$$\frac{1}{\cos\theta} = \sqrt{2}$$

$$\cos\theta = \frac{1}{\sqrt{2}}$$

$$\theta = 45°$$

(the only value in this domain)

## Example 2

Solve $\sec x - 16\cos x = 0$ for $|x| < \pi$

Give your answer to 2 decimal places.

**Solution**

$$\sec x - 16\cos x = 0$$

$$\frac{1}{\cos x} - 16\cos x = 0$$

$$1 - 16\cos^2 x = 0$$

$$1 = 16\cos^2 x$$

$$\frac{1}{16} = \cos^2 x$$

$$\pm\frac{1}{4} = \cos x$$



$$\cos x = \frac{1}{4} \quad \cos x = -\frac{1}{4}$$

$x = 1.32$ $x = 1.82$ (to 2 d.p.) from your calculator for $0 \leq x \leq \pi$

So in the domain $|x| < \pi$

$x = \pm 1.32 \qquad x = \pm 1.82$

correct to 2 d.p.

## Exercise 5.1

Give answers that are non-exact to 1 decimal place for $\theta$, or 2 decimal places for $x$.

**A1** For $0 < \theta < 360$ solve

(a) $\sec\theta° = 2$

(b) $\text{cosec}(2x - 1.8) = 4$

(c) $\cot\theta° = 0.5$

**A2** For $-\pi < x < \pi$ solve

(a) $\sec\left(x - \dfrac{\pi}{3}\right) = -2$

(b) $\text{cosec}\ (2x - 1.8) = 4$

(c) $\cot(1 - 2x) = -1$

**A3** Solve $\sec^2\theta° = 2$ if $-180 < \theta < 180$

**A4** Solve for $|\theta| \leq 180$

Hint: in each case find the values for $\tan\theta$

(a) $4\sin\theta° = 5\cos\theta°$

(b) $\cos\theta° + \sin\theta° = 0$

**A5** Solve for $-180 < \theta < 180$

(a) $\text{cosec}\theta° = 2\sin\theta°$

(b) $\sec\theta° - 4\cos\theta° = 0$

**A6** Solve for $0 \leq \theta \leq 360$

(a) $\cot\theta° = 2\cos\theta°$

(b) $\tan\theta° - 3\sin\theta° = 0$

**A7** Find $x$ if $\sec x = 1 + 2\cos x$ and $|x| \leq 2\pi$

**A8** Solve for $-180 < \theta < 180$,
$3\ \sin\theta° = 1 + 2\text{cosec}\theta°$

**A9** If $0 \leq \theta \leq 360$, solve $\tan\theta° - 6\cot\theta° = 1$

**A10**

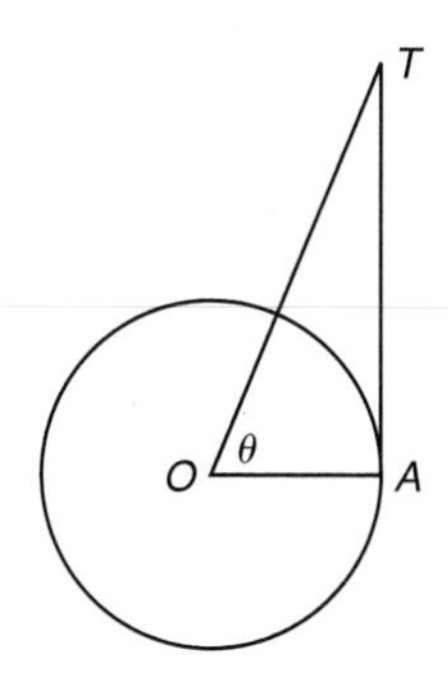


In the diagram the circle, centre $O$, has radius $r$ and $AT$ is a tangent at $A$ to the circle.

Angle $AOT = \theta$, which is acute. By considering the lengths of $OA$, $AT$ and $OT$ show that

(a) $\sec\theta > \tan\theta$

(b) $\sec\theta < 1 + \tan\theta$

## 5.2 Simple identities and disguised quadratic equations

### Key points

- $\sin^2\theta + \cos^2\theta \equiv 1$
- $\sec^2\theta \equiv 1 + \tan^2\theta$
- $\text{cosec}^2\theta \equiv 1 + \cot^2\theta$

When you are trying to establish a trigonometrical identity, in general start with the more difficult side and try to simplify it to give the other side.

## Example 1

Solve $6\sin^2\theta + 5\cos\theta = 5$ for $0° < \theta < 360°$

**Solution**

Use $\cos^2\theta + \sin^2\theta = 1$ to give $\sin^2\theta = 1 - \cos^2\theta$

So

$$6(1 - \cos^2\theta) + 5\cos\theta = 5$$

replacing $\sin^2\theta$ by $1 - \cos^2\theta$

$$6 - 6\cos^2\theta + 5\cos\theta = 5$$

$$0 = 6\cos^2\theta + 5\cos\theta - 1$$

you now have a quadratic

$$0 = (6\cos\theta - 1)(\cos\theta + 1)$$

$$6\cos\theta - 1 = 0$$

$$\cos\theta = \frac{1}{6}$$

$\theta = 80.4°, .279.6°$ to 1 d.p.

$$\cos\theta + 1 = 0$$

$$\cos\theta = -1$$

$$\theta = 180°$$

## Example 2

Show that $\tan^2 x - \tan^2 y \equiv \dfrac{\sin^2 x - \sin^2 y}{\cos^2 x\cos^2 y}$

**Solution**

$$\tan^2 x - \tan^2 y \equiv \frac{\sin^2 x}{\cos^2 x} - \frac{\sin^2 y}{\cos^2 y}$$

$$\equiv \frac{\sin^2 x\cos^2 y - \sin^2 y\cos^2 x}{\cos^2 x\cos^2 y}$$

$$\equiv \frac{\sin^2 x(1 - \sin^2 y) - \sin^2 y(1 - \sin^2 x)}{\cos^2 x\cos^2 y}$$

$$\equiv \frac{\sin^2 x - \sin^2 y}{\cos^2 x\cos^2 y}$$

## Exercise 5.2

Give non-exact values of $\theta$ to 1 decimal place.

**A1** (a) If $\operatorname{cosec}\theta = \frac{13}{12}$, find the possible exact values of $\tan\theta$.

(Hint: use $\operatorname{cosec}^2\theta \equiv 1 + \cot^2\theta$)

(b) If $\cot\theta = -\frac{8}{15}$, find the possible exact values of $\sec\theta$.

(Hint: use $\sec^2\theta \equiv 1 + \tan^2\theta$)

In **A2** to **A7**, solve for $0° \leq \theta \leq 360°$

**A2** (a) $2\sin^2\theta - 7\sin\theta + 3 = 0$

(b) $\cos^2\theta + \cos\theta = 2$

**A3** (a) $6\cos^2\theta + \sin\theta = 5$

(b) $4\sin^2\theta + 8\cos\theta = 7$

**A4** (a) $\sec^2\theta + 3\tan\theta + 1 = 0$

(b) $2\tan^2\theta + 8 = 7\sec\theta$

**A5** (a) $\operatorname{cosec}^2\theta = 2\cot\theta$

(b) $\cot^2\theta + \operatorname{cosec}^2\theta = 5$

**A6** $\tan^2\theta + (1 + \sqrt{3})\tan\theta + \sqrt{3} = 0$

**A7** (a) $8\cot\theta + 3\sin\theta = 0$

(b) $15\tan\theta = 4\cos\theta$

**A8** Eliminate $\theta$ from the following. This means, find a relationship between $x$ and $y$ which does not involve $\theta$.

(a) $x = \sin\theta$, $y = \cos\theta$

(b) $x = 2\sin\theta$, $y = \cos\theta$

**A9** Simplify:

(a) $(1 - \cos\theta)(1 + \cos\theta)$

(b) $\sec\theta\cos\theta + \operatorname{cosec}\theta\sin\theta$

(c) $(\operatorname{cosec}\theta + 1)(\operatorname{cosec}\theta - 1)$

**A10** Eliminate $\theta$ from the following

(a) $x = 2\sec\theta$, $y = 3\tan\theta$

(b) $x = \frac{3}{\sin\theta}$, $y = \frac{2}{\tan\theta}$

In questions **B1–B5** prove the identities.

**B1** $\sin^2\theta + 4\cos^2\theta \equiv 4 - 3\sin^2\theta$

**B2** $(\sin\theta + \operatorname{cosec}\theta)^2 \equiv \sin^2\theta + \cot^2\theta + 3$

**B3** $\cos\theta - \sec\theta \equiv -\sin\theta\tan\theta$

**B4** $\operatorname{cosec}^2\theta(\tan^2\theta - \sin^2\theta) \equiv \tan^2\theta$

**B5** $(\cos\theta + \sin\theta)^2 + (\cos\theta - \sin\theta)^2 \equiv 2$

**B6** Show that $\tan\theta + \cot\theta \equiv \sec\theta\operatorname{cosec}\theta$

**B7** Prove that $\frac{1 - \tan^2\theta}{1 + \tan^2\theta} \equiv 1 - 2\sin^2\theta$

**B8** Show that $\operatorname{cosec}x - \sin x \equiv \cos x\cot x$. Find a similar expression for $\sec x - \cos x$.

Hence, or otherwise, show that $(\operatorname{cosec}x - \sin x)(\sec x - \cos x) \equiv \sin x\cos x$.

**B9** Eliminate $t$ from the following:

(a) $x = 2\tan t - 1$, $y = 2\sec t + 3$

(b) $x = 3 - 2\cos t$, $y = 2 - 3\sin t$

(c) $x = \cos t + \sin t$, $y = \cos t - \sin t$

**B10** Express $z \equiv \frac{1}{\sec\theta - 1} - \frac{1}{\sec\theta + 1}$ as a single fraction and simplify it.

Hence find $\theta$ when $z = 6$ if $\theta$ is obtuse.

## 5.3 Expansion of sin(A ± B), cos(A ± B), tan(A ± B), double angles and simple multiple angles

### Key points

- $$\sin(A + B) = \sin A\cos B + \sin B\cos A$$
- $$\sin(A - B) = \sin A\cos B - \sin B\cos A$$
- $$\cos(A + B) = \cos A\cos B - \sin A\sin B$$
- $$\cos(A - B) = \cos A\cos B + \sin A\sin B$$
- $$\tan(A + B) = \frac{\tan A + \tan B}{1 - \tan A\tan B}$$
- $$\tan(A - B) = \frac{\tan A - \tan B}{1 + \tan A\tan B}$$

You can use these to establish the double angle formulae.

$\sin 2A = \sin(A + A) = \sin A\cos A + \sin A\cos A = 2\sin A\cos A$

$\therefore$ $$\sin 2A = 2\sin A\cos A$$

$\cos 2A = \cos(A + A) = \cos A\cos A - \sin A\sin A = \cos^2 A - \sin^2 A$

Two other identities for cos2A are extremely important

$$\cos 2A = (1 - \sin^2 A) - \sin^2 A$$
$$= 1 - 2\sin^2 A$$

and $$\cos 2A = \cos^2 A - (1 - \cos^2 A)$$
$$= 2\cos^2 A - 1$$

$\therefore$
$$\begin{aligned}\cos 2A &= \cos^2 A - \sin^2 A\\ &= 1 - 2\sin^2 A\\ &= 2\cos^2 A - 1\end{aligned}$$

$$\tan 2A = \tan(A + A) = \frac{2\tan A}{1 - \tan^2 A}$$

The double angles crop up in either identities or solving trigonometrical equations.

You will frequently need to use $\sin^2 A = \frac{1}{2}(1 - \cos 2A)$

and $\cos^2 A = \frac{1}{2}(1 + \cos 2A)$

which come directly from the double angle formulae.

## Example 1

Solve $\cos 2\theta = 3\cos\theta - 2$ for $0° \leq \theta \leq 360°$

**Solution**

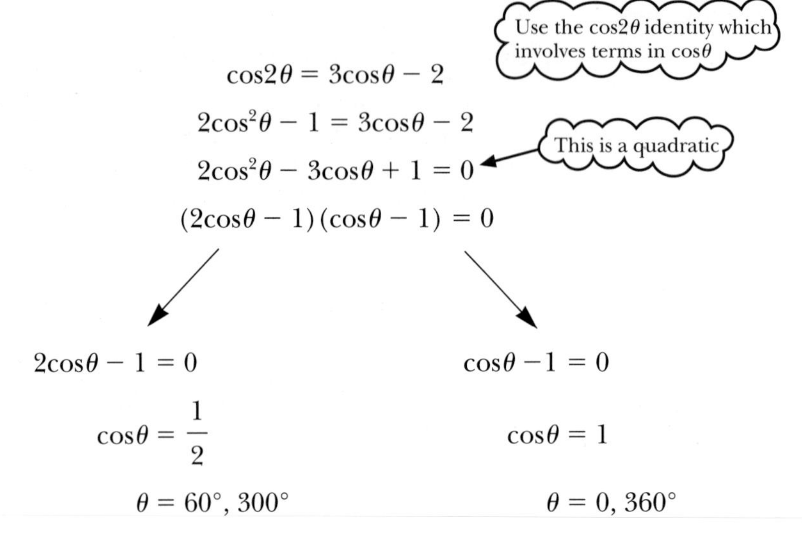


$$\cos 2\theta = 3\cos\theta - 2$$
$$2\cos^2\theta - 1 = 3\cos\theta - 2$$
$$2\cos^2\theta - 3\cos\theta + 1 = 0$$
$$(2\cos\theta - 1)(\cos\theta - 1) = 0$$

$$2\cos\theta - 1 = 0 \qquad \cos\theta - 1 = 0$$
$$\cos\theta = \frac{1}{2} \qquad \cos\theta = 1$$
$$\theta = 60°, 300° \qquad \theta = 0, 360°$$

in our given domain

## Example 2

If $\sin\theta = \frac{8}{17}$ and $\theta$ is obtuse, find the exact value of $\sec\theta$.

**Solution**

To find $\sec\theta$, we should first find $\cos\theta$.

Using $\sin^2\theta + \cos^2\theta = 1$

$\cos^2\theta = 1 - \sin^2\theta$

$= 1 - \frac{64}{289}$

$= \frac{225}{289}$

$\cos\theta = \pm\frac{15}{17}$

$\theta$ is *obtuse* so $\cos\theta = -\frac{15}{17}$ ← think of your $\cos\theta$ graph

So $\sec\theta = -\frac{17}{15}$

## Example 3

Solve $3\sin x - 4\sin^3 x = 2\sin^2 x$ for $0 \leq x < 2\pi$

**Solution**

Do **not** cancel out $\sin x$, as you will lose some answers.

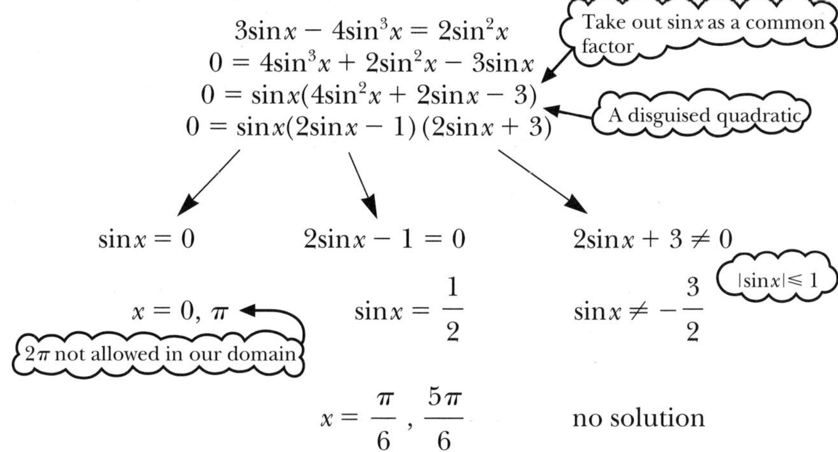


## Exercise 5.3

**A1** If $\sin\theta = \frac{5}{13}$ and $\theta$ is an acute angle, find the exact values of

(a) $\sin 2\theta$

(b) $\cos 2\theta$

(c) $\tan 2\theta$

**A2** If $\sin\theta = \frac{3}{5}$ and $\theta$ is obtuse, find the exact values of

(a) $\sin 2\theta$

(b) $\sec 2\theta$

(c) $\tan 2\theta$

**A3** If $\tan\theta = -\frac{8}{15}$ and $90° < \theta < 180°$, find exactly

(a) $\cos\theta$

(b) $\sin\theta$

(c) $\sin 2\theta$

**A4** If $\cos 2\theta = \frac{1}{3}$ and $0° < \theta < 90°$ find the exact values of

(a) $\sin\theta$

(b) $\cos\theta$

**A5** If $2\sin\theta = \cos(\theta + 60°)$ show that

$$\tan\theta = \frac{1}{4 + \sqrt{3}}$$

**A6** Solve for $0° \leq \theta \leq 360°$

(a) $3\sin 2\theta = \sin\theta$

(b) $4\sin 2\theta - \cos\theta = 0$

Give your answers to 1 decimal place.

Don't miss out any solutions

**A7** Solve for $|\theta| \leq 180°$

$3\cos 2\theta - 7\cos\theta - 2 = 0$

**A8** If $\sin(3\theta + 45°) = \cos 3\theta$ show that $\tan 3\theta = \sqrt{2} - 1$

## Exercise 5.3 *continued*

**A9** Find the values of $\tan\frac{\theta}{2}$ when

(a) $\tan\theta = \frac{8}{15}$

(b) $\tan\theta = -\frac{5}{12}$

**A10** Prove the identities

(a) $\frac{\sin 2\theta}{1 - \cos 2\theta} \equiv \cot\theta$

(b) $\frac{1 + \cos 2\theta}{\sin 2\theta} \equiv \cot\theta$

**B1** Given that angle $A$ is obtuse with $\tan A = -\frac{4}{3}$ and that angle $B$ is acute with $\tan B = \frac{7}{24}$, find the exact values of

(a) $\tan(A - B)$

(b) $\sin(A - B)$

(c) $\cos(B - A)$

**B2** If $\tan\theta = -\frac{3}{4}$ find the exact values of

(a) $\tan 2\theta$

(b) $\cos 2\theta$

(c) $\sin 2\theta$

(iv) $\sin 4\theta$

(v) $\tan 4\theta$

**B3** For $-\pi \leq x \leq \pi$ solve

(a) $\sin 2x = \tan x$

(b) $\cos 2x = \cos x$

(c) $\sin 2x + \cos 2x = 1$

**B4** Given that $\tan\theta = \frac{3}{4}$, find the possible values of

(a) $\sin 2\theta$

(b) $\tan\left(\frac{\theta}{2}\right)$

**B5** Given that $\cos 2\theta = \frac{1 - \tan^2\theta}{1 + \tan^2\theta}$, show that

$$\sec 2\theta + \tan 2\theta = \frac{1 + \tan\theta}{1 - \tan\theta}.$$

Express this answer in terms of $\cot\theta$, in its simplest form.

**B6** Use the formula for $\sin(A - B)$ together with a useful choice for $A$ and $B$ to show that $\sin 15° = \frac{\sqrt{3} - 1}{2\sqrt{2}}$. Obtain a similar expression for $\cos 15°$.

Hence obtain $\tan 15°$ and show that this can be written in the form $a + b\sqrt{3}$ where $a$ and $b$ are integers which should be found.

**B7** If $y = 2\sin\theta°\cos 27° - 2\cos\theta°\sin 27°$, $0 \leq \theta \leq 360$, find

(a) the values of $\theta$ when $y = 0$

(b) the maximum value of $y$ and the value of $\theta$ for which it occurs

(c) the minimum value of $y$ and the corresponding value of $\theta$.

**B8** Given that $\sin\left(x + \frac{\pi}{6}\right) = 2\cos x$ find the exact value of $\tan x$.

Hence solve the equation if $|x| < 2\pi$

**B9** Show that $\tan(45° + \theta) = \frac{1 + \tan\theta}{1 - \tan\theta}$

Hence show that

$$\tan(45° + \theta) - \tan(45° - \theta) = \frac{4\tan\theta}{1 - \tan^2\theta}$$

Find $\tan\theta$ if
$\tan(45° + \theta) - \tan(45° - \theta) = 1.5$

Also simplify $\tan(45° + \theta) \times \tan(45° - \theta)$.

**B10** By writing $\cos 3x$ in the form $\cos(2x + x)$ and expanding, show that $\cos 3x = 4\cos^3 x - 3\cos x$.

Hence solve the equation $\cos 3x = \cos^2 x$ when $0 \leq x \leq 2\pi$ giving any non exact solutions correct to 2 decimal places.

## 5.4 Transformations of y=sin$\theta$, y=cos$\theta$, y=tan$\theta$

### Key points

$y = \sin 2x$ is obtained from the $y = \sin x$ graph by a stretch of scale factor $\frac{1}{2}$ parallel to the $x$ axis.

Similarly $y = \sin 3x$ is obtained from $y = \sin x$ by a stretch of scale factor $\frac{1}{3}$ parallel to the $x$ axis.

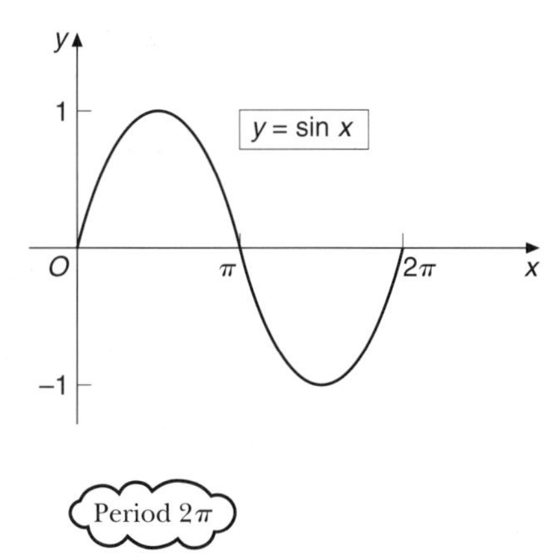


Period $2\pi$

For $y = \sin nx$ the period is $\dfrac{2\pi}{n}$

There are $n$ full cycles for $0 \leq x \leq 2\pi$

For example,

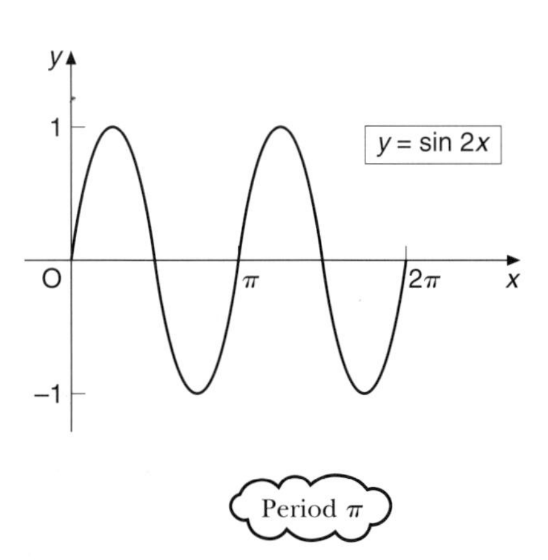


Period $\pi$

The other trigonometrical functions $y = \cos nx$, $y = \tan nx$, say, behave in exactly the same way.

## Example 1

Sketch $y = \sin\left(x - \frac{\pi}{3}\right) \quad 0 \le x \le 2\pi$

**Solution**

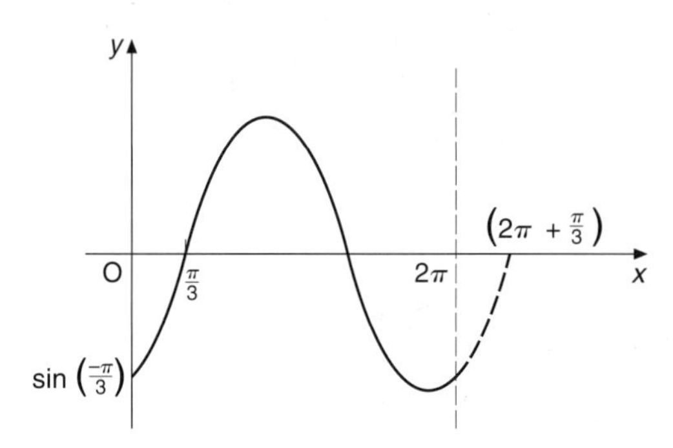


N.B. (a) Translation $\begin{pmatrix} \frac{\pi}{3} \\ 0 \end{pmatrix}$ from $y = \sin x$

(b) Period $2\pi$

(c) $-1 \le y \le 1$

(d) $y$ intercept at $\sin\left(-\frac{\pi}{3}\right)$

## Example 2

Sketch $y = \cos\left(2x - \frac{\pi}{4}\right) \quad 0 \le x \le 2\pi$

**Solution**

Think about the zeros of $y$. We know that $\cos\frac{\pi}{2}, \cos\frac{3\pi}{2}, \cos\frac{5\pi}{2}, \ldots = 0$.

So for our $y$

$$2x - \frac{\pi}{4} = \frac{\pi}{2}, \frac{3\pi}{2}, \frac{5\pi}{2}, \frac{7\pi}{2} \ldots$$

$$2x = \frac{3\pi}{4}, \frac{7\pi}{4}, \frac{11\pi}{4}, \frac{15\pi}{4} \ldots$$

$$x = \frac{3\pi}{8}, \frac{7\pi}{8}, \frac{11\pi}{8}, \frac{15\pi}{8} \ldots$$

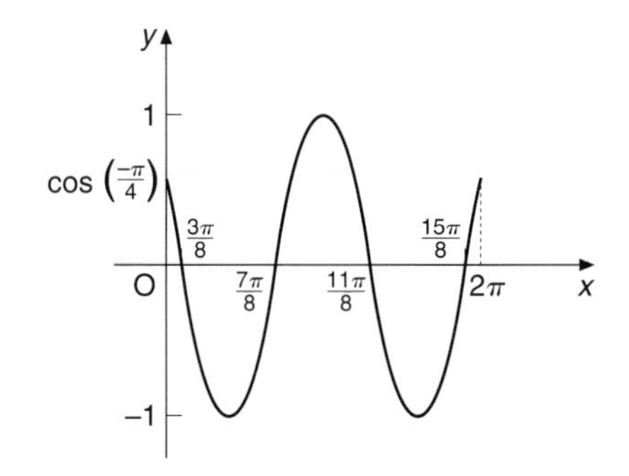


N.B. (a) $y = \cos 2x$ translated $\begin{pmatrix} \frac{\pi}{8} \\ 0 \end{pmatrix}$

(b) Period $\pi$

(c) $-1 \leq y \leq 1$

(d) Intercept at $\cos\left(-\frac{\pi}{4}\right)$

## Exercise 5.4

**1** Describe how each of the following graphs may be obtained from the graph of $y = \sin\theta$

(a) $y = \sin(\theta - 25)^\circ$

(b) $y = 3\sin(\theta + 57)^\circ$

(c) $y = \sin(\theta - \alpha)^\circ + \mathrm{k}$

**2** Repeat question **1** but for $y = \cos x$

(a) $y = 2\cos\left(x - \frac{\pi}{3}\right)$

(b) $y = \frac{1}{2}\cos\left(x + \frac{\pi}{6}\right)$

(c) $y = \mathrm{a}\cos(x + \beta) + \mathrm{b}$

**3** Repeat question **1** but for $y = \tan\theta^\circ$

(a) $y = 3\tan(\theta - 17)^\circ$

(b) $y = -2\tan\theta^\circ$

(c) $y = \frac{1}{3}\tan(\theta + 42)^\circ$

**4** For $0 \leq x \leq 2\pi$, sketch the graphs of

(a) $y = 2\sin\left(x + \frac{\pi}{3}\right)$

(b) $y = 3\cos\left(x - \frac{\pi}{4}\right)$

(c) $y = \frac{1}{2}\tan\left(x - \frac{\pi}{5}\right)$

showing the coordinates of any points of intersection with the axes and the coordinates of any maximum or minimum points.

**5** Sketch the graphs of $y$ in the given domain

(a) $y = \sin 3\theta^\circ$, $-180 \leq \theta \leq 180$

(b) $y = 3\sin\left(\frac{1}{2}\theta\right)^\circ$, $-360 \leq \theta \leq 360$

(c) $y = -\sin 2\theta^\circ$, $0 \leq \theta \leq 360$

(d) $y = 1 - \cos 2\theta^\circ$, $|\theta| \leq 180$

## Chapter 5: A level questions

**C1**

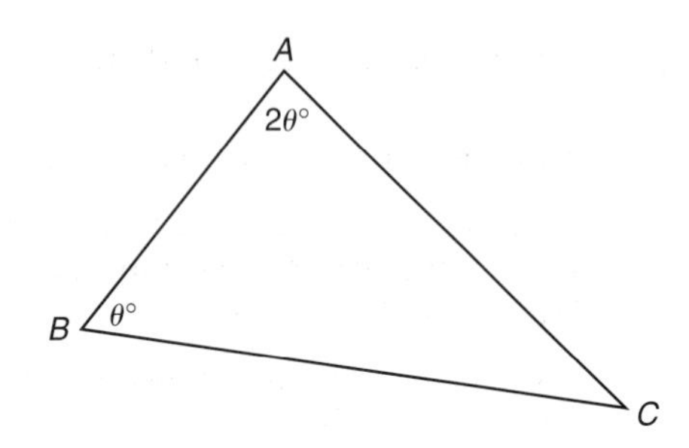


In triangle $ABC$, $\angle ABC = \theta°$ and $\angle BAC = 2\theta°$. $BC = \sqrt{3}AC$

(a) Use the sine rule to find the value of $\theta$

(b) Show that $AB = 2AC$

(c) Find the area of triangle $ABC$ if $AB = 6$ cm

**C2** (a) Show that

$$\frac{1}{\sec\theta + \tan\theta} + \frac{1}{\sec\theta - \tan\theta} \equiv \frac{2}{\cos\theta}$$

(b) Simplify $\dfrac{1}{\sec\theta - \tan\theta} - \dfrac{1}{\sec\theta + \tan\theta}$

**C3** Find $\theta$ to one decimal place, when $0° \leq \theta \leq 360°$ if

(a) $6\cot^2\theta - \cot\theta - 1 = 0$

(b) $\sin^2\theta + \sin\theta\cos\theta - 6\cos^2\theta = 0$

(c) $\cos 2\theta = 5\cos\theta - 3$

**C4** (a) Obtain $\cos 2x$ in terms of $\sin x$

(b) Given that $0 \leq x \leq 2\pi$ find the three values of $x$ for which $\cos 2x = 1 + \sin x$

(c) Given that $0 \leq x \leq 4\pi$, solve the equation $\cos x = 1 + \sin\frac{1}{2}x$.

**C5** If the geometric series $S = 1 + \sin^2\theta + \sin^4\theta + \sin^6\theta + \ldots$ write down its sum to infinity. ($\sin^2\theta \neq 1$)

If the geometric series $T = 1 - \tan^2\theta + \tan^4\theta - \tan^6\theta + \ldots$ (where $|\tan\theta| < 1$) write down the value of $T$ and show that $S \times T = 1$

**C6**

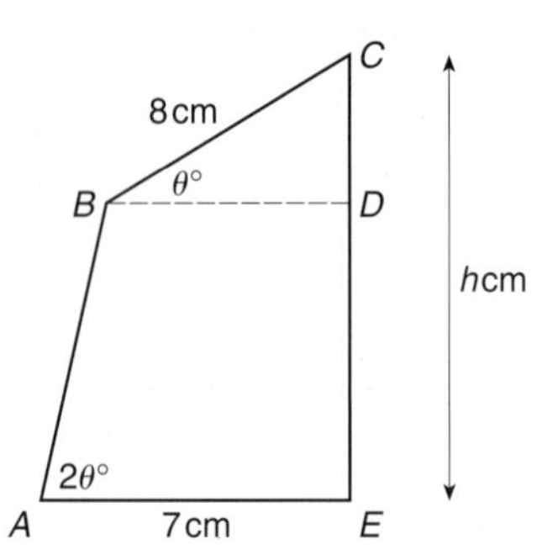


In the diagram (not to scale) $0 < \theta < 45$, $AB = BC = 8$ cm, $AE = 7$ cm, $CE = h$ cm and angle $AEC = 90° =$ angle $BDC$

(a) Show that $8\cos 2\theta° + 8\cos\theta° = 7$ and solve this equation to show that $\cos\theta° = \dfrac{3}{4}$

(b) Write down an expression for $h$ in terms of $\theta$ and show that $h = 20\sin\theta°$

(c) Find $h$ in exact surd form.

**C7** In the diagram $ABCD$ is a rectangle with $AB = 3a$, $AD = a$ and $P$ is a point on the circle centre $A$, radius $a$, such that angle $PAB = \theta°$ ($\theta°$ is acute). $PM$ is parallel to $AB$ and $PN$ is parallel to $AD$.

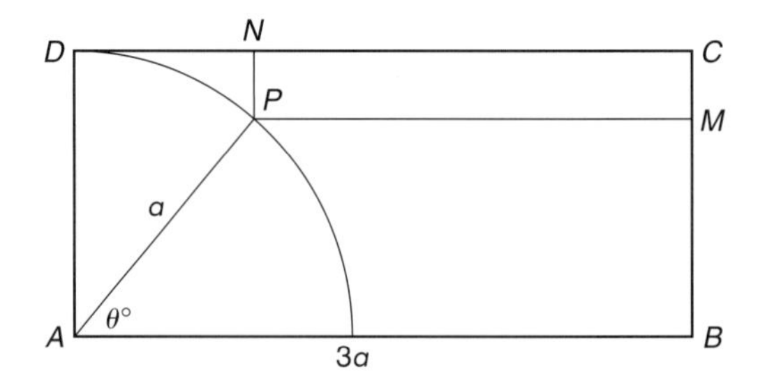


(a) Show that $PM = a(3 - \cos\theta)$

(b) Find $PN$ in terms of $\theta$

(c) Show that $PC = a\sqrt{11 - 2\sin\theta - 6\cos\theta}$

## Chapter 5: A level questions *continued*

**C8** For $-\pi < x < \pi$ solve

(a) $\cos 2x = \sin x$

(b) $\sqrt{3}\tan^2 x + (1 - \sqrt{3})\tan x - 1 = 0$

(c) $\sin 2x = \sin x$

**C9** The points $\left(\frac{\pi}{4}, y_1\right)$, $(0, y_2)$, $\left(-\frac{\pi}{6}, y_3\right)$ lie on the graph of $y = 3\cos\left(2x - \frac{\pi}{6}\right)$.

(a) Find the exact values of $y_1$, $y_2$, $y_3$.

(b) Find $x$ at the points where the line $y = \frac{3\sqrt{3}}{2}$ meets the curve

$$y = 3\cos\left(2x - \frac{\pi}{6}\right) \text{ if } -\pi \leq x \leq \pi.$$

**C10** (a) If the angle $\alpha$ is acute and $\tan\alpha = \frac{4}{3}$, find the exact values of $\sin\alpha$ and $\cos\alpha$.

(b) By using the expansion for $\sin(A - B)$ show that $10\sin(\theta - \alpha)$ simplifies to $6\sin\theta - 8\cos\theta$.

(c) Sketch the graph of $y = 6\sin\theta - 8\cos\theta$ for $0° \leq \theta \leq 360°$.

(d) State the maximum and minimum values of $y$ and the values of $\theta$ (to 1 decimal place) for which they occur.

# Chapter 6

## COORDINATE GEOMETRY

### 6.1 Distance between two points; gradient of a line; equations $y = mx + c$, $ax + by + c = 0$; finding the equation of a linear graph

**Key points**

A gentle reminder

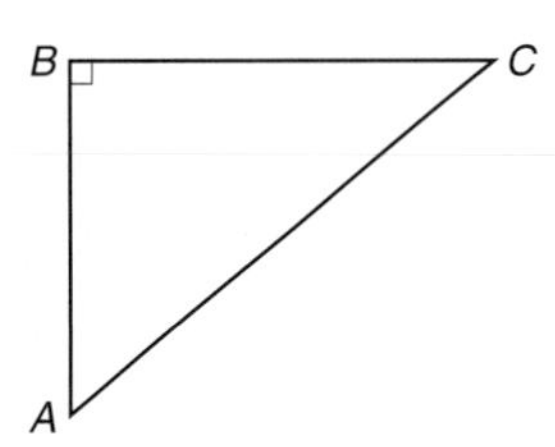


If the triangle is right angled then, using Pythagoras' Theorem, $AC^2 = AB^2 + BC^2$

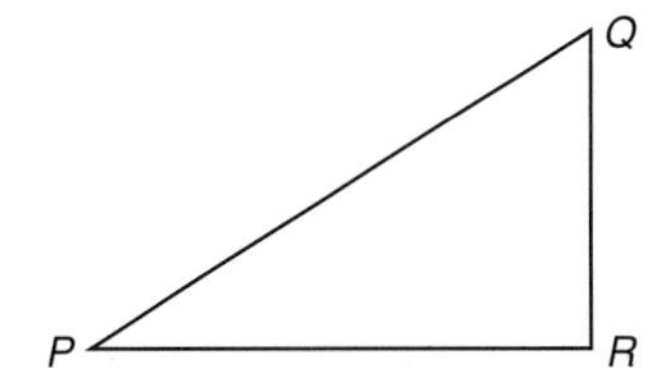


If you can show that $PQ^2 = PR^2 + QR^2$ then the triangle has a right angle at $R$.

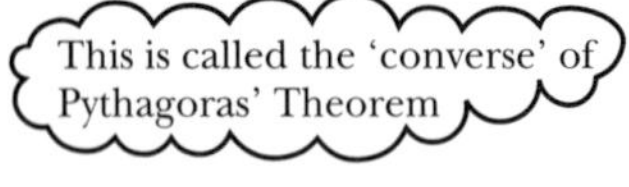


For the points $A(x_1,y_1)$ and $B(x_2,y_2)$

- the distance $AB = \sqrt{(x_2 - x_1)^2 + (y_2 - y_1)^2}$
- the gradient of $AB = \dfrac{y_2 - y_1}{x_2 - x_1}$
- $y = mx + c$ represents a straight line, gradient $m$, passing through $(0,c)$
- $ax + by + c = 0$ represents a straight line.

Re-arranging gives $y = -\frac{ax}{b} - \frac{c}{b}$ $(b \neq 0)$ so the gradient is $-\frac{a}{b}$

and the intercept $-\frac{c}{b}$.

- $y - y_1 = m(x - x_1)$ represents a line, gradient m, through $(x_1,y_1)$.
- To find the equation of the line through two given points it is sensible to find the gradient first and then use $y - y_1 = m(x - x_1)$

Note: It is usually sensible to give your answers without fractions – a question may say 'find the equation of the line with integral coefficients'.

## Example 1

Find the equation of the line $L$ which has the same gradient as $3x + 4y = 4$ and passes through $A(1,-2)$. Find the distance of $A$ from the point $B$ which lies on $L$ and has $x$ coordinate $-3$.

**Solution**

The line $3x + 4y = 4$ has gradient $-\frac{3}{4}$

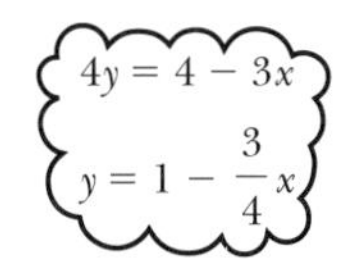


So using $y - y_1 = m(x - x_1)$ where $(x_1,y_1)$ is the point $A(1,-2)$ you will get:

$$y - (-2) = -\frac{3}{4}(x - 1)$$

$$y + 2 = -\frac{3}{4}(x - 1)$$

$$4y + 8 = -3(x - 1)$$

$$\Rightarrow \quad 4y + 3x + 5 = 0$$

The point $B$ lies on $4y + 3x + 5 = 0$ when $x = -3$

So substituting for $x$ you will get

$$4y - 9 + 5 = 0$$

$$4y = 4$$

$$y = 1 \qquad \text{so } B(-3,1)$$

You now have to find the distance $AB$.

$AB = \sqrt{(-3 - 1)^2 + (1 + 2)^2} = \sqrt{16 + 9} = 5$

## Example 2

The line through the points $P\left(3,\frac{1}{2}\right)$ and $Q\left(5,1\frac{1}{2}\right)$ meets the $x$ axis at $S$, and $R$ is the point $\left(\frac{13}{4},0\right)$. Find the area of $\Delta PSR$ and, by considering the lengths of the sides, show that the triangle is right angled.

**Solution**

You need to find the equation of line $PQ$ first and then find where the line cuts the $x$ axis.

The gradient of $PQ$ $= \dfrac{1\frac{1}{2} - \frac{1}{2}}{5 - 3} = \dfrac{1}{2}$

So the equation of $PQ$ is $y - \dfrac{1}{2} = \dfrac{1}{2}(x - 3)$

$$2y - 1 = x - 3$$

$$2y = x - 2$$

When $y = 0$, $x = 2$, so $S$ is the point (2,0)

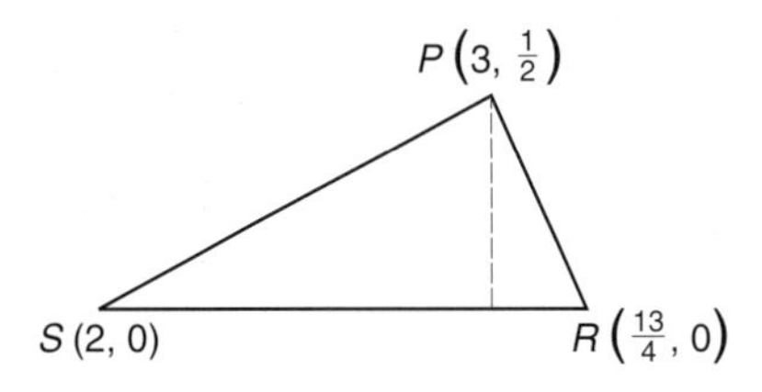


Area of $\Delta PSR = \dfrac{1}{2}$ base $\times$ height

$$= \frac{1}{2}\left(\frac{5}{4}\right) \times \frac{1}{2} = \frac{5}{16} \text{ sq. units}$$

$$PS^2 = \left(\frac{1}{2} - 0\right)^2 + (3 - 2)^2 = \frac{1}{4} + 1 = \frac{5}{4}\left(= \frac{20}{16}\right)$$

$$PR^2 = \left(\frac{1}{2} - 0\right)^2 + \left(3 - \frac{13}{4}\right)^2 = \frac{1}{4} + \frac{1}{16} = \frac{5}{16}$$

$$SR^2 = \left(\frac{5}{4}\right)^2 = \frac{25}{16}$$

So you can see that $SR^2 = PR^2 + PS^2$ and hence the triangle is right angled ($\angle P = 90°$).

This is using the 'converse' of Pythagoras.

## Exercise 6.1

**A1** Find the distance $AB$ if

(a) $A(3,5)$, $B(7,9)$

(b) $A(7,-2)$, $B(-3,0)$

(c) $A(6,-4)$, $B(9,-4)$

**A2** For each of the pairs of points given in question **A1** find the gradient of the line $AB$.

**A3** State the gradients of the following lines and write down the coordinates of the point of intersection with the $y$ axis

(a) $y = 7x - 2$

(b) $y = 5 - 3x$

(c) $x + y = 5$

(d) $y = 7$

**A4** Using your results from question 3 sketch, on separate axes, the lines

(a) $y = 7x - 2$

(b) $y = 5 - 3x$

(c) $x + y = 5$

(d) $y = 7$

**A5** Use the equation $y - y_1 = m(x - x_1)$ [line with gradient $m$ passing through $(x_1,y_1)$] to find the equation of the lines

(a) gradient 6 through $(1,-5)$

(b) gradient $-\frac{1}{6}$ through $(1,-5)$

(c) gradient $-4$ through $(1,0)$

(d) gradient $\frac{1}{4}$ through $(1,0)$

**A6** Find the gradient of the line passing through points $A$ and $B$ and then use $y = mx + c$ to find the equation of the line $AB$ if

(a) $A(6,2)$, $B(8,5)$

(b) $A(-3,0)$, $B(6,-1)$

(c) $A(4,-1)$, $B(8,1)$

(d) $A(4,1)$, $B(8,1)$

**A7** Find the equation of the line which is

(a) parallel to the $y$ axis and passes through the point $(7,6)$

(b) parallel to the $x$ axis and passes through $(4,9)$

(c) parallel to the line $y = 6x - 5$ and with $y$ intercept zero

(d) parallel to $x - 2y + 5 = 0$ and passing through $(-3,-2)$

(Remember, parallel lines have the same gradient)

**A8** The line with gradient $-2$ which passes through $P(1,3)$, meets the $x$ axis at $A$ and the $y$ axis at $B$

(a) find the coordinates of $A$ and $B$

(b) find the area of $\Delta APB$ (a diagram always helps).

**B1** Points $A$, $B$ and $C$ have coordinates $(-1,0)$, $(2,2)$ and $(8,6)$ respectively. Show that $AC = 3AB$.

**B2** Obtain the gradient of each of the following lines

(a) $4x = 6 - 3y$

(b) $7 - 2y - 3x = 0$

(c) $\frac{x}{2} - \frac{y}{5} = 1$

(d) $ax + by + c = 0$, $b \neq 0$

In **B3–B5**, find the equations of the lines in the form $ax + by + c = 0$, where $a$, $b$, $c$ are integers

**B3** (a) through $(0,5)$ and with gradient $-\frac{3}{4}$

(b) through $(0,-2)$ and with gradient $\frac{4}{5}$

**B4** (a) through $(-3,-4)$ and with gradient 3

(b) through $(5,0)$ and with gradient $-\frac{2}{7}$

(c) through $(-2,1)$ and with gradient 1.4

## Exercise 6.1 *continued*

**B5** (a) through (2,5) and $(-1,9)$

(b) through $(-4,-1)$ and $(-4,4)$

(c) joining $(-3,0)$ to (0,4)

(d) joining $(4,-2)$ to $(-3,5)$

(e) through $(3,-2)$ and $(-7,-2)$

**B6** Show that the triangle $ABC$ with $A(1,2)$, $B(5,5)$, $C(-2,6)$ is isosceles.

**B7** The line containing the points $A(-4,6)$ and $B(2,1\frac{1}{2})$ meets the $x$ axis at $P$ and the $y$ axis at $Q$. Find the area of the triangle $OPQ$ where $O$ is the origin.

**B8** Find the coordinates of the vertices of a triangle $ABC$ whose sides have equations

$AB$: $y + 4 = 0$

$BC$: $2y + 5x - 27 = 0$

$CA$: $y - 2x = 0$

Show that $AC = k\sqrt{5}$ and $BC = h\sqrt{29}$ where $k$ and $h$ are integers to be found.

**B9** Straight lines of gradients $-\dfrac{1}{4}$ and $+3$ are drawn through the point $A(3,5)$ to meet the $y$ axis at $C$ and $B$ respectively. Find the area of triangle $ABC$.

**B10** $A$ is $(-3,0)$, $B$ is $(0,-7)$ and $O$ is the origin. Lines of gradient 5 and $-\dfrac{1}{2}$ are drawn through $A$ and $B$ respectively to intersect at $C$. Find the area of the quadrilateral $OACB$.

## 6.2 Parallel and perpendicular lines; midpoints

### Key points

Suppose that the lines $L_1$ and $L_2$ have gradients $m_1$ and $m_2$ respectively.

•

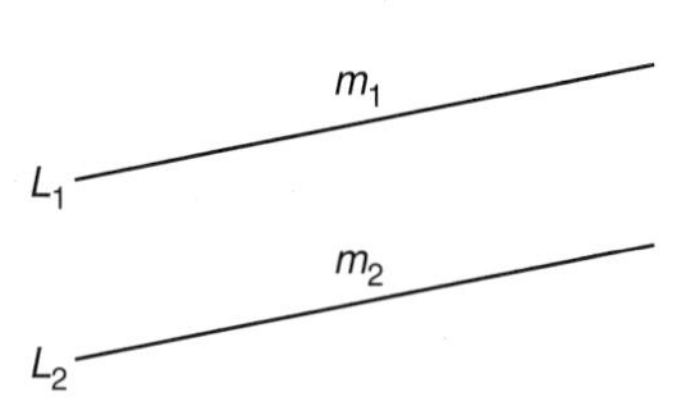


(a) If $L_1$ is parallel to $L_2$ then $m_1 = m_2$

(b) If $m_1 = m_2$ then $L_1$ is parallel to $L_2$

•

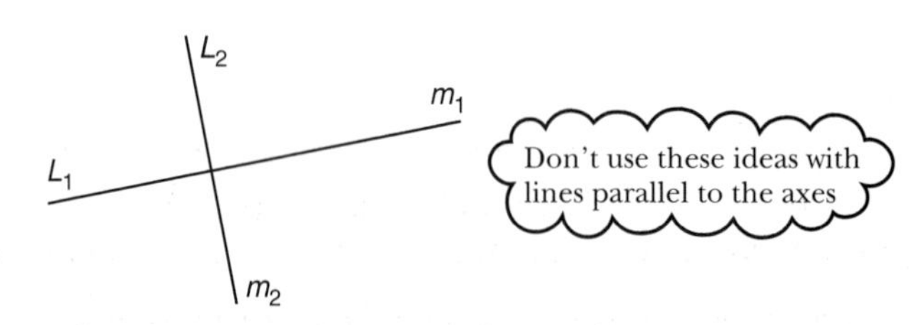

(a) If $L_1$ is perpendicular to $L_2$ then $m_1 m_2 = -1$

(b) If $m_1 m_2 = -1$ then $L_1$ is perpendicular to $L_2$

- The midpoint of the line joining $A(x_1,y_1)$ to $B(x_2,y_2)$ is $M\left(\frac{x_1 + x_2}{2}, \frac{y_1 + y_2}{2}\right)$.

## Example 1

Find the equation of the line through the midpoint of $AB$ and perpendicular to $4y - 3x = 2$ if $A$ is the point $(7,-1)$ and $B$ is $(2,-3)$.

**Solution**

For points $A(7,-1)$ and $B(2,-3)$ the midpoint $M$ of $AB$ is

$$\left(\frac{7+2}{2}, \frac{(-1)+(-3)}{2}\right)$$

i.e. $M$ is $\left(\frac{9}{2}, -2\right)$

The line $4y - 3x = 2$ can be written $4y = 3x + 2$

$$y = \frac{3}{4}x + \frac{1}{2}$$

and so the gradient of $AB$ is $\frac{3}{4}$.

The gradient of any line perpendicular to $AB$ is $-\frac{4}{3}$

$m_1 m_2 = -1$

Hence the required line passes through $\left(\frac{9}{2}, -2\right)$ and has gradient $-\frac{4}{3}$.

Using $y - y_1 = m(x - x_1)$ $\quad y - \frac{9}{2} = -\frac{4}{3}(x + 2)$

Multiply by 6 to remove fractions

$$6y - 27 = -8(x + 2)$$

$$6y - 27 = -8x - 16$$

The required equation is $\quad 6y + 8x = 11$

## Example 2

If $P$ is the point $(1,5)$ and $Q$ the point $(5,13)$, find the coordinates of the point $X$ where the line through $R(4,6)$ perpendicular to $PQ$, meets $PQ$.

Hence show that the distance of $R$ from $PQ$ is $\sqrt{5}$.

### Solution

Sketches help

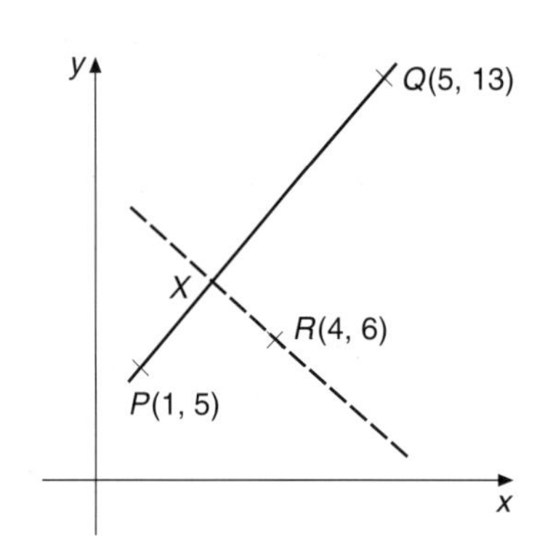


You need to find the coordinates of $X$, so if you find the equations of lines $PQ$ and $RX$ you can solve them simultaneously.

$P(1,5)$, $Q(5,13)$

Gradient of $PQ = \dfrac{13-5}{5-1} = \dfrac{8}{4} = 2.$

Using $y - y_1 = m(x - x_1)$

The equation of $PQ$ is $y - 5 = 2(x - 1)$

i.e.

$$y = 2x + 3$$

Line $RX$ is perpendicular to $PQ$ so the gradient of $RX = -\dfrac{1}{2}$. $\quad 2\left(-\dfrac{1}{2}\right) = -1$

Using $\qquad y - y_1 = m(x - x_1)$

The equation of $RX$ is $\qquad y - 6 = -\dfrac{1}{2}(x - 4)$

$$2y - 12 = -(x - 4)$$

$$2y = -x + 16$$

The lines $y = 2x + 3$ and $2y = -x + 16$ intersect when
$2y = 4x + 6 = -x + 16$

Hence $5x - 10$ so $x = 2$

When $x = 2$, $y = 7$ and so

$$X \text{ is } (2,7)$$

$RX = \sqrt{(2-4)^2 + (7-6)^2} = \sqrt{(-2)^2 + 1^2} = \sqrt{4+1} = \sqrt{5}$

The distance of $R$ from the line $PQ$ is $\sqrt{5}$.

## Exercise 6.2

**A1** Write down the coordinates of the midpoint of $AB$ if

(a) $A(7,2)$, $B(3,8)$

(b) $A(2,0)$, $B(6,1)$

(c) $A(-3,2)$, $B(1,-4)$

**A2** The straight line $L$ has equation $y = 3x + 1$. Find the equation of the line

(a) parallel to $L$ and passing through $(5,7)$

(b) perpendicular to $L$ and passing through $(5,7)$

**A3** Find the equation of the line passing through the origin that is

(a) parallel to $2x + 3y + 4 = 0$

(b) perpendicular to $2x + 3y + 4 = 0$

**A4** Find

(a) the gradient of the line joining $A(8,4)$, $B(-2,6)$

(b) the midpoint $M$ of $AB$

(c) the line through $M$ at right angles to $AB$

(This line is known as the perpendicular bisector of $AB$.)

**A5** Find the equation of the perpendicular bisector of the line joining $P$ and $Q$ if

(a) $P(7,1)$ and $Q(3,5)$

(b) $P(7,1)$ and $Q(13,1)$

**A6** Find the equation of the line through $P(-2,7)$ perpendicular to the line $3x + 4y = 1$. Write your answer without fractions.

**A7** Find the gradients of the line segments $AB$ and $BC$ if $A(2,5)$, $B(3,9)$ and $C(4,13)$. What does this mean about the points $A$, $B$ and $C$? (Looking at the gradient of segment $AC$ should convince you of your answer.)

**A8** If $A(6,3)$ and $B(12,3)$ are the end points of the diameter of a circle, find the coordinates of the centre of the circle and the radius of the circle. Draw a sensible sketch.

**B1** Show that the points $A(2,2)$, $B(-3,4)$ and $C(12,-2)$ lie on a straight line. Find its equation.

**B2** Points $A$, $B$ have coordinates $(-3,-5)$ and $(7,11)$ respectively.

Find the coordinates of

(a) $C$, the midpoint of $AB$

(b) $D$, the midpoint of $CB$

(c) $E$, the point on $BA$ produced (i.e. extended) such that $A$ is the midpoint of $EB$.

**B3** Line $l$ has equation $y + 2x = 5$. Find the equations of

(a) the line through $A(2,6)$
 (i) parallel to $l$
 (ii) perpendicular to $l$

(b) the line through $B(-3,-1)$
 (i) parallel to $l$
 (ii) perpendicular to $l$

**B4** The points $A(0,1)$, $B(6,3)$, $C(7,6)$ are three of the vertices of a parallelogram $ABCD$. Find the coordinates of $D$.

**B5** Show that the points $A(-2,3)$, $B(4,0)$, $C(6,4)$ and $D(0,7)$ form a rectangle $ABCD$. Find the area of the rectangle.

**B6** Triangle $ABC$ has $A(-2,-1)$, $B(4,7)$, $C(6,-3)$. $M$ is the midpoint of $BC$. Find

(a) the coordinates of the midpoint of $AM$

(b) the length of $AM$

(c) the equation of $AM$.

**B7** The line $l$ has equation $2x - 3y - 6 = 0$. Find the equation of the line through $A(-1,-7)$ perpendicular to $l$. Hence find the coordinates of the foot of the perpendicular from $A$ to $l$ and the distance of $A$ from $l$.

**B8** Show that triangle $ABC$ with $A(-5,2)$,

## Exercise 6.2 *continued*

$B(-1,4)$ and $C(4,8)$ is right angled. Find its area.

**B9** Triangle $ABC$ has $A(2,0)$, $B(4,8)$ and $C(0,4)$.

Write down the coordinates of $D$, $E$ and $F$, the midpoints of $BC$, $CA$ and $AB$ respectively. Obtain the equations of the lines $BE$ and $CF$ and find the coordinates of their point of intersection, $G$. Show that $G$ lies on $AD$.

**B10** Triangle $ABC$ has $A(-1,6)$, $B(-2,-1)$ and $C(7,2)$. Find the coordinates of $D$, the foot of the perpendicular from $A$ to $BC$. Hence show that the area of the triangle is 30. Show that $AC = 4\sqrt{5}$. Hence obtain, in the form $k\sqrt{5}$, where $k$ is an integer, the length of the perpendicular from $B$ to $AC$.

## 6.3 The circle, its tangents and other geometrical properties

### Key points

$$(x - a)^2 + (y - b)^2 = r^2$$

represents a circle centre $(a, b)$ radius $r$. In particular

$$x^2 + y^2 = r^2$$

represents a circle centre the origin and radius $r$. Remember that at any point on the circumference of the circle, the tangent and radius are perpendicular.

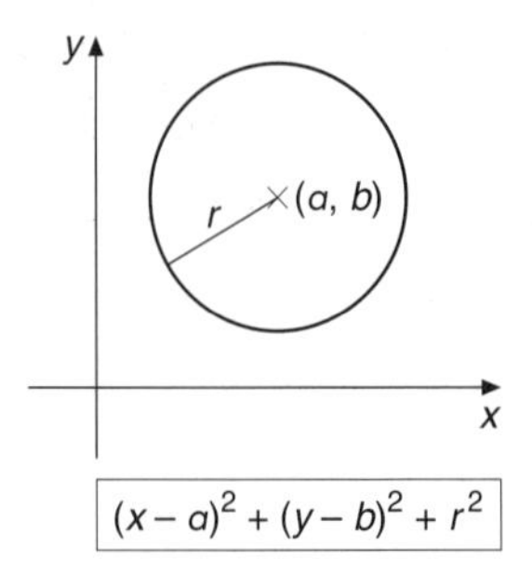


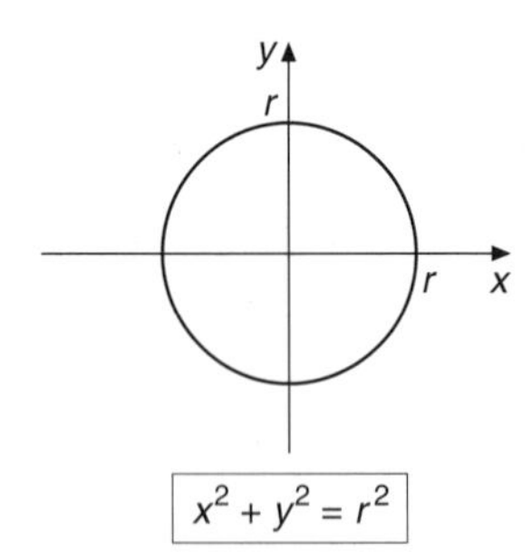


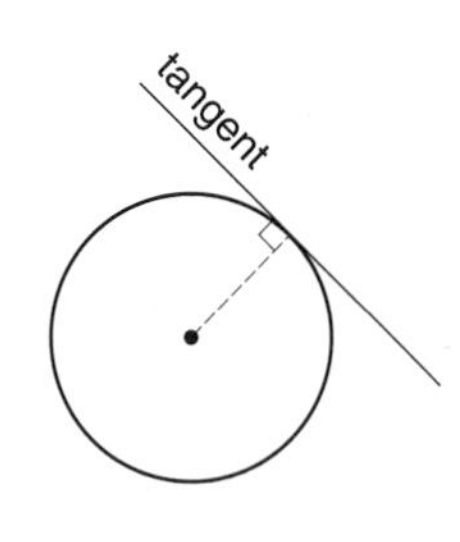


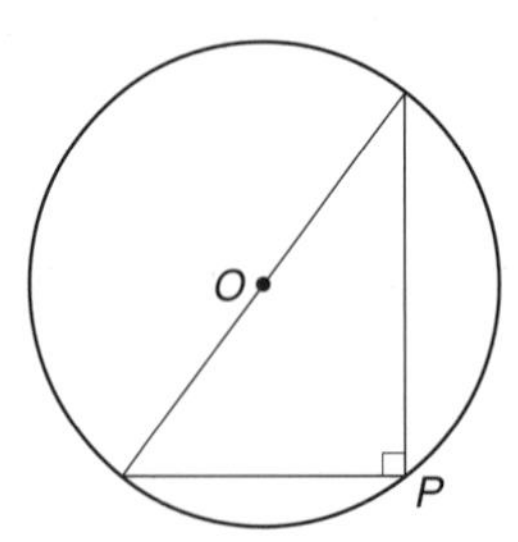


The angle in a semi-circle is a right angle.

## Example 1

Points $A(7,9)$ and $B(-5,3)$ are the end points of diameter $AB$ of a circle. Find the centre of the circle and its radius. Hence write down the equation of the circle.

**Solution**

The centre of the circle is the midpoint of $AB$ and has coordinates

$$C\left(\frac{7+(-5)}{2}, \frac{9+3}{2}\right) \text{ or } C(1,6)$$

The radius is the length $AC$ (or $BC$).

$$AC = \sqrt{(7-1)^2 + (9-6)^2} = \sqrt{6^2 + 3^2} = \sqrt{36 + 9} = \sqrt{45} = 3\sqrt{5}$$

So $r^2 = 45$

$\therefore$ The equation of the circle is

$$(x-1)^2 + (y-6)^2 = 45.$$

## Example 2

By writing the equation $x^2 + y^2 - 6x - 8y + 9 = 0$ in the form $(x-a)^2 + (y-b)^2 = r^2$ show that the equation represents a circle and state the coordinates of the centre and the length of the radius. Sketch the circle and draw a square with sides that are both tangents to the circle and parallel to the axes. Mark the coordinates of the points of contact, the coordinates of the vertices of the square and find the area of the square.

**Solution**

$(x-a)^2 + (y-b)^2 - r^2 \equiv x^2 + y^2 - 6x - 8y + 9$

Squaring out the brackets on the left hand side

so $x^2 - 2ax + a^2 + y^2 - 2by + b^2 - r^2 = x^2 + y^2 - 6x - 8y + 9$

comparing coefficients of $x$, $y$ and constant term respectively

then $-2a = -6$, $-2b = -8$ and $a^2 + b^2 - r^2 = 9$

i.e. $a = 3$, $b = 4$ and $3^2 + 4^2 - r^2 = 9$

$$25 - 9 = r^2$$

$$16 = r^2$$

$\therefore$ The required form is

$$(x-3)^2 + (y-4)^2 = 16$$

This is a circle centre (3,4) radius 4.

The diameter of the circle is 8. The area of the square is $8 \times 8 = 64$ sq. units

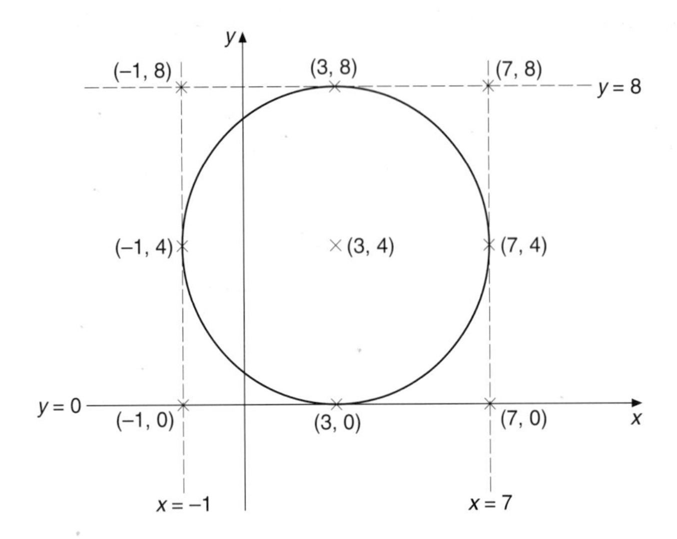


## Exercise 6.3

**A1** Write down the equation of the circle with

(a) centre $(-1,0)$, radius 3

(b) centre $(0,-4)$, radius 2

(c) centre $(-2,3)$, radius 1

(d) centre $(4,-3)$, radius 5.

**A2** For the circles in **A1** find the coordinates of any points of intersection with the axes. If there are none, write down the coordinates of the point on the circle nearest the axis.

**A3** (a) Show that the equation $x^2 + y^2 + 6x - 10y - 6 = 0$ can be written in the form $(x + 3)^2 + (y - 5)^2 = r^2$ where $r^2 = 40$. Hence write down the coordinates of the centre, the exact value of the radius and the area of the circle.

(b) State which of the following equations represent circles. Where the equation represents a circle, find the coordinates of the centre, and the length of the radius.

(i) $x^2 + y^2 - 2x - 4y - 11 = 0$

(ii) $x^2 + y^2 + 4x - 6y + 13 = 0$

(iii) $x^2 + y^2 - 6x - 2y + 6 = 0$

(iv) $x^2 + y^2 - 8x + 16 = 0$

(v) $x^2 + y^2 - 4x - 4y + 4 = 0$

**A4** Find the equation of the circle concentric with $(x - 2)^2 + (y - 1)^2 = 4$ but which has

(a) half its radius

(b) 3 times its radius

concentric circles have the same centre

**A5** Show that the circles $(x + 2)^3 + (y - 1)^2 = 9$ and $(x - 2)^2 + (y - 4)^2 = 4$ touch each other externally. Sketch the situation.

**B1** Show that the point $A(3,-4)$ lies on the circle $x^2 + y^2 = 25$. Write down the gradient of $OA$ where $O$ is the origin. Hence find the equation of the tangent to the circle at $A$. Obtain the equation of the parallel tangent.

**B2** (a) Find the equation of the circle with centre $(-3,2)$ which passes through $(4,-1)$

(b) Find the equation of the circle which has points $(5,-3)$ and $(-1,9)$ as the extremities of a diameter.

**B3** Show that triangle $ABC$ with $A(-3,0)$, $B(-1,4)$ and $C(7,0)$ is right angled. Hence find the equation of the circumcircle of the triangle (i.e. the circle which passes through $A$, $B$ and $C$).

Remember: The angle in a semi circle is 90°.

After finding the expressions for $Y$ and $X$, you should

(a) Draw up a table of values connecting $Y$ and $X$
(b) Plot the points
(c) Draw the line of best fit
(d) From the line, estimate the gradient ($m$) and intercept ($c$) **or** find two points on the line and use them to find the equation of the line and hence the values of $m$ and $c$
(e) From these values of $m$ and $c$ write down the values of constants $a$ and $b$.

## Example 1(a)

Find a relation connecting $y$ and $x$ in 1(a) and 1(b)

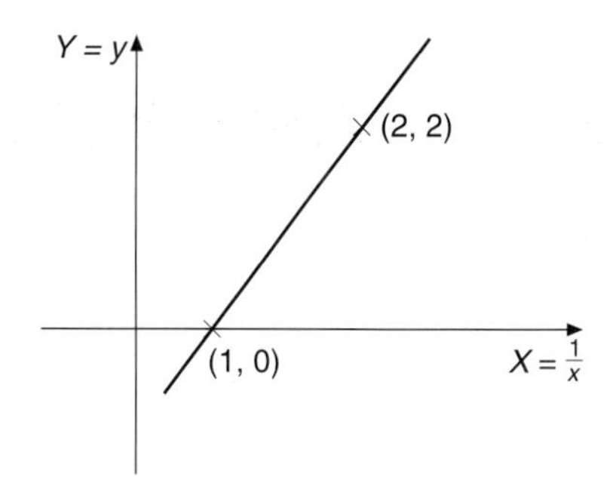


### Solution

Gradient $= 2$ $(= m)$
so $Y = 2X + c$

You can use either (1,0) or (2,2) now for $(X,Y)$ to find $c$.

Let $X = 1$ and $Y = 0$
$0 = 2 + c$
$-2 = c$

so $$Y = 2X - 2$$

The required relation is

$$y = 2\left(\frac{1}{x}\right) - 2$$

i.e. $$y = \frac{2}{x} - 2$$

**Exercise 6.3** *continued*

**B4** Write down the coordinates of the centre and the length of the radius of the circle $x^2 + y^2 - 4x - 8y - 5 = 0$. Show that the point $A(5,8)$ lies on this circle and find the equation of the tangent at $A$. Obtain the equation of the tangent at the point $B$ diametrically opposite $A$.

**B5** Triangle $ABC$ has $A(0,6)$, $B(0,-4)$ and $C(8,4)$. $E$ is the midpoint of $AC$, and $F$ is the midpoint of $AB$. Write coordinates of $E$ and bisector of $AC$ (i.e. th right angles to $AC$) m perpendicular bisecto is $(3,1)$. Show that $AP$ write down the equati passes through $A$, $B$ ar that the line joining $F$ $BC$ is perpendicular tc

## 6.4 The concept of a linear relation. Reduction of a relation to linear form and determination of th constants from graphs

### Key points

You will be given data connecting two variables with a suggested p relationship (or law) between them. To test this law you try to fit a relationship $Y = mX + c$ to the data by finding appropriate expres $Y$ and $X$.

The table should help.

| Suggested law | Explanations | Compare $Y = mX$ | | |
|---|---|---|---|---|
| | | $Y$ | $X$ | $m$ |
| $y = ax^2 + b$ | Simple comparison | $y$ | $x^2$ | $a$ |
| $y = ax^2 + bx$ | Divide by $x$<br>$\frac{y}{x} = ax + b$ | $\frac{y}{x}$ | $x$ | $a$ |
| $\frac{1}{x} + \frac{1}{y} = \frac{1}{a}$ | Reorganise<br>$\frac{1}{y} = -\frac{1}{x} + \frac{1}{a}$ | $\frac{1}{y}$ | $\frac{1}{x}$ | $-1$ |
| $y = ax^b$ | $\ln y = \ln(ax^b)$<br>$\ln y = \ln a + \ln x^b$<br>$\ln y = b\ln x + \ln a$ | $\ln y$ | $\ln x$ | $b$ |
| $y = ab^x$ | $\ln y = \ln(ab^x)$<br>$\ln y = \ln a + \ln b^x$<br>$\ln y = \ln a + x\ln b$ | $\ln y$ | $x$ | $\ln b$ |

## Example 1(b)

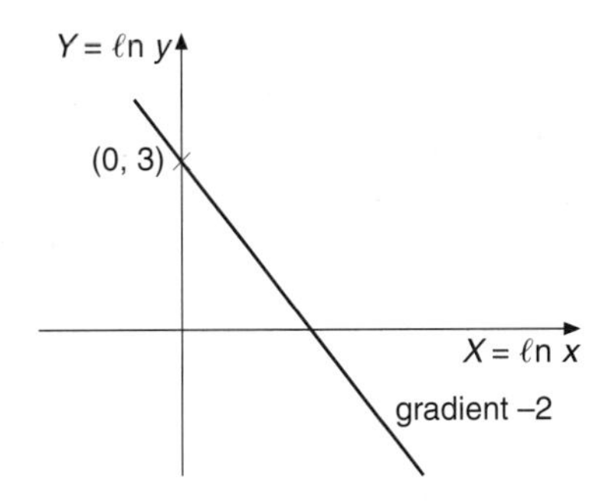


**Solution**

$m = -2$
$c = 3$

so $$Y = -2X + 3$$

i.e. $\ln y = -2\ln x + 3$
$\ln y + 2\ln x = 3$
$\ln y + \ln x^2 = 3$
$\ln(yx^2) = 3$
$yx^2 = e^3$

Hence $$y = \frac{k}{x^2} \text{ where } k = e^3$$

## Example 2

The table gives the results of an experiment where for chosen values of $x$ appropriate values of $y$ were found.

| $x$ | 1 | 2 | 3 | 4 | 5 |
|---|---|---|---|---|---|
| $y$ | 8.91 | 3.01 | 1.71 | 1.15 | 0.87 |

It was expected that a relationship of the form $y = \frac{a}{x} + \frac{b}{x^2}$ would connect $x$ and $y$. By drawing a suitable linear graph show that this is indeed the case and find $a$, $b$ each correct to 1 decimal place.

**Solution**

If $y = \dfrac{a}{x} + \dfrac{b}{x^2}$ then $yx^2 = ax + b$

Comparing with $Y = mX + c$

$$Y = yx^2$$
$$X = x$$
$$m = a$$
$$c = b$$

We need a table of values for $Y$ against $X$ now, so use the information in the given table to calculate $X$ and $Y$.

| $x = X$ | 1 | 2 | 3 | 4 | 5 |
|---|---|---|---|---|---|
| $yx^2 = Y$ | 8.91 | 12.04 | 15.39 | 18.40 | 21.75 |

Plot the graph of $Y$ and $X$ and draw in the line of best fit.

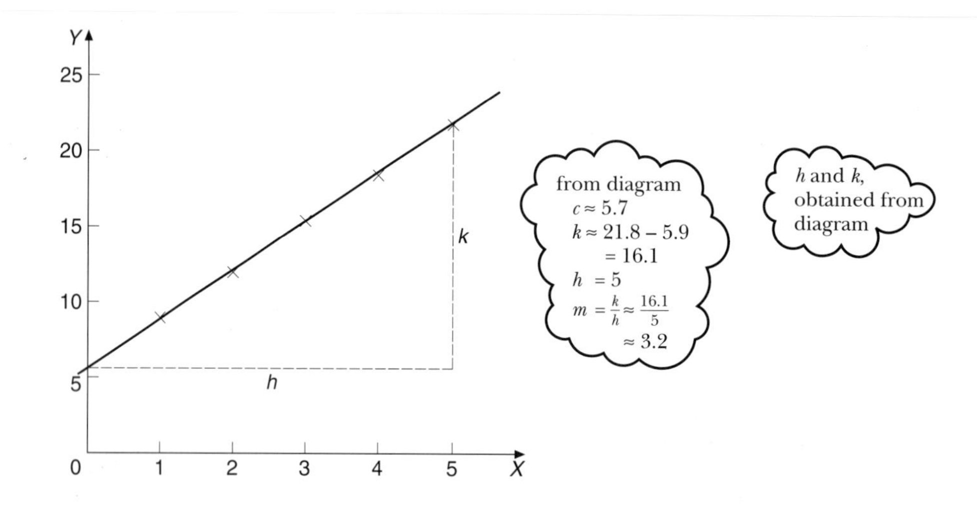


From the line find:

(a) Gradient $\dfrac{k}{h} \approx 3.2 = m$

(b) Intercept $\approx 5.7 = c$
So $a = m = 3.2$
$b = c = 5.7$
and we have

$$y = \frac{3.2}{x} + \frac{5.7}{x^2}$$

for the relationship.

## Exercise 6.4

In the diagrams, not drawn to scale, all the lines are straight.

**A1** In each case find $Y$ in terms of $X$.

a)

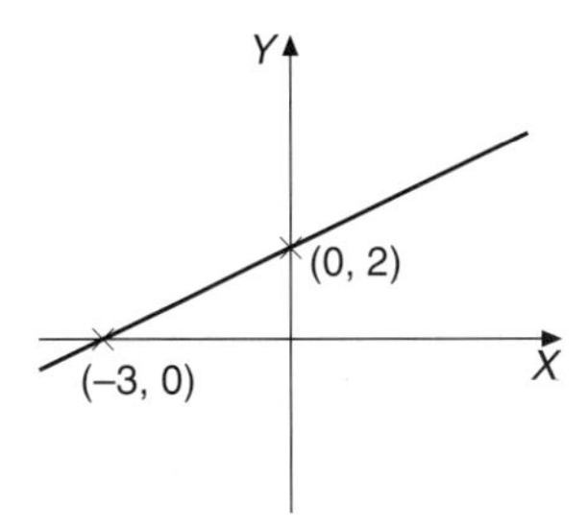


b)

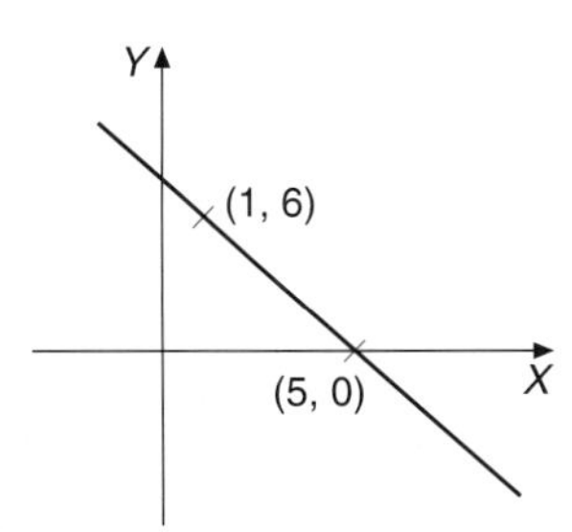


c)

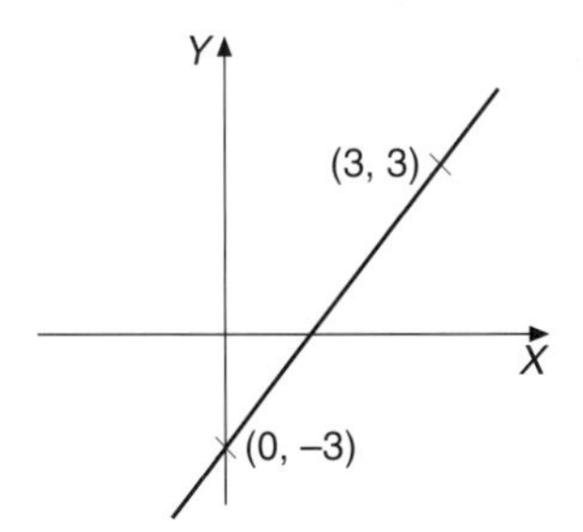


**A2** Find a relation connecting $y$ and $x$.

a)

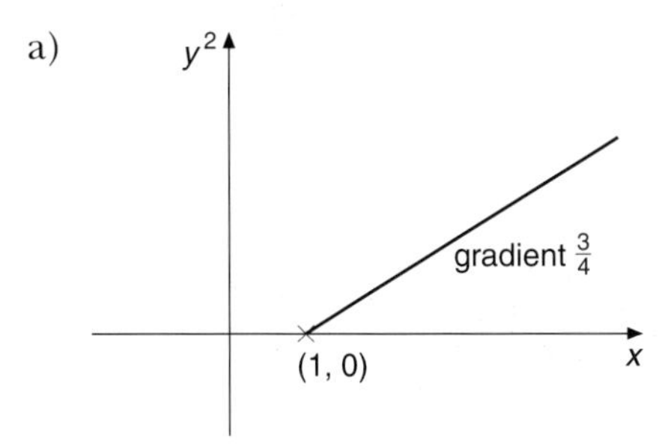


b)

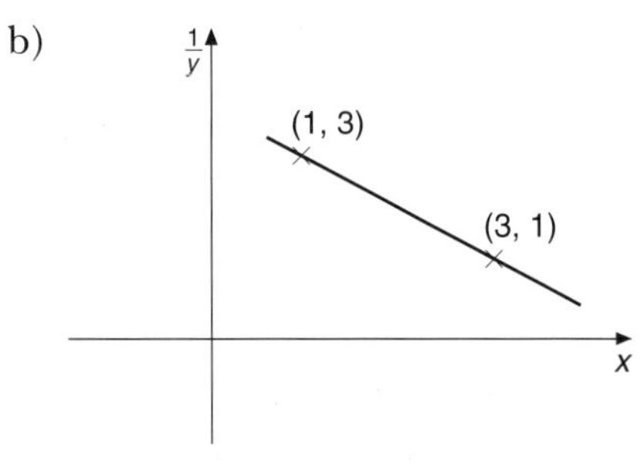


**A3** Find a formula connecting $y$ and $x$ with $y$ as the subject.

a)

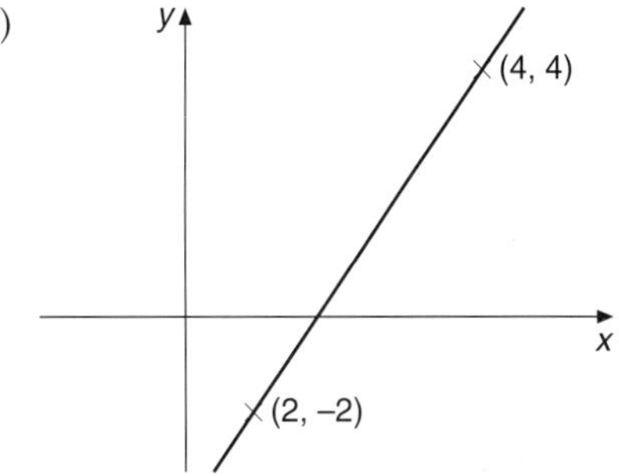


b)

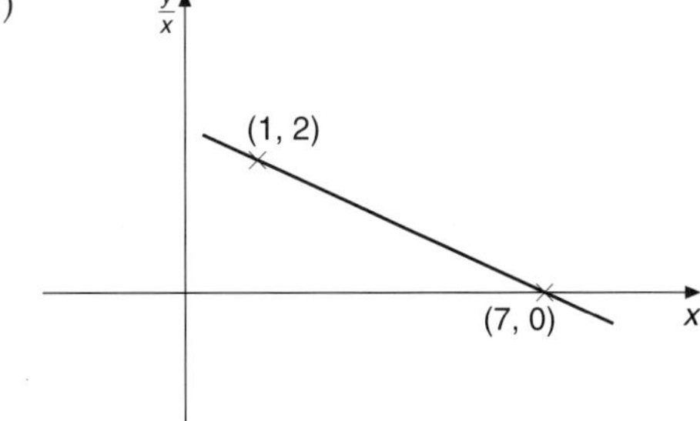


**A4**

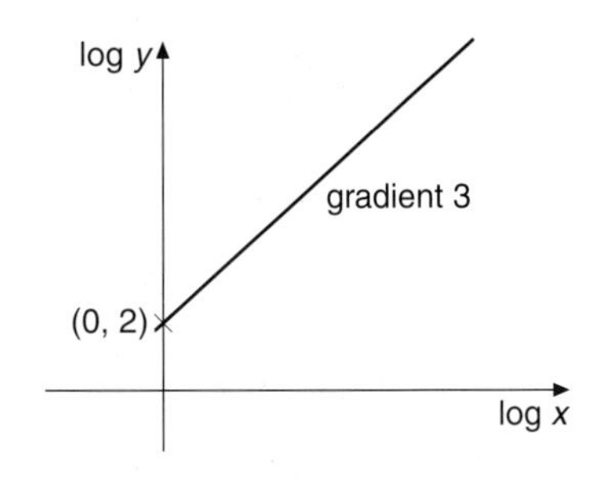

## Exercise 6.4 *continued*

Show that $y = ax^3$ and state the value of the constant $a$.

**A5**

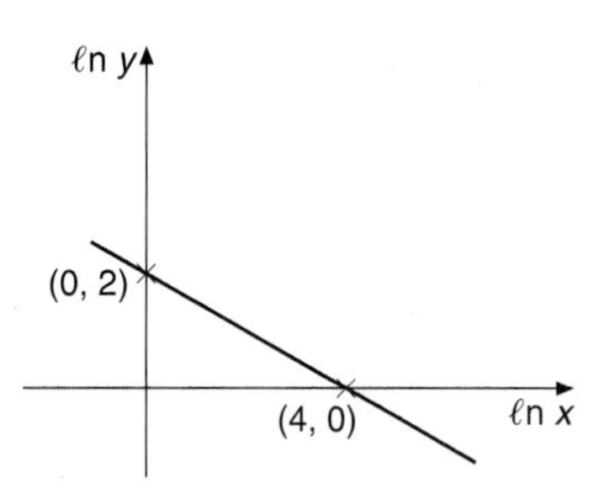


Show that $y = ab^x$ where $a$ and $b$ are constants that satisfy the relation $ab^4 = 1$.

**B1** A car moves along a straight road. The distance $s$ metres moved by the car after it passes a bus stop is measured at one second intervals.

The following data is collected.

| $t$ | 1 | 2 | 3 | 4 | 5 |
|---|---|---|---|---|---|
| $s$ | 12.8 | 27.5 | 43.0 | 60.5 | 78.8 |

It is believed that $s$ and $t$ are related by the formula $s = at + bt^2$. By drawing a suitable straight line graph, verify the relationship and estimate the values of $a$ and $b$ giving your answers to 1 decimal place.

**B2** The period $T$ seconds of oscillation of a pendulum and its length $l$ metres are related by the law $T = al^b$. The following experimental data was collected.

| $l$ | 0.6 | 0.8 | 1.0 | 1.2 | 1.4 |
|---|---|---|---|---|---|
| $T$ | 1.55 | 1.80 | 2.01 | 2.19 | 2.37 |

Estimate the values of $a$ and $b$ and the period of oscillation of a pendulum of length 1.1 metres.

**B3** It is believed that $x$ and $y$ are connected by the relationship $y = ab^x$ when the following experimental data is examined.

| $x$ | 1 | 3 | 5 | 7 | 9 |
|---|---|---|---|---|---|
| $y$ | 3.8 | 6.7 | 11.6 | 20.3 | 35.3 |

By drawing a straight line graph based on the data estimate the values of $a$ and $b$.

**B4** In an experiment to find the focal length $f$ cm of a lens, the distance $u$ cm of the object and the distance $v$ cm of its images from the centre of the lens were measured and the following data collected.

| $u$ | 10 | 15 | 20 | 25 | 30 |
|---|---|---|---|---|---|
| $v$ | 57.0 | 19.8 | 14.8 | 13.0 | 11.9 |

It is known that the formula $\frac{1}{f} = \frac{1}{u} + \frac{1}{v}$ connects $u$, $v$, and $f$.

By plotting a suitable graph estimate $f$ to 2 significant figures.

## Chapter 6: A level questions

Remember: Diagrams always help

**C1** Line $L_1$ has gradient $\frac{2}{3}$ and passes through $A(-2,1)$.

Line $L_2$ passes through $B(10,-4)$ and is perpendicular to $L_1$.

Lines $L_1$ and $L_2$ intersect at point $C$.

Show that the area of triangle $ABC$ is 39 square units.

**C2** The triangle $ABC$ has $A(-1,-4)$, $B(2,5)$ and $C(8,2)$

Find

(a) the equation of $AB$.

## Chapter 6: A level questions *continued*

(b) the equation of $BC$.

Show that the point $F(1,2)$ lies on the line $AB$.

A line through $F$ parallel to $AC$ meets $BC$ at $D$.

Find the coordinates of $D$ and show that the length of $FD = \sqrt{13}$ and that $AC = 3 \times FD$.

**C3**

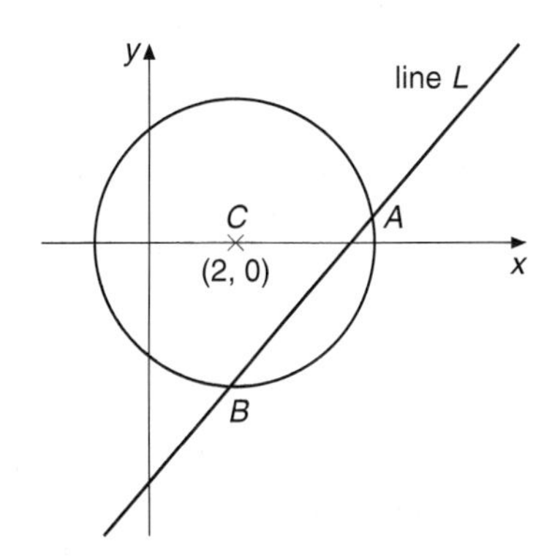


In the diagram (not to scale) circle centre $C$ has equation $x^2 + y^2 - 4x - 9 = 0$ and line $L$ has equation $2x - y - 8 = 0$. Line $L$ cuts the circle at points $A$ and $B$.

(a) Show that $A$ is the point $(5,2)$

(b) Find the coordinates of the point $B$

(c) Show that the midpoint $M$ of $AB$ has coordinates $\left(\frac{18}{5}, -\frac{4}{5}\right)$ and that $CM$ is perpendicular to $AB$.

**C4** (a) If $A$ is $(0,7)$, $B(-10,-3)$, $C(5,-3)$ and $D(4,4)$ show that
- (i) $AC$ is at right angles to $BD$
- (ii) the lines $AC$ and $BD$ intersect at $E(2,3)$.

(b) Find the exact lengths of $BE$, $ED$, $AE$ and $EC$ and show that $BE \times ED = AE \times EC$

**C5** (a) Show that the point $C(7,-11)$ is the same distance from point $A(-2,-4)$ as it is from point $B(4,0)$.

(b) Find the equation of the circle with centre $C$ which passes through the points $A$ and $B$.

(c) If $C$ is the midpoint of $AD$ then find the coordinates of $D$ and show that angle $DBA$ is $90°$.

**C6**

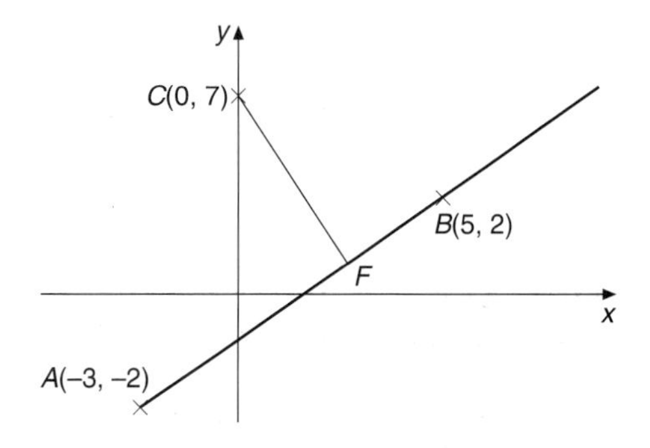


$A$, $B$ and $C$ are the points shown in the diagram (not drawn to scale).

$CF$ is at right angles to $AB$.

(a) Show that $F$ has coordinates $(3,1)$

(b) If the point $C$ is reflected in the line $AB$ find the coordinates of the image $C'$.

**C7** The diagram shows point $A(2,4)$ on the circle, centre $O$, with equation $x^2 + y^2 = 20$

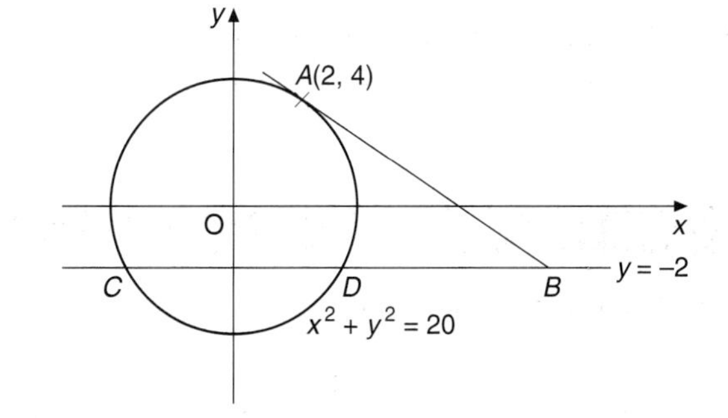


(a) Find the equation of the tangent at $A$

(b) If the tangent at $A$ meets line $y = -2$ at $B$ then find the coordinates of $B$ and show that distance $AB$ is $6\sqrt{5}$

## Chapter 6: A level questions *continued*

(c) The line $y = -2$ meets the circle at points $C$ and $D$. Find the coordinates of $C$ and $D$.

(d) Write down the lengths of $BC$ and $BD$ and show that $BC \times BD = AB^2$.

**C8** The point $A(p,q)$ lies on a circle centre $O(0,0)$.

Find, in terms of $p$ and $q$

(a) the gradient of $OA$

(b) the gradient of the tangent at $A$

(c) the equation of the tangent at $A$

(d) the coordinates of the point $T$ where the tangent at $A$ meets the $x$ axis

(e) the area of triangle $OAT$.

**C9** The values of $x$ and $y$, given below, are believed to be connected by a formula of the form $\frac{1}{y} = a + b\sqrt{x}$, where $a$, $b$ are constants.

Show, by drawing a suitable linear graph, that this belief has some foundation, and use your graph to estimate the values of $a$ and $b$, each correct to 1 decimal place.

| $x$ | 1 | 2 | 3 | 4 | 5 |
|---|---|---|---|---|---|
| $y$ | 0.091 | 0.112 | 0.136 | 0.167 | 0.207 |

**C10**

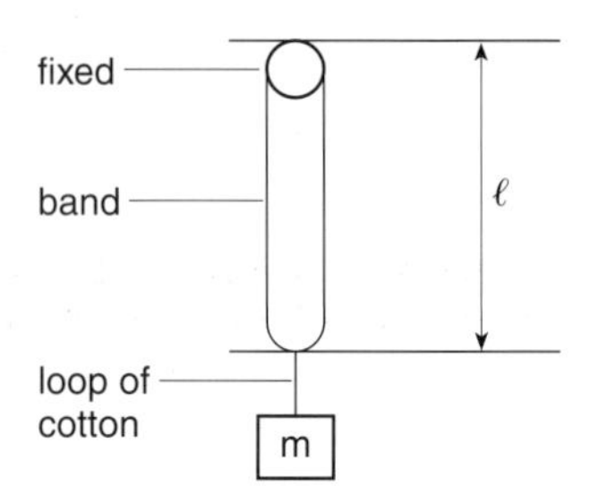


In an experiment to determine the elastic properties of a rubber band a student obtained the following results when a mass was hung by a loop of cotton from the free end of the band.

| mass $m$ in gm | 200 | 400 | 600 | 800 | 1000 | 1200 |
|---|---|---|---|---|---|---|
| length $l$ in cm | 13.2 | 15.4 | 17.7 | 20.0 | 22.4 | 24.6 |

The student's teacher has suggested that the connection between $l$ and $m$ was probably linear. By drawing an appropriate graph confirm that this suggestion is reasonable and find an approximate formula connecting $l$ and $m$, with $l$ as subject.

From your graph estimate the unstretched length of the band and the value of $l$ when the load is 750 gm.

# Chapter 7

## FUNCTIONS

### 7.1 Functions and composite functions

#### Key points

- If, for any relationship between two variabls $x$ and $y$, each input value $x$ has *one and only one* output value $y$, then the relationship is called a **function.**

  The set of input values is called the **domain** of the function and the set of output values is called the **range** of the function.

- The idea of a 'simple' function is illustrated here by

$$x \xrightarrow[\text{DOMAIN}]{\text{INPUT}} \boxed{\begin{array}{c}\text{FUNCTION}\\ \text{MACHINE f}\end{array}} \xrightarrow[\text{RANGE}]{\text{OUTPUT}} y$$

  We write this as $y = \mathrm{f}(x)$

  The function could be 'square', 'sin', 'log', 'reciprocal', 'cube', 'positive square root', or many others which you already know and use on your 'function machine' (i.e. your calculator!)

- The idea of a **'composite' function** is illustrated here by

$$x \xrightarrow[\text{DOMAIN of f}]{\text{INPUT}} \boxed{\text{FUNCTION f}} \xrightarrow[\text{RANGE of f, DOMAIN of g}]{\mathrm{f}(x)} \boxed{\text{FUNCTION g}} \xrightarrow[\text{RANGE of g}]{} \mathrm{g}[\mathrm{f}(x)]$$

  We write this as $y = \mathrm{gf}(x)$

#### Example 1

If $\mathrm{f}(x) \equiv x^2 - 2x + 3$ find $\mathrm{f}(4), \mathrm{f}(2a), \mathrm{f}(-x), \mathrm{f}(x+1)$

**Solution**

$\mathrm{f}(4) = 4^2 - 2(4) + 3 = 16 - 8 + 3 = 11$
$\mathrm{f}(2a) \equiv (2a)^2 - 2(2a) + 3 \equiv 4a^2 - 4a + 3$
$\mathrm{f}(-x) \equiv (-x)^2 - 2(-x) + 3 \equiv x^2 + 2x + 3$
$\mathrm{f}(x+1) \equiv (x+1)^2 - 2(x+1) + 3 \equiv (x^2 + 2x + 1) - 2x - 2 + 3 \equiv x^2 + 2$

#### Example 2

(a) If $\mathrm{f}(x) \equiv x^2 - 2$ and $\mathrm{g}(x) \equiv 3x + 4$ find (a) $\mathrm{fg}(x)$, (b) $\mathrm{gf}(x)$ in terms of $x$

(b) Show that $fg(x) - 3gf(x) \equiv 24x + 20$

**Solution**

(a) (i) $fg(x) \equiv f(3x + 4)$

$f(3x + 4) \equiv (3x + 4)^2 - 2 \equiv (9x^2 + 24x + 16) - 2$

$\equiv 9x^2 + 24x + 14$

(ii) $gf(x) \equiv g(x^2 - 2)$

$g(x^2 - 2) \equiv 3(x^2 - 2) + 4 \equiv 3x^2 - 6 + 4 \equiv 3x^2 - 2$

(b) $fg(x) - 3gf(x) \equiv 9x^2 + 24x + 14 - 3(3x^2 - 2)$

$\equiv 9x^2 + 24x + 14 - 9x^2 + 6$

$\equiv 24x + 20$

## Exercise 7.1

**A1** If $f(x) \equiv x^3 - 3x + 1$ find

(a) $f(4)$

(b) $f(-2)$

(c) $f(-x)$

(d) $f(x) + f(-x)$

**A2** If $g(x) \equiv \dfrac{x+1}{x-5}$ $(x \neq 5)$ find

(a) $g(2)$

(b) $g(-1)$

(c) $g(x + 6)$

**A3** If $h(x) \equiv \dfrac{x+1}{x-1}$ $(x \neq 1)$

(a) Find (i) $h(2)$ (ii) $h(-2)$ (iii) $h\left(\dfrac{1}{x}\right)$

(iv) $h(x) + h\left(\dfrac{1}{x}\right)$

(b) Show that $h(-x) = \dfrac{1}{h(x)}$

**A4** If $f : x \rightarrow x^2$ and $g : x \rightarrow 3x + 1$ find

(a) $g(3)$

(b) $fg(3)$

(c) $fg(x)$

If $fg(x) = 4f(x)$ find the two values of $x$ which satisfy this equation.

**A5** If $f : x \rightarrow 3x - 1$ and $g : x \rightarrow \dfrac{2}{3x-1}$ $(x \neq \frac{1}{3})$

show that $x = \dfrac{1}{9}$ is a solution of

$f(x) = gf(x)$ and find the other solution.

**B1** If $f(x) \equiv (x + 1)(2x - 1)(x - 3)$ find $f(x - 3)$ as a product of three linear factors. Solve

(a) $f(x) = 0$

(b) $f(x - 3) = 0$

**B2** The function f is defined by $f : x \rightarrow 2x^2 - 5$. Show that $ff(x) = 8x^4 - 40x^2 + 45$ and solve $ff(x) = 13$.

**B3** If $g : x \rightarrow \dfrac{x}{1 + 2x}$ $(x \neq -\frac{1}{2})$ find $g\left(\dfrac{1}{x}\right)$ in the form $\dfrac{1}{x + a}$ where $a$ has to be stated.

Find

(a) $g(a)$

(b) $g(-a)$

(c) $g\left(\dfrac{1}{a}\right)$

using your value of $a$.

**B4** If $h(x) \equiv (2x + 1)(x + 5)(3x - 2)$ find $h(x - 2)$ and solve $h(x - 2) = 0$. Write

## Exercise 7.1 *continued*

down expressions for the solutions of $h(x - p) = 0$

**B5** (a) Solve $|x^2 - 20| = 5$

(b) Solve $|x^2 - 5| = 20$

(c) If $f(x) \equiv x^2$ and $g(x) \equiv |x - a|$ find $gf(x)$ and state the condition for the equation $gf(x) = b$ to have only two solutions, where both $a$ and $b$ are positive.

**B6** If $f(x) \equiv \ln x$ and $g(x) \equiv e^x$ find and simplify

(a) (i) $f(1)$ (ii) $f(e)$ (iii) $f(e^3)$ (iv) $f(e^{-1})$

(b) (i) $g(0)$ (ii) $g(\ln x)$ (iii) $g(\ln e)$ (iv) $g(2\ln x)$

(c) Solve $g(2x) - 4g(x) + 3 = 0$

## 7.2 Inverse functions

### Key points

Associated with any function is an 'inverse relationship' which 'undoes' what the function 'does'

i.e. changes output $y$ back to input $x$

Such a relationship may or may not be a function.

(a) For a one-to-one function any output value $y$ is obtained from a unique input value $x$

$x$ → FUNCTION f → $y$
ONE INPUT — ONE OUTPUT

$y = f(x)$

The 'inverse relationship' here gives only one output $x$

$x$ ← INVERSE RELATIONSHIP ← $y$
ONE OUTPUT — ONE INPUT

i.e. this inverse relationship is a 'function'

(b) For a many-to-one function at least one output value $y$ is obtained from more than one input value $x$

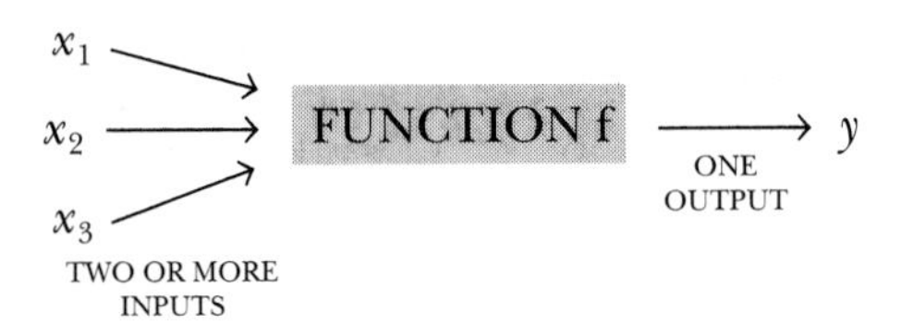

The ‘inverse relationship’ here gives more than one output ($x_1$, $x_2$, $x_3$)

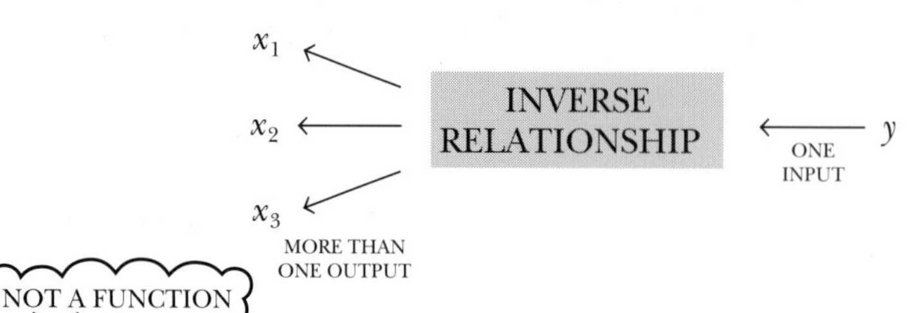


This inverse relationship is not a function.

- Only a one-to-one function has an inverse relationship which is itself a function.
- $y = f^{-1}(x)$ is defined as the inverse function of $y = f(x)$
- Geometrically using equal scales on the axes the graph of $y = f^{-1}(x)$ is the reflection of the graph of $y = f(x)$ in the line $y = x$
- To find the inverse fucntion interchange $x$ and $y$ and then express $y$ in terms of $x$
- The **domain** of $f(x)$ is the **range** of $f^{-1}(x)$

  The **range** of $f(x)$ is the **domain** of $f^{-1}(x)$
- If $f(a) = b$ then $f^{-1}(b) = a$.

  The inverse function takes you back to where you started from.
- (a) Geometrically, if at least one vertical line crosses a graph more than once, this graph is **not** the graph of a function

  (b) If the graph of a function is crossed more than once by at least one horizontal line then there is no inverse function.

## Example 1

Given that $f(x) \equiv \dfrac{2x-3}{x+1}$ $(x \neq -1)$ find $f^{-1}(x)$ and state the domain of $f^{-1}(x)$ and the range of $f(x)$

**Solution**

Let $y = \dfrac{2x-3}{x+1}$

For the inverse function $x = \dfrac{2y-3}{y+1}$

interchange $x$ and $y$

$$x(y+1) = 2y - 3$$

$$xy + x = 2y - 3$$

$$x + 3 = 2y - xy = y(2 - x)$$

rearrange to make $y$ the subject

$$\frac{x+3}{2-x} = y$$

So $$f^{-1}(x) \equiv \frac{x+3}{2-x}$$

for all $x$ except $x = 2$. i.e. Domain of $f^{-1}(x)$ is $x \in R$, $x \neq 2$

This is also the range of $f(x)$

N.B. In the examination it is always sensible to do a quick check to see if your $f^{-1}(x)$ is reasonable.

Here $f(0) = \frac{-3}{1} = -3, f^{-1}(-3) = \frac{0}{5} = 0$

## Example 2

We are given $f: x \rightarrow x^2 + 1, 1 \leq x \leq 4$

The function g is defined by transforming $y = f(x)$ under the translation vector $\begin{pmatrix} 4 \\ 2 \end{pmatrix}$ (this means 4 units in the positive $x$ direction and 2 units in the positive $y$ direction).

(a) find an expression for $g(x)$ and sketch $y = g(x)$ stating its domain and range

(b) find an expression for $g^{-1}(x)$ and state the domain and range.

**Solution**

(a)
$$f(x) \equiv x^2 + 1$$
$$f(x-4) \equiv (x-4)^2 + 1 = x^2 - 8x + 17$$

this has translated $f(x)$ 4 units in the positive $x$ direction

$$f(x-4) + 2 \equiv x^2 - 8x + 19$$

this has 'lifted' the graph 2 units in the positive $y$ direction

Hence $$g(x) \equiv x^2 - 8x + 19$$

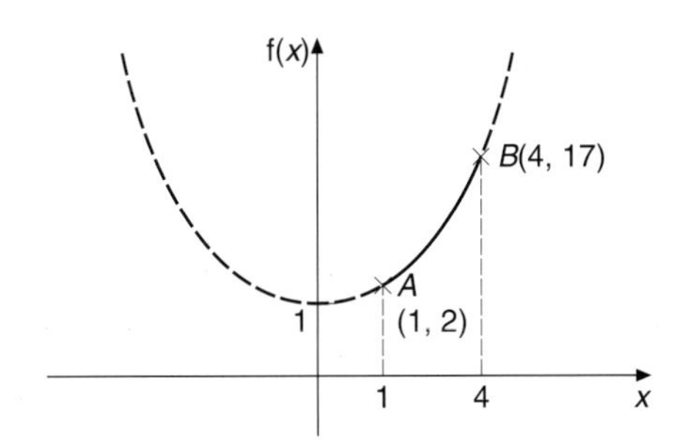


$y = f(x)$ is part of a parabola, vertex (0,1)

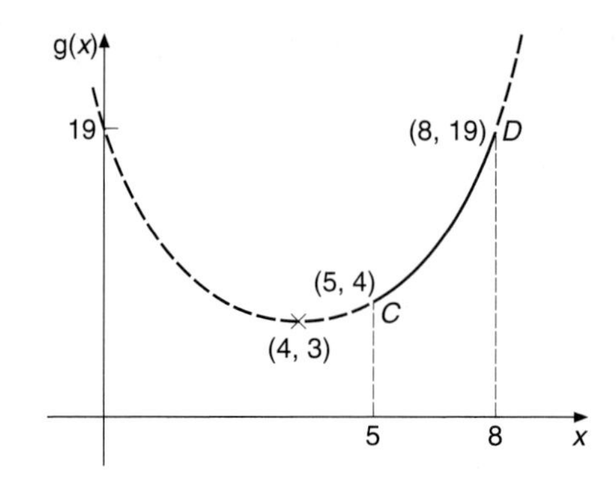


$y = g(x)$ is part of a parabola, vertex (4,3) intersecting the $y$ axis at (0,19)

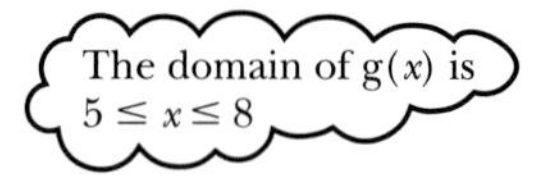


The range of $g(x)$ is $4 \leq g(x) \leq 19$

(b) Let $y = g(x)$

i.e. $y = x^2 - 8x + 19$

For the inverse function

$$x = y^2 - 8y + 19$$

completing the square

$$x = (y - 4)^2 + 3$$

$$x - 3 = (y - 4)^2$$

$$\sqrt{x - 3} = y - 4$$

the positive root is needed as we know that $5 \leq g^{-1}(x) \leq 8$

$$4 + \sqrt{x - 3} = y$$

$$\text{i.e. } g^{-1}(x) = 4 + \sqrt{x - 3}$$

The domain of $g^{-1}(x)$ is $4 \leq x \leq 19$

The range of $g^{-1}(x)$ is $5 \leq g^{-1}(x) \leq 8$

Always check your inverse function by choosing a suitable value for $x$, 7, say and find $g(7) = 12$ then $g^{-1}(12) = 7$ so you know you should be right

## Exercise 7.2

In questions **A1** to **A6** find the inverse functions and state the range of these functions

**A1** (a) $f(x) = 3x - 1, x \in R$

(b) $g(x) = \dfrac{x + 4}{2}, x \in R$

**A2** (a) $h(x) = e^x, x \in R$

(b) $g(x) = 1 - e^{2x}, x \in R$

(c) $f(x) = e^{2x-3}, x \in R$

**A3** $f : x \rightarrow \dfrac{x + 1}{x - 2}, x \neq 2$

**A4** (a) $f : x \rightarrow \dfrac{1}{3}(x + 5), x \in R$

(b) $g : x \rightarrow \dfrac{1}{2}(7 - x), x \in R$

(c) $h : x \rightarrow \dfrac{1}{3}x + 5, x \in R$

**A5** $g : x \rightarrow \dfrac{2 - x}{2x - 1}, x \neq \frac{1}{2}$

**A6** (a) $f(x) = \ln(2x + 1), x > -\frac{1}{2}$

(b) $g(x) = 2 + \ln 3x, x > 0$

**A7** Given that $f : x \rightarrow 2x - 3, 0 \leq x \leq 2$ find $f^{-1}(x)$ and state its domain and range.

Sketch $f(x)$ and $f^{-1}(x)$ on the same graph

**B1** If $h : x \rightarrow (x + 2)^2 - 1$ for $x \geqslant -2$

## Exercise 7.2 *continued*

(a) find the range of h

(b) find the inverse function $h^{-1}(x)$ and state its domain and range.

**B2** A function f is called a self-inverse function if $f(x) = f^{-1}(x)$. Show that

$f(x) = \dfrac{1}{x}$ $(x \neq 0)$ and $g(x) = 1 - x$ are

self-inverse functions.

**B3** The function f changes a temperature given in degrees Celsius to degrees Fahrenheit and is such that

$f : x \to \dfrac{9}{5}x + 32$

(a) Find $f^{-1}(x)$

(b) Sketch $y = f(x)$ and $y = f^{-1}(x)$ on the same graph using equal scales on the axes and dotting in the line of symmetry.

(c) If t° Celsius is the same as t° Fahrenheit then find the value of t.

**B4** If (a) $f(x) \equiv -2x$ (b) $g(x) \equiv 3 - 2x$

show that $f[f^{-1}(x)] \equiv f^{-1}[f(x)] \equiv x$ and similarly that

$g[g^{-1}(a^2)] = g^{-1}[g(a^2)] = a^2$

**B5** (a) If $f(x) = \begin{cases} 2x & 0 \leq x \leq 1 \\ \dfrac{1}{2}(x+3) & 1 \leq x \leq 3 \end{cases}$ find $f^{-1}(x)$ and state its domain

(b) Sketch $y = f(x)$ and $y = f^{-1}(x)$ on the same graph.

**B6** (a) For each of the graphs (i), (ii), (iii), and (iv), state whether or not it represents a function.

(b) Suggest an equation for each function.

(c) One of the functions sketched has an inverse function. Assuming equal scales on the axes, sketch the graph of the inverse function.

(i)

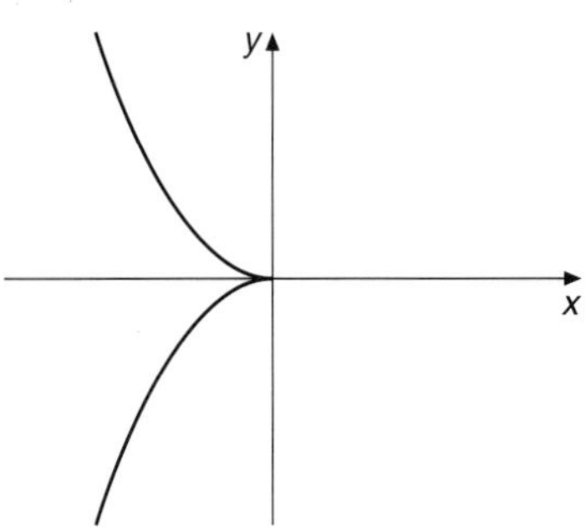


(ii)

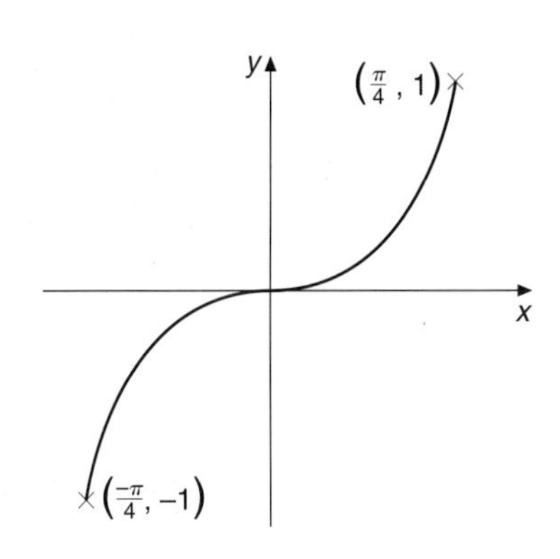


(iii)

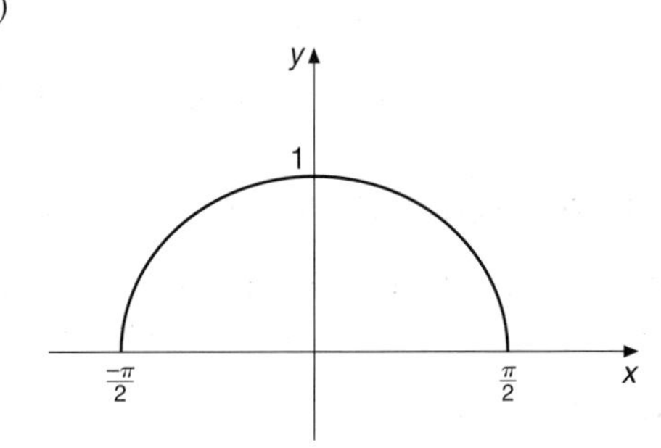


(iv)

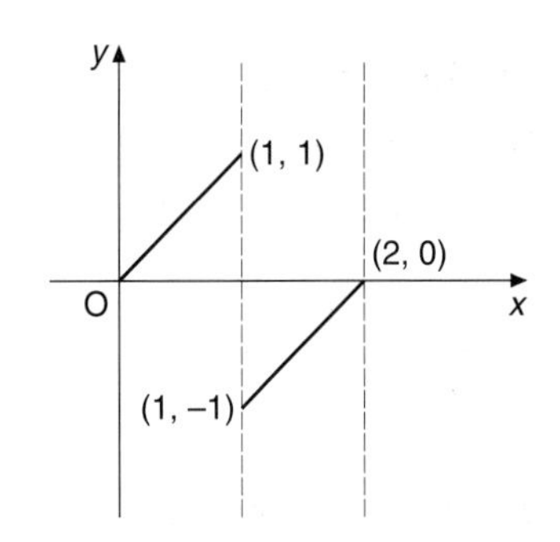

## 7.3 Even and odd functions and simple transformations

### Key points

If $f(-x) = f(x)$ then the function is said to be an **'even' function**

If $f(-x) = -f(x)$ then the function is an **'odd' function**

The graph of an 'even' function is symmetrical about the $y$ axis

The graph of an 'odd' function has rotational symmetry about the origin

In particular $\sin(-x) = -\sin x$ so $\sin x$ is an odd function

$\cos(-x) = \cos x$ so $\cos x$ is even

$\tan(-x) = -\tan x$ so $\tan x$ is odd

- The graph of $y = f(x - a)$ is the graph of $y = f(x)$ translated $\begin{pmatrix} a \\ 0 \end{pmatrix}$
- The graph of $y = -f(x)$ is the graph of $y = f(x)$ reflected in the $x$ axis
- The graph of $y = af(x)$ is the graph of $y = f(x)$ stretched by a scale factor $a$ parallel to the $y$ axis
- The graph of $y = f(x) + a$ is the graph of $y = f(x)$ translated $\begin{pmatrix} 0 \\ a \end{pmatrix}$
- The graph of $y = f(ax)$ is the graph of $y = f(x)$ stretched scale factor $\frac{1}{a}$ parallel to the $x$ axis
- The graph of $y = f(-x)$ is the graph of $y = f(x)$ reflected in the $y$ axis

### Example 1

Show that

(a) $f(x) = x^3 + \frac{4}{x}$ is an odd function $(x \neq 0)$

(b) $f(x) = 2^x + 2^{-x}$ is an even function

**Solution**

(a) $f(x) = x^3 + \frac{4}{x}$

$$f(-x) = (-x)^3 + \frac{4}{(-x)} = -x^3 - \frac{4}{x} = -\left(x^3 + \frac{4}{x}\right) = -f(x)$$

So $f(x)$ is an odd function

(b) $f(x) = 2^x + 2^{-x}$

$f(-x) = 2^{-x} + 2^{-(-x)} = 2^{-x} + 2^x = f(x)$

So $f(x)$ is an even function.

## Example 2(a)

Given that $f(x) = x^3$ sketch the graphs of (a) $y = f(x + 2)$ and (b) $y = 2f(x + 2) + 1$ on separate axes. Describe the transformations from the graph of $y = f(x)$ and on each graph mark the coordinates of the point corresponding to the origin on the graph of $y = f(x)$ and the intersection with the $y$ axis.

**Solution**

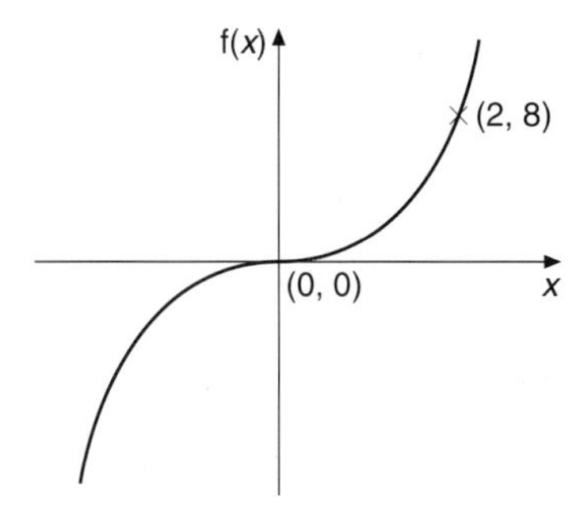


(a) translation vector $\begin{pmatrix} -2 \\ 0 \end{pmatrix}$

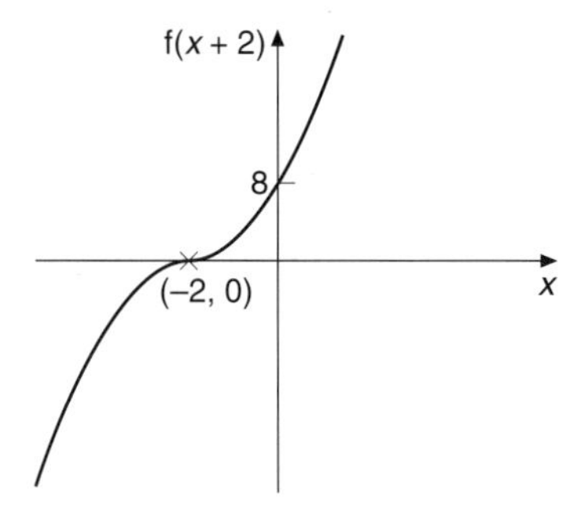


(b) translation vector $\begin{pmatrix} -2 \\ 0 \end{pmatrix}$ followed by a stretch scale factor 2 parallel to the $y$ axis followed by translation $\begin{pmatrix} 0 \\ 1 \end{pmatrix}$

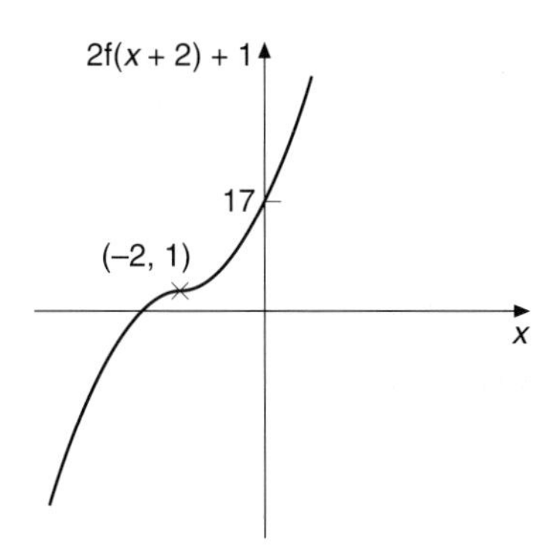

## Example 2(b)

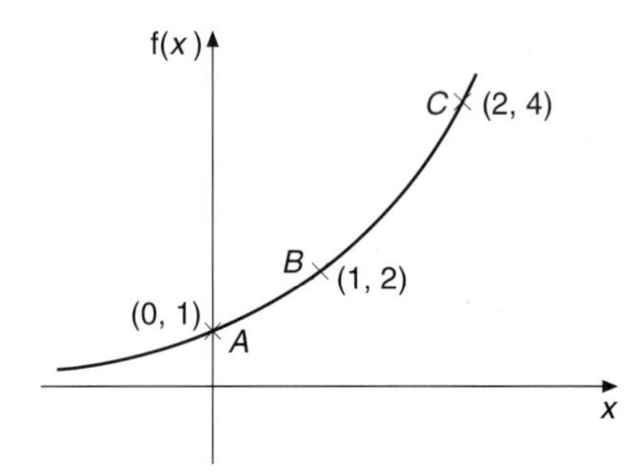


The diagram shows the curve $f(x) = 2^x$ and the points $A$, $B$ and $C$ on that curve.

Sketch the graphs of (a) $y = f(x + 1)$ (b) $y = f(-x)$ (c) $y = -f(x) + 4$ and mark the new positions of $A$, $B$ and $C$ and their coordinates.

**Solution**

(a) $y = f(x)$ is translated $\begin{pmatrix} -1 \\ 0 \end{pmatrix}$ so

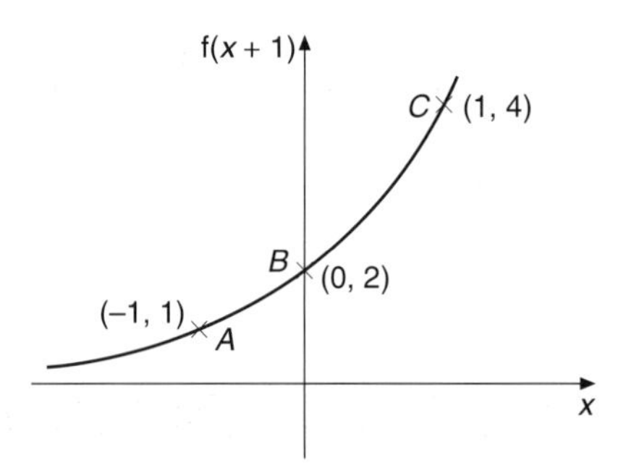


(b) $y = f(x)$ is reflected in the $y$ axis

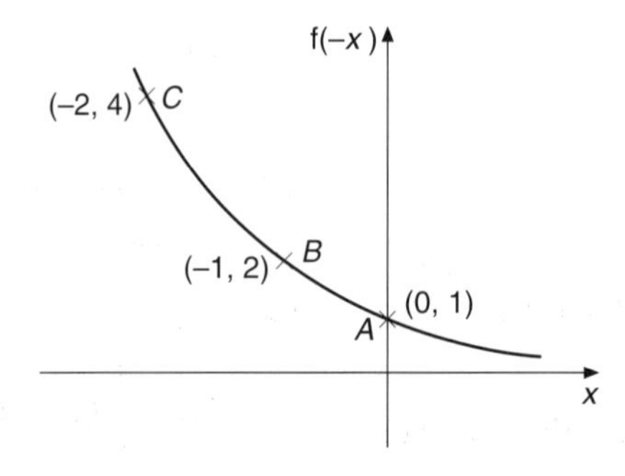

(c) $y = f(x)$ is reflected in the $x$ axis and then translated $\begin{pmatrix} 0 \\ 4 \end{pmatrix}$

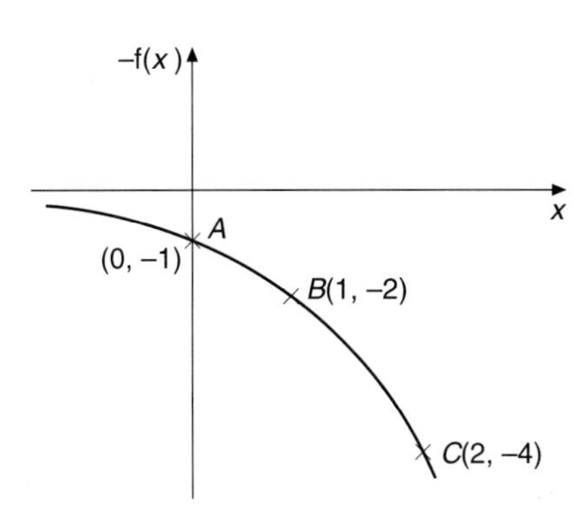


so first

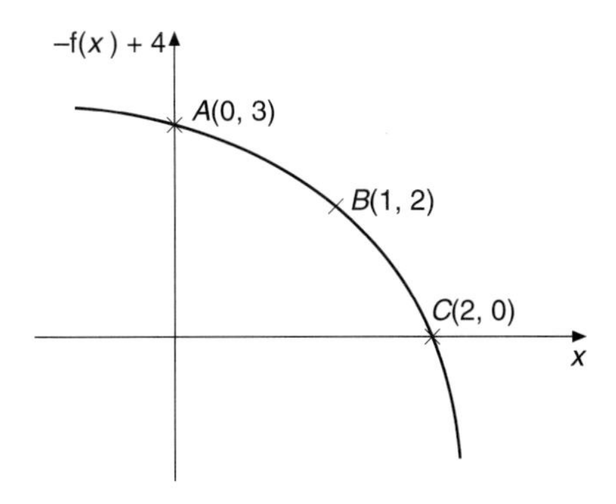


## Exercise 7.3

and then

In questions **A1–A6** the domain is $x \in \mathbb{R}$

**A1** Determine if the following functions are even or odd functions or neither.

(a) $f(x) \equiv x^2 + 3$

(b) $f(x) \equiv (x - 3)^2$

(c) $f(x) \equiv -x^2$

**A2** Show that $f(x) \equiv x\cos x$ is an odd function and that $g(x) \equiv x\sin x$ is an even function.

**A3** If $f(x) \equiv 4 - x^2 + 3x^4$ and $g(x) \equiv 6x^5 - 2x^3 + 4x$ show that f is even and g is odd.

**A4** Are the following functions even, odd, or neither?

(a) $h : x \rightarrow \frac{7}{x}$ $(x \neq 0)$

(b) $g : x \rightarrow |x| + 3$

(c) $f : x \rightarrow x^3 + x^{-3}$ $(x \neq 0)$

**A5** Show that $x\cos 2x + \sin 3x$ is an odd function.

**A6** Are

(a) $\frac{1}{2}(e^x - e^{-x})$

## Exercise 7.3 *continued*

(b) $3x^2 - \frac{2}{x^2}$, $(x \neq 0)$

(c) $\tan 2x$

even or odd functions?

In questions **B1–B4** on your sketches mark the coordinates of the points corresponding to those whose coordinates are given.

**B1**

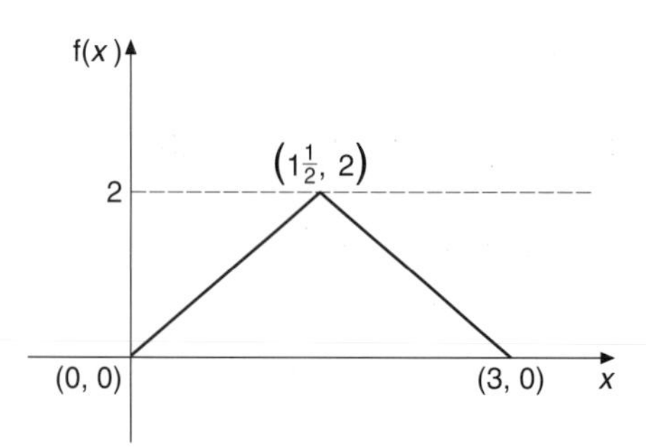


The diagram shows part of the graph of $y = f(x)$. Given that $f(x) = f(-x)$ copy and complete the sketch.

**B2**

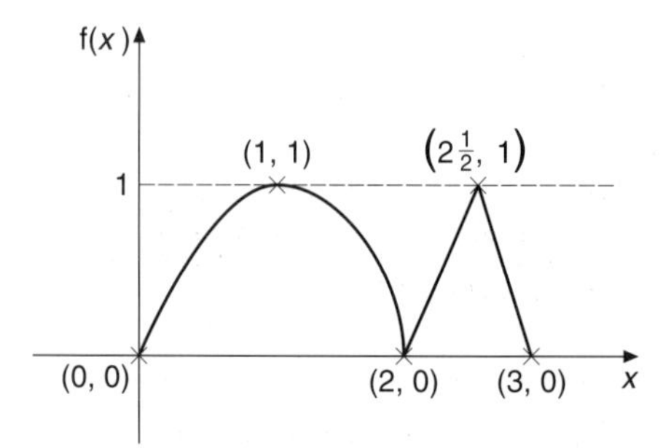


The diagram shows part of a graph of $y = f(x)$. Draw separate sketches to illustrate

(a) $y = 2f(x)$

(b) $y = f(x + 1)$

(c) $y = f(2x)$

(d) $y = f\left(\frac{x}{2}\right)$

**B3**

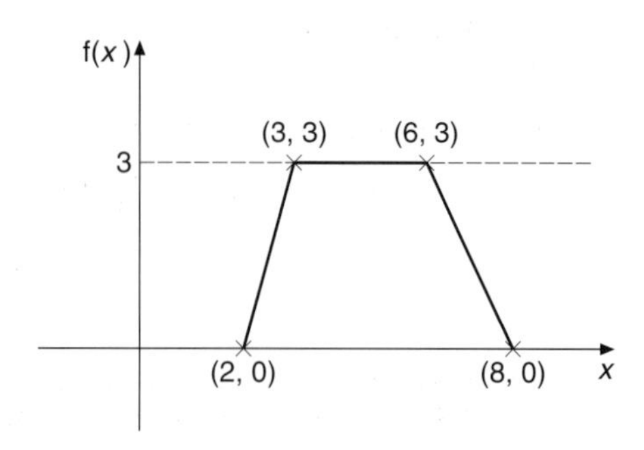


The diagram shows part of the graph of $y = f(x)$.

Sketch, on separate axes, the graphs of

(a) $y = f(x - 2)$

(b) $y = \frac{1}{2}f(x + 2)$ (iii) $y = \frac{1}{3}f(2x)$

**B4**

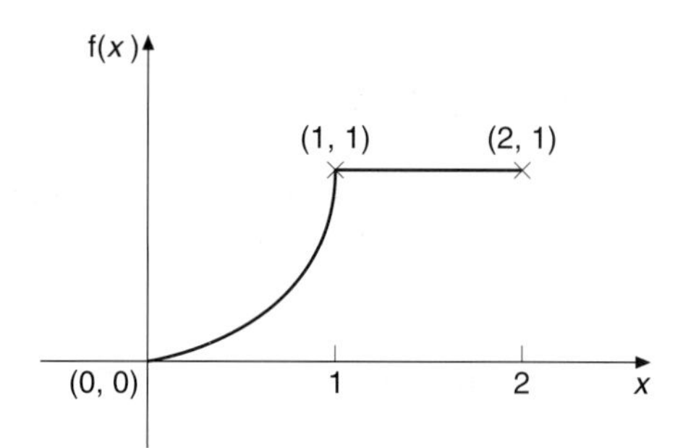


The diagram shows part of the graph of $y = f(x)$

(a) Given that $f(x)$ is an odd function copy and complete the sketch.

(b) Sketch $y = f(x - 1) + 2$ on a separate graph and mark the intersection with the $y$ axis.

**B5**

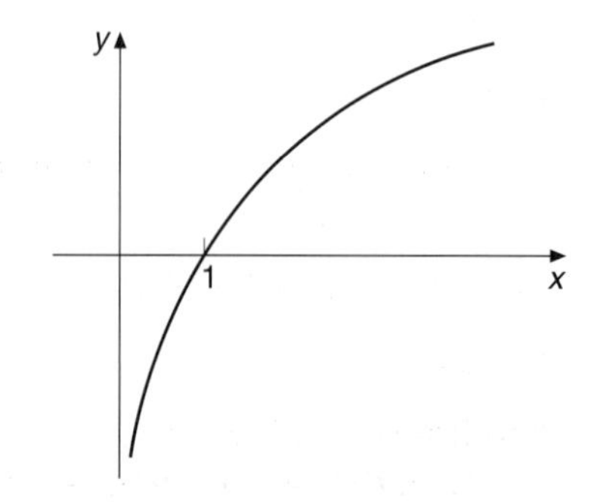

## Exercise 7.3 *continued*

The diagram shows the graph of $y = \ln x = \text{f}(x),\ x > 0$

Draw separate diagrams to illustrate

(a) $y = \text{f}(x - 1)$

(b) $y = \text{f}(x) - 1$

(c) $y = \text{f}(2x)$

marking the intersection with the $x$ axis in each case.

## 7.4 The remainder theorem and the factor theorem

### Key points

- Remainder theorem. When a polynomial $\text{P}(x)$ is divided by $(x - a)$ the remainder is $\text{P}(a)$
- Factor theorem. (a) If $\text{P}(a) = 0$ then $(x - a)$ is a factor of $\text{P}(x)$
  (b) Conversely, if $(x - a)$ is a factor of $\text{P}(x)$ then $\text{P}(a) = 0$
- Roots of equations. If $\text{f}(a) = 0$ then $x = a$ is a root of the equation $\text{f}(x) = 0$

### Example 1

Find the remainder when $\text{P}(x) \equiv 2x^3 - 3x^2 + 5x - 4$ is divided by (a) $x - 3$ (b) $x + 2$ (c) $x - 1$

**Solution**

(a) remainder is $\text{P}(3) = 54 - 27 + 15 - 4 = 38$

(b) remainder is $\text{P}(-2) = -16 - 12 - 10 - 4 = -42$

(c) remainder is $\text{P}(1) = 2 - 3 + 5 - 4 = 0$

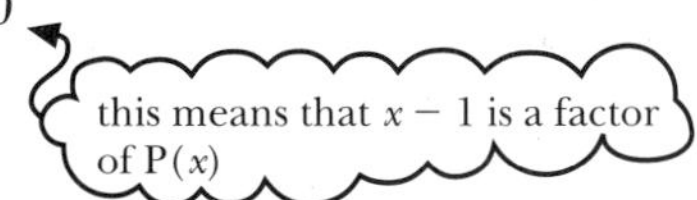


### Example 2

Use the factor theorem to express $\text{P}(x) \equiv x^3 + 2x^2 - 5x - 6$ as a product of three linear factors. Hence solve the equation $x^3 + 2x^2 = 5x + 6$

**Solution**

$\text{P}(x) \equiv x^3 + 2x^2 - 5x - 6$

To find a factor the only values worth trying are $\pm 1, \pm 2, \pm 3, \pm 6$ which are the factors of $-6$

$\text{P}(1) = 1 + 2 - 5 - 6 \neq 0$ so $(x - 1)$ is **not** a factor of $\text{P}(x)$

$\text{P}(-1) = -1 + 2 + 5 - 6 = 0$ so $(x + 1)$ **is** a factor of $\text{P}(x)$

You know that $\text{P}(x) = (x + 1) \times$ (quadratic in $x$) and you can choose either of the two methods shown now to get to the answer.

*Method 1* – further use of the factor theorem.

6 can't have another factor 2 so don't try P(−2)

$P(2) = 8 + 8 - 10 - 6 = 0 \qquad \therefore (x - 2)$ is a factor.

$P(3) = 27 + 18 - 15 - 6 \neq 0$

$P(-3) = -27 + 18 + 15 - 6 = 0 \qquad \therefore (x + 3)$ is a factor.

Hence $\quad P(x) = (x + 1)(x - 2)(x + 3)$

*Method 2* – division of $P(x)$ by $(x + 1)$

**either**

$$
\begin{array}{r}
x^2 + x - 6 \\
x + 1\overline{)x^3 + 2x^2 - 5x - 6} \\
\underline{x^3 + x^2 \qquad\qquad} \\
x^2 - 5x \qquad \\
\underline{x^2 + x \qquad} \\
-6x - 6 \\
\underline{-6x - 6} \\
0
\end{array}
$$

$\therefore P(x) = (x + 1)(x^2 + x - 6) = (x + 1)(x - 2)(x + 3)$

**or** by 'inspection' to give
$P(x) = (x + 1)(x^2 + x - 6) = (x + 1)(x - 2)(x + 3)$

If $x^3 + 2x^2 = 5x + 6$ then $x^3 + 2x^2 - 5x - 6 = 0$
i.e. $(x + 1)(x - 2)(x + 3) = 0$
and so $x = -1, 2$ or $-3$.

## Example 3

Given that $x + 4$ is a factor of $f(x) \equiv x^3 + ax^2 + 11x - 4$

(a) find the value of $a$

(b) factorise $f(x)$

(c) Sketch the graph of $y = f(x)$ showing the exact points of intersection with the axes.

(d) Use your graph to help you solve, exactly, the inequality $f(x) > 0$ if $x$ is negative.

### Solution

(a) $f(x) \equiv x^3 + ax^2 + 11x - 4$
$f(-4) = 0 \qquad$ i.e. $-64 + 16a - 44 - 4 = 0$
$16a = 112$
$a = 7$

(b) $f(x) \equiv x^3 + 7x^2 + 11x - 4$
$f(x) \equiv (x + 4)(x^2 + 3x - 1)$

by inspection
or
long division
as shown in example 2

(c) the graph meets the $x$ axis where $(x + 4)(x^2 + 3x - 1) = 0$

i.e. $x + 4 = 0$ or $x + 3x - 1 = 0$

$x = -4$ $\qquad x = \dfrac{-3 \pm \sqrt{13}}{2}$

$x = -\dfrac{3}{2} \pm \dfrac{\sqrt{13}}{2}$ ← ≈ −3.3 or 0.3 helps your sketch

the graph meets the $y$ axis (when $x = 0$) at the point $(0,-4)$

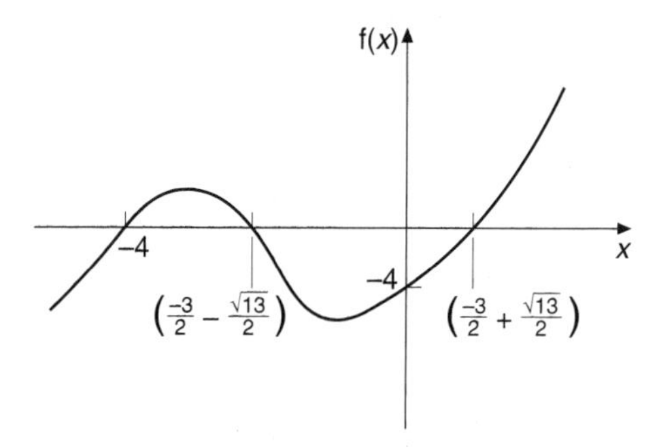


(d) When $f(x) > 0$ and $x < 0$ then from the graph $-4 < x < \dfrac{-3}{2} - \dfrac{\sqrt{13}}{2}$

## Exercise 7.4

**A1** Show that $x - 3$ is a factor of

(a) $4x^2 - 13x + 3$

(b) $x^3 - x^2 + 6x - 36$

(c) $x^4 - 81$

**A2** If $x + 2$ is a factor of $x^3 + 2x^2 - ax + 2$ find the value of $a$.

**A3** Find the remainder when $x^3 - 3x^2 + 2x - 1$ is divided by

(a) $(x - 1)$

(b) $(x + 2)$

(c) $(x - a)$

**A4** Show that $(x + 3)$ is not a factor of $P(x) \equiv x^3 + x^2 - 14x + 6$ but that $(x - 3)$ is a factor.

**A5** Show that if $x^2 - 16$ is a factor of $f(x) \equiv x^3 + x^2 + ax + b$ then $a = b$. Express $f(x)$ as a product of three linear factors.

**A6** Given that $(x + 3)$ is a factor of $f(x) \equiv 4x^3 + 12x^2 - 9x - 27$ solve the equation $f(x) = 0$.

**B1** The function g is given by $g(x) \equiv x^3 - 2x^2 - 5x + 10$

(a) Show that $(x - 2)$ is a factor of $g(x)$

(b) Write $g(x)$ in the form $(x - 2)f(x)$ where $f(x) = px^2 + qx + r$ and find the values of $p$, $q$, and $r$

(c) Solve $g(x) = 0$.

**B2** (a) Show that $(x + 2)$ is a factor of $P(x) \equiv x^3 + 3x^2 - 10x - 24$

(b) Write $P(x)$ as a product of three linear factors

## Exercise 7.4 *continued*

(c) Find the set of values of $x$ for which $x^3 + 3x^2 - 10x - 24 > 0$.

**B3** If $f(x) \equiv x^3 + ax^2 + bx + 6$ and both $(x - 2)$ and $(x + 1)$ are factors of $f(x)$, find $a$ and $b$ and verify that $a + 4b = 0$.

**B4** (a) If $f(x) \equiv x^3 - 8x^2 + 14x - 4$ show that $(x - 2)$ is a factor of $f(x)$

(b) Find the exact solutions of $f(x) = 0$.

**B5** (a) Given that $P(x) \equiv x^3 + 3x^2 - 11x + 2$ and that $P(x) \equiv (x - 2)(ax^2 + bx + c)$ find $a, b, c$.

(b) Sketch the graph of $y = P(x)$ marking the exact values of the points of intersection with the axes.

(c) Solve $P(x) > 0$.

## Chapter 7: A level questions

**C1** The functions f and g are defined by $f : x \to x^2 - 8,\ x \in \mathbb{R}$ and $g : x \to |x - 2|,\ x \in \mathbb{R}$.

(a) Show that $ff(x) \equiv x^4 - 16x^2 + 56$ and find the values of $x$ for which $ff(x) = 56$

(b) Show that $gf(x) \equiv |x^2 - 10|$ and solve the equation $gf(x) = 6$

**C2**

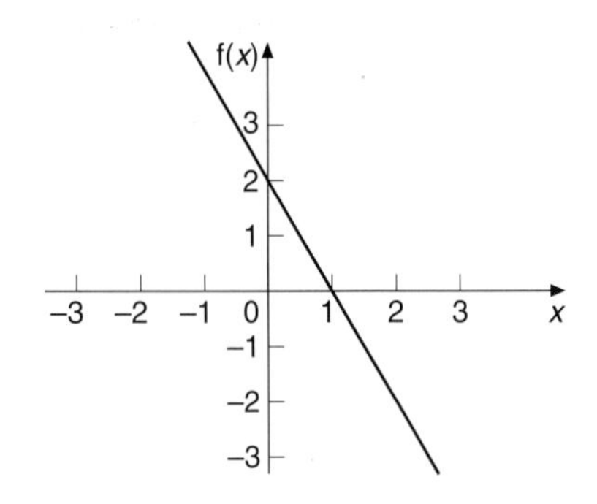


A sketch graph for the function $f(x)$ is shown in the diagram.

On separate axes sketch the graphs of

(a) $f\left(\frac{1}{2}x\right)$

(b) $-f(2x)$

(c) $f^{-1}(x)$

marking where the graphs cross the axes

**C3** (a) Explain why $(x - 2)$ is not a factor of $g(x) \equiv 2x^3 - 9x^2 - 20x + 12$

(b) The function $g(x)$ may be written in the form $g(x) \equiv (x + 2)(px^2 + qx + r)$. Find the values of $p$, $q$ and $r$ and hence express $g(x)$ as the product of three linear factors.

(c) Find the value of $x$ such that $g(x) \leq 0$

**C4** If $P(x) \equiv x^3 - 9x^2 + 14x + 24$ show that $P(x) = 0$ has a root $x = 4$ and find the other two roots.

Hence find the solutions of $f(x + 4) = 0$

**C5** Given that $f(x) \equiv e^x$, $g(x) \equiv f(x - 1)$ and $h(x) \equiv g(2x)$

(a) find (i) $g(x)$ (ii) $h(x)$ (iii) $h^{-1}(x)$

(b) find the exact value of $x$ such that $f^{-1}(x) = h^{-1}(x)$

**C6** (a) Given that $x^2 - a^2$ is a factor of $P(x) \equiv x^3 + x^2 + px + q$ show that $p$ and $q$ are both equal to $ka^2$ where $k$ has to be found.

(b) Write $P(x)$ in the form $(x^2 - a^2)(x + r)$ and state the value of $r$.

(c) If $0 < a < 1$ sketch the graph of $P(x)$ and use your graph to solve the inequality $P(x) < 0$.

**C7** Find the inverse of $f(x) = \dfrac{1}{1 - x} + 4$, $x \neq 1,\ x \in \mathbb{R}$, and state the domain and

## Chapter 7: A level questions *continued*

range of the inverse function. Using equal scales on the axes sketch the graph of $y = f^{-1}(x)$, dotting in the asymptotes.

**C8** Given that

$$f(x) = \begin{cases} x^2 & 0 \leq x \leq 2 \\ \frac{1}{2}(x+6) & 2 \leq x \leq 6 \end{cases}$$

find $f^{-1}(x)$ giving the domains

On a large diagram, using equal scales on the axes, draw the graphs of $y = f(x)$ and $y = f^{-1}(x)$ marking all points of intersection and dot in the line of symmetry $y = x$.

**C9** A sketch of the function f given by

$f(x) = \dfrac{3}{1+x^2}$ is shown in the diagram

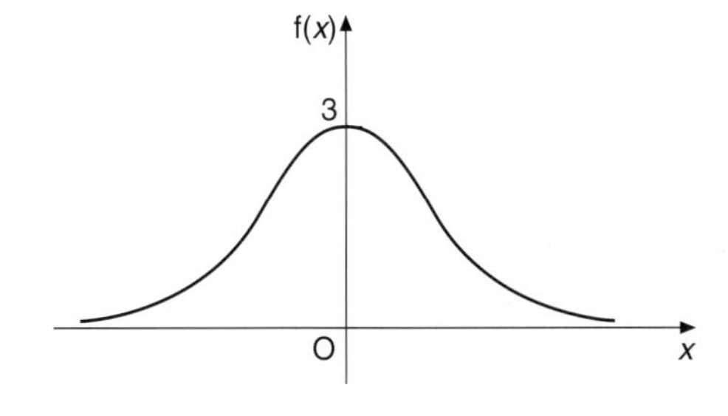


(a) Sketch the graph of $y = -\dfrac{1}{3}f(x)$

(b) Obtain an expression for $f(x-2)$ and sketch the graph of $y = f(x-2)$

**C10**

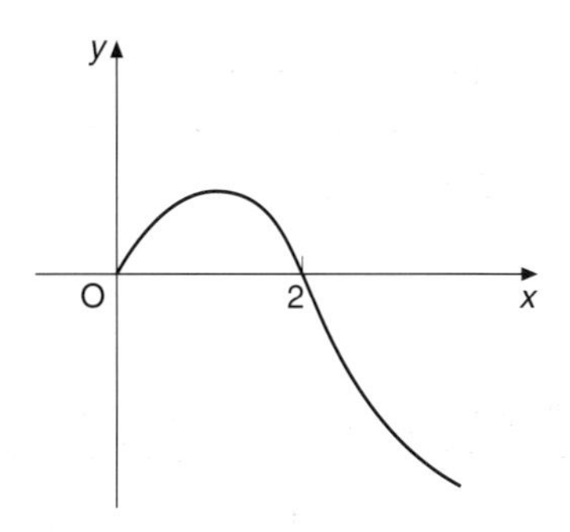


The function $f(x)$ is defined for all $x$. The diagram shows part of the graph of $y = f(x)$

(a) If f is an odd function copy and complete the sketch.

(b) Draw a separate sketch to illustrate the graph of $y = f(x-2)$ marking the intersections with the axes.

# Chapter 8

## DIFFERENTIATION I

### 8.1 Practice in basic differentiation including the second and higher derivatives

#### Key points

- If $y = f(x) = x^n$

  then $\dfrac{dy}{dx} = f'(x) = nx^{n-1}$ (for all rational $n$)

  and $\dfrac{d^2y}{dx^2} = \dfrac{d}{dx}\left(\dfrac{dy}{dx}\right) = f''(x)$

  Similarly for the higher derivatives, $\dfrac{d^3y}{dx^3} = \dfrac{d}{dx}\left(\dfrac{d^2y}{dx^2}\right) = f'''(x)$, etc.

  (N.B. If $y = f(x) =$ constant then $\dfrac{dy}{dx} = f'(x) =$ zero)

- If $y = f(x) + g(x)$

  You have to understand the notation

  then $\dfrac{dy}{dx} = f'(x) + g'(x)$

  (N.B. For the straight line $y = mx + c$, gradient m, then $\dfrac{dy}{dx} = m$ which is entirely consistent)

  If $y = f(x)g(x)$ then $\dfrac{dy}{dx} \neq f'(x)g'(x)$. You must use the product rule here.

#### Example 1

If $y = x(x + 2)(2x - 5)$ find $\dfrac{dy}{dx}$ and $\dfrac{d^2y}{dx^2}$

**Solution**

$y = x(x + 2)(2x - 5)$

$y = x(2x^2 - x - 10)$ First, multiply out the brackets

$y = 2x^3 - x^2 - 10x$

$$\frac{dy}{dx} = 6x^2 - 2x - 10$$

$$\frac{d^2y}{dx^2} = 12x - 2$$

## Example 2

If $f(x) = \dfrac{(\sqrt{x} - 3)^2}{x}$ expand the brackets and write f(x) as the sum of powers of $x$ then (a) find $f'(x)$ (b) show that $f''(x) = ax^{-\frac{5}{2}} + bx^{-3}$ where $a$ and $b$ are such that $4a + b = 0$

**Solution**

$$f(x) = \frac{(\sqrt{x} - 3)^2}{x} = \frac{x - 6\sqrt{x} + 9}{x}$$

You need to divide each of the three terms in the numerator by $x$

so $\quad f(x) = 1 - 6x^{-\frac{1}{2}} + 9x^{-1}$

$\frac{x^a}{x^b} = x^{a-b}$

$$f'(x) = -6\left(-\frac{1}{2}x^{-\frac{3}{2}}\right) + 9(-1x^{-2})$$

$$= 3x^{-\frac{3}{2}} - 9x^{-2}$$

$$f''(x) = 3\left(-\frac{3}{2}x^{-\frac{5}{2}}\right) - 9(-2x^{-3})$$

$$= -\frac{9}{2}x^{-\frac{5}{2}} + 18x^{-3}$$

So we have $a = -\dfrac{9}{2}$ and $b = 18$

$$4a + b = 4\left(-\frac{9}{2}\right) + 18 = -18 + 18 = 0$$

## Exercise 8.1

**A1** Find $\dfrac{dy}{dx}$ and $\dfrac{d^2y}{dx^2}$ for the following

(a) $y = (2x + 1)(x + 3)$

(b) $y = (3x - 1)^2$

(c) $y = (2 - 5x)(2 + 5x)$

**A2** Find $f'(x)$ if

(a) $f(x) = x^3 - 4x^2 + 9x + 1$

(b) $f(x) = \dfrac{1}{x^3} + x^3$

**A3** If $y = \dfrac{1}{x} + \dfrac{1}{x^2} - \dfrac{1}{x^3}$ find $\dfrac{dy}{dx}$

**A4** If $f(x) = \left(x + \dfrac{1}{x}\right)^2$ find $f'(x)$

**A5** If $y = (x - 2)^3$ multiply out the brackets and then find $\dfrac{dy}{dx}$ in factorised form.

## Exercise 8.1 *continued*

**A6** Find $\dfrac{ds}{dt}$ if

(a) $s = \dfrac{4}{t^2}$

(b) $s = t\sqrt{t}$

**A7** Find $g'(x)$ if $g(x) = (x - 1)\sqrt{x}$

**A8** If $v = \dfrac{t^2 + 3t + 1}{t^2}$ then write $v$ as the sum of three separate fractions and hence find $\dfrac{dv}{dt}$.

**A9** If $h(t) = \left(t - \dfrac{2}{t}\right)^2$ find $h'(t)$.

**A10** If $y = x^8 - x^2$ write down $\dfrac{dy}{dx}, \dfrac{d^2y}{dx^2}, \dfrac{d^3y}{dx^3}$.

**B1** If $y = x^5(2x + 3)$ find $\dfrac{d^2y}{dx^2}$ and factorise your answer.

**B2** If $y = \sqrt{x} + \dfrac{1}{\sqrt{x}}$ find $\dfrac{dy}{dx}$ and $\dfrac{d^2y}{dx^2}$.

**B3** If $y = a\sqrt{x} + bx^4$ and $\dfrac{d^2y}{dx^2} = -\dfrac{3}{2x^{\frac{3}{2}}} + 6x^2$ then find $a$ and $b$.

**B4** If $y = \sqrt{x}\left(x^2 + \dfrac{3x}{2} + 1\right)$ multiply out the bracket being careful with the indices and then find $\dfrac{dy}{dx}$. Write your answer in the form $\dfrac{1}{4\sqrt{x}}(ax^2 + bx + c)$ and show that $a + 2b + c = 30$.

**B5** If $f(x) = \dfrac{(2x + 3)^2}{x}$ find $f'(x)$, $f'(2)$ and $f''(x)$.

**B6** If $z = \dfrac{2t + 3}{t^6}$ find $\dfrac{dz}{dt}$ and factorise your answer.

**B7** If $g(x) = \left(\sqrt{x} + \dfrac{2}{\sqrt{x}}\right)^2$ find $g'(x)$.

**B8** If $y = x^3(4 - x)$ find the values of $x$ when

(a) $\dfrac{dy}{dx} = 0$ (b) $\dfrac{d^2y}{dx^2} = 12$.

**B9** If $f(x) = (x^2 + 1)(x - 3)$ find $f'(x)$, $f'(0)$, $f''(x)$, $f''(0)$.

**B10** If $f(x) = \dfrac{3x^2}{2} - \dfrac{4}{x}$ find $f'(x)$, $f''(x)$ and also find the value of $x$ when $f''(x) = 4$.

## 8.2 Product and quotient rules. Differentiation of $e^x$ and $\ln x$

### Key points

- If $u$ and $v$ are functions of $x$ then

$$\frac{d}{dx}(uv) = u\frac{dv}{dx} + v\frac{du}{dx}$$

$$\frac{d}{dx}\left(\frac{u}{v}\right) = \frac{v\dfrac{du}{dx} - u\dfrac{dv}{dx}}{v^2}$$

- If $y = e^x$ then

$$\frac{dy}{dx} = e^x$$

- If $y = \ln x \ (x > 0)$ then

$$\frac{dy}{dx} = \frac{1}{x}$$

## Example 1

1a) If $y = x^2e^x$ find $\frac{dy}{dx}$

1b) If $y = \frac{x}{x+2}$ find $\frac{dy}{dx}$

### Solution

1a)

$$\frac{dy}{dx} = x^2(e^x) + e^x(2x)$$

$$= x^2e^x + 2xe^x$$

Using the product rule

$$= xe^x(x+2)$$

1b)

$$\frac{dy}{dx} = \frac{(x+2)(1) - x(1)}{(x+2)^2}$$

$$= \frac{x+2-x}{(x+2)^2}$$

Using the quotient rule

$$= \frac{2}{(x+2)^2}$$

## Example 2

If $y = x^2 + \ln x^2 - 3\ln x^3 - \ln x$ find $\frac{dy}{dx}$ and the value of $x$ when $\frac{dy}{dx} = 0$.

### Solution

$$y = x^2 + \ln x^2 - 3\ln x^3 - \ln x$$

$$y = x^2 + 2\ln x - 9\ln x - \ln x$$

rules for logs here

$$y = x^2 - 8\ln x$$

$$\frac{dy}{dx} = 2x - \frac{8}{x}$$

$$\frac{dy}{dx} = 0 \text{ when } 2x - \frac{8}{x} = 0$$

$$2x^2 - 8 = 0$$

neglect the negative root as $x > 0$ here

$$x^2 = 4 \qquad \text{so } x = 2$$

## Exercise 8.2

**A1** If $y = xe^x$ find $\frac{dy}{dx}$

**A2** If $y = \frac{x}{e^x}$ find $\frac{dy}{dx}$. When is $\frac{dy}{dx}$ zero?

**A3** If $f(x) = \frac{x^2}{x+3}$ find $f'(x)$.

**A4** If $f(x) = \frac{x-3}{x^2}$ find $f'(x)$

(a) by dividing by $x$

(b) by using the quotient rule.

**A5** If $f(x) = x^2 + 3$ and $g(x) = e^x$ find

(a) $\frac{d}{dx}[f(x)g(x)]$

(b) $\frac{d}{dx}\left[\frac{g(x)}{f(x)}\right]$

(c) $\frac{d}{dx}\left[\frac{f(x)}{g(x)}\right]$

**A6** If $g(x) = \frac{e^x}{x^4}$ $(x \neq 0)$ find $g'(x)$ and the value of $x$ when $g'(x) = 0$.

**A7** If $h(x) = x^4e^x$ find the values of $x$ for which $h'(x) = 0$.

**A8** If $y = x^4\ln x$ $(x > 0)$ find $x$ when $\frac{dy}{dx} = 0$.

**A9** If $y = x^3(4x - 3)$ find $\frac{dy}{dx}$

(a) by multiplying out the brackets

(b) by using the product rule

**A10** By writing $e^{2x}$ as $e^x \times e^x$ and using the product rule show that $\frac{d}{dx}(e^{2x}) = 2e^{2x}$

Use your result to show that $\frac{d}{dx}(e^{3x}) = 3e^{3x}$.

**B1** If

(a) $y = x^3\ln x$

(b) $y = \frac{\ln x}{x^3}$

find expressions for $\frac{dy}{dx}$.

**B2** By using your rules for logarithms find $\frac{dy}{dx}$ if

(a) $y = \ln 5x$

(b) $y = \ln\frac{5}{x}$

(c) $y = \ln x^5$

**B3** Find the values of $x$ when $\frac{dy}{dx}$ is zero if

(a) $y = x^5\ln x$

(b) $y = x^3e^x$

**B4** If $y = 2\ln x^2 + 4\ln x^3 + 2\ln x - x^3$ show that $\frac{dy}{dx} = 0$ when $x^3 = 6$.

**B5** If $f(x) = \frac{\sqrt{x}}{x+3}$ show that $f'(x) = 0$ when $x = 3$.

## 8.3 The chain rule

### Key points

$$\frac{dy}{dx} = \frac{dy}{dz} \times \frac{dz}{dx}$$

$z$ is a function of $x$ and $y$ is a function of $z$ implies that $y$ is a function of $x$

## Example 1

Find $\frac{dy}{dx}$ if (a) $y = e^{5x}$ b) $y = (3x - 7)^6$

**Solution**

a) $y = e^{5x}$ Let $z = 5x$

then $y = e^z$ $\frac{dz}{dx} = 5$

and $\frac{dy}{dz} = e^z$

$$\frac{dy}{dx} = \frac{dy}{dz} \times \frac{dz}{dx} = e^z \times 5$$

$$= 5e^{5x}$$

Using the chain rule

b) $y = (3x - 7)^6$ Let $z = 3x - 7$

then $y = z^6$ $\frac{dz}{dx} = 3$

and $\frac{dy}{dz} = 6z^5$

$$\frac{dy}{dx} = \frac{dy}{dz} \times \frac{dz}{dx} = 6z^5 \times 3$$

$$= 18(3x - 7)^5$$

## Example 2

If $y = \ln\left|\frac{1 + 2x}{1 - 2x}\right|$, $|x| < \frac{1}{2}$ find $\frac{dy}{dx}$ and show that $\frac{dy}{dx} = 8$ when $x = \pm\frac{1}{2\sqrt{2}}$

**Solution**

Using your rules for logs here, $y = \ln|1 + 2x| - \ln|1 - 2x|$

$$\frac{dy}{dx} = \frac{2}{1 + 2x} - \frac{(-2)}{1 - 2x} = \frac{2}{1 + 2x} + \frac{2}{1 - 2x}$$

$$= 2\left(\frac{1}{1 + 2x} + \frac{1}{1 - 2x}\right)$$

When $\frac{dy}{dx} = 8$ $\frac{1}{1 + 2x} + \frac{1}{1 - 2x} = 4$

$$(1 - 2x) + (1 + 2x) = 4(1 - 4x^2)$$

Multiply through by $(1 + 2x)(1 - 2x)$

$$2 = 4(1 - 4x^2)$$

$$\frac{1}{2} = 1 - 4x^2 \qquad 4x^2 = \frac{1}{2}$$

$$x^2 = \frac{1}{8}$$

$$x = \pm\frac{1}{2\sqrt{2}}$$

## Exercise 8.3

**A1** If $y = (4x + 1)^5$ find $\frac{dy}{dx}$ (Let $z = 4x + 1$).

**A2** If $y = e^{-3x}$ find $\frac{dy}{dx}$ (Let $z = -3x$).

**A3** If $y = \ln(5 - 3x)$ find $\frac{dy}{dx}$ (Let $z = 5 - 3x$).

**A4** If $f(x) = \sqrt{1 - x^2}$ find $f'(x)$ (Let $z = 1 - x^2$).

**A5** If $f(x) = \frac{1}{\sqrt{1 - x^2}}$ find $f'(x)$ (Let $z = 1 - x^2$).

**A6** Find $\frac{dy}{dx}$ if

(a) $y = (2x - 3)^4$

(b) $y = \frac{1}{(2x - 3)^4}, x \neq \frac{3}{2}$

**A7** Find $\frac{ds}{dt}$ if

(a) $s = e^{4t-5}$

(b) $s = \ln(4t - 5), t > \frac{5}{4}$

**A8** Find $\frac{dv}{dt}$ if

(a) $v = (2 - 3t)^3$

(b) $v = \frac{1}{2 - 3t}, t \neq \frac{2}{3}$

**A9** If $z = 3e^{5x}$ obtain $\frac{dz}{dx}$ and $\frac{d^2z}{dx^2}$

Hence show that $\frac{dz}{dx} = 5z$ and $\frac{d^2z}{dx^2} = 25z$

**A10** If $y = \sqrt{4 - x^2}$ show that

$$\frac{dy}{dx} + \frac{x}{y} = 0.$$

**B1** If $f(x) = (2x + 5)^4$ find $f'(x)$ and $f'(0)$

**B2** If $y = \frac{3}{e^{4x}}$ find $\frac{dy}{dx}$ and $\frac{d^2y}{dx^2}$.

Show that $\frac{d^2y}{dx^2} + 4\frac{dy}{dx} = 0$.

**B3** If $f(x) = \frac{3}{(6x + 1)^5}$ find $f'(x)$ and $f'(0)$.

**B4** If $f(x) = x^2e^{5x}$ use the chain rule to differentiate $e^{5x}$ with respect to $x$ and then the product rule to find $f'(x)$.

Write your result in factorised form and then find the two values of $x$ for which $f'(x) = 0$.

**B5** If $f(x) = x^2e^{5x}$ show that $f''(x) + 2e^{5x} = (5x + 2)^2e^{5x}$. (Hint: use your result from question **B4**)

**B6** If $y = ae^{-bx}$ where a and b are constants show

that $\frac{dy}{dx} + by = 0$.

**B7** Show that $\frac{1}{1 - x} - \frac{1}{1 + x} = \frac{2x}{1 - x^2}$

$(x \neq \pm 1)$

Hence if $y = \frac{2x}{1 - x^2}$ shows that $\frac{dy}{dx}$ can be written as the sum of two squares. What can be deduced about the sign of $\frac{dy}{dx}$?

**B8** Write down or obtain the derivatives of

(a) $e^{2t}$

(b) $e^{-2t}$

Given that $x = 3e^{2t} + 4e^{-2t}$ write down expressions for $\frac{dx}{dt}$ and $\frac{d^2x}{dt^2}$. Show that

$$\frac{d^2x}{dt^2} = 4x.$$

## Exercise 8.3 *continued*

**B9** (a) Obtain the derivative of $\ln(ax + b)$ where a and b are constants, and $ax + b > 0$

(b) If $y = \ln\dfrac{2x+1}{x-1}$, $(x > 1)$, write $y$ as the difference of two logarithms.

(c) Find $\dfrac{dy}{dx}$ and use this result to show that $\dfrac{d^2y}{dx^2} = \dfrac{1}{(x-1)^2} - \dfrac{4}{(2x+1)^2}$.

**B10** (a) Find $\dfrac{d}{dx}(2x-5)^4$

(b) Given that $y = x(2x-5)^4$ use the product rule to find an expression for $\dfrac{dy}{dx}$.

(c) Show that $\dfrac{dy}{dx}$ can be written in the form $5(2x-1)(2x-5)^3$ and hence find the values of $x$ for which $\dfrac{dy}{dx}$ is zero.

## 8.4 Differentiation of trigonometrical functions

### Key points

| $y$ | $\dfrac{dy}{dx}$ |
|---|---|
| $\sin x$<br>$\cos x$ | $\cos x$<br>$-\sin x$ |

### Example 1

(a) Find $\dfrac{d}{dx}(\tan x)$ (b) $\dfrac{d}{dx}(\sin 3x)$

**Solution**

(a) Let $y = \tan x = \dfrac{\sin x}{\cos x}$ (Using the quotient rule)

$$\frac{dy}{dx} = \frac{\cos x(\cos x) - \sin x(-\sin x)}{\cos^2 x}$$

$$= \frac{\cos^2 x + \sin^2 x}{\cos^2 x}$$

$$= \frac{1}{\cos^2 x} = \sec^2 x$$

(b) Let $y = \sin 3x$

$y = \sin 3x$ Let $z = 3x$

$y = \sin z$ $\dfrac{dz}{dx} = 3$ (Using the chain rule)

$$\frac{dy}{dz} = \cos z$$

$$\frac{dy}{dx} = \frac{dy}{dz} \times \frac{dz}{dx} = \cos z \times 3$$

$$= 3\cos 3x$$

## Example 2

(a) Find $\frac{d}{dx}(\cos^3 x)$

(b) if $y = e^{-x}\sin 2x$ find $\frac{dy}{dx}$ and the values of $x$ when $\frac{dy}{dx} = 0$ if $0 \leq x \leq \pi$

### Solution

(a) Let $y = \cos^3 x$ Let $z = \cos x$

so $y = z^3$ $\qquad \frac{dz}{dx} = -\sin x$ (use the chain rule)

$$\frac{dy}{dz} = 3z^2$$

$$\frac{dy}{dx} = \frac{dy}{dz} \times \frac{dz}{dx}$$

$$\frac{dy}{dx} = 3z^2 \times (-\sin x)$$

$$= -3\sin x\cos^2 x$$

(b) $y = e^{-x}\sin 2x$

First you need to differentiate $\sin 2x$ using the chain rule to get $2\cos 2x$ (look at example 1(b) again if you are unsure of this)

$$\frac{dy}{dx} = e^{-x}(2\cos 2x) + (-e^{-x})\sin 2x$$

(using the product rule)

$$= e^{-x}(2\cos 2x - \sin 2x)$$

When $\frac{dy}{dx} = 0$ $\qquad e^{-x}(2\cos 2x - \sin 2x) = 0$

$$2\cos 2x = \sin 2x$$

$e^{-x} \neq 0$ for any $x$

$$2 = \tan 2x$$

(Divide by $\cos 2x$)

From your calculator $2x = 1.107$

So in the given domain $0 \leq x \leq \pi$ (radians remember)

$$2x = 1.107 \text{ or } 2x = 1.107 + \pi = 4.249$$

Hence $x = 0.55$ or $x = 2.12$ to 2 d.p.

## Exercise 8.4

**A1** Find $\frac{dy}{dx}$ if

(a) $y = \sin 2x$ (Let $z = 2x$)

(b) $y = \cos 3x$ (Let $z = 3x$)

(c) $y = \tan 4x$ (Let $z = 4x$)

**A2** Find $\frac{dy}{dx}$ if

(a) $y = \sin\frac{1}{4}x$ $\left(\text{Let } z = \frac{1}{4}x\right)$

(b) $y = \tan\left(x + \frac{\pi}{4}\right)$ $\left(\text{Let } z = x + \frac{\pi}{4}\right)$

(c) $y = \cos\left(\frac{\pi}{3} - 2x\right)$ $\left(\text{Let } z = \frac{\pi}{3} - 2x\right)$

**A3** Find $\frac{ds}{dt}$

(a) $s = (1 + 4\sin t)^2$ (Let $z = 1 + 4\sin t$)

(b) $s = \frac{1}{(1 - 4\cos t)^3}$ (Let $z = 1 - 4\cos t$)

**A4** Find $\frac{dy}{dx}$

(a) $y = e^{\sin x}$

(b) $y = e^{\cos x}$

(c) $y = e^{\tan x}$

**A5** Find $f'(t)$ if

(a) $f(t) = \ln(\sin t)$ (Let $z = \sin t$)

(b) $f(t) = \ln(1 + \cos t)$ (Let $z = 1 + \cos t$)

**A6** Write down $\frac{dy}{dx}$ if

(a) $y = \sin 3x$

(b) $y = \cos 3x$

(c) $y = \tan 5x$

**A7** Find $f'(x)$ if

(a) $f(x) = \sin^3 x$

(b) $f(x) = \cos^2 x$

(c) $f(x) = \tan^3 x$

**A8** Find $\frac{dx}{dt}$ if

(a) $x = e^{\sin 2t}$

(b) $x = e^{-\cos t}$

**A9** Find $f'(t)$ if

(a) $f(t) = \ln(\sin\frac{t}{2})$

(b) $f(t) = \ln(\cos 3t)$

**A10** Given that $f(x) = \sin^2 x$ and $g(x) = \cos^2 x$ obtain $f'(x)$ and $g'(x)$.

Simplify $\frac{d}{dx}[f(x) + g(x)]$.

**B1** If $f(x) = \sin x + \cos x$ find when $f'(x) = 0$ if $|x| < \pi$

**B2** Find $\frac{d}{dx}(\sin^3 2x)$

**B3** If $y = e^{-x}\sin x$ show that $\frac{dy}{dx} = 0$ when $x = \frac{\pi}{4}$

**B4** If $x = 2\sin t + 3\cos t$ write down $\frac{dx}{dt}$ and $\frac{d^2x}{dt^2}$

Show that $\frac{d^2x}{dt^2} + x = 0$

**B5** Write down the derivatives of $\cos 2t$ and $\sin 2t$.

If $s = 3\cos 2t - 4\sin 2t$ show that $\frac{d^2s}{dt^2} = -4s$

**B6** Find $\frac{d}{dx}(\tan^2 3x)$

**B7** If $f(t) = 2\sin t + \cos 2t$ find an expression for $f'(t)$. Find values of $t$ if $f'(t) = 0$ and $0 \leq t \leq 2\pi$

## Exercise 8.4 *continued*

**B8** If $y = \ln\cot x$ and $0 < x < \frac{\pi}{2}$ write $y$ as the difference of two logarithms and hence show that $\frac{dy}{dx} = -\frac{1}{\sin x \cos x}$

**B9** (a) By writing $\sec x$ as $(\cos x)^{-1}$ show that $\frac{d}{dx}(\sec x) = \sec x \tan x$.

(b) Given that $y = \ln(\sec x + \tan x)$ show that $\frac{dy}{dx} = \sec x$ and write down the value of $\frac{d^2y}{dx^2}$

**B10** (a) Write down the derivatives of $e^{2t}$ and $\cos 2t$.

(b) If $f(t) = e^{2t}\cos 2t$ obtain an expression for $f'(t)$ and factorise this expression.

(c) Show that $f'(t) = 0$ when $\tan 2t = 1$

(d) If $t = t_1$ is a solution of this equation in the interval $0 < t < \frac{\pi}{2}$, show that

$$f(t_1) = \frac{\sqrt{2}}{2}e^{\frac{\pi}{4}}$$

## 8.5 Parametric and implicit differentiation

### Key points

It can be shown that, in general,

$$\frac{dy}{dx} = \frac{1}{\frac{dx}{dy}}$$

y is a function of x and x is a function of y

- For Parametric differentiation;

  If $x = f(t)$ and $y = g(t)$ then, in general,

$$\frac{dy}{dx} = \frac{\frac{dy}{dt}}{\frac{dx}{dt}} = \frac{g'(t)}{f'(t)}$$

- For Implicit differentiation, in general,

$$\frac{d}{dx}f(y) = f'(y)\frac{dy}{dx}$$

$$\text{e.g. } \frac{d}{dx}(y^n) = \frac{d}{dy}(y^n) \times \frac{dy}{dx}$$

$$= ny^{n-1}\frac{dy}{dx}$$

when $f(y) = y^n$

$$\text{Also } \frac{d}{dx}(xy) = x\frac{dy}{dx} + 1y$$

using the product rule

$$= x\frac{dy}{dx} + y$$

## Example 1

(a) If $x = t^2$, $y = 2t$ find $\frac{dy}{dx}$ in terms of $t$

(b) If $x = t^2$, $y = 2t$ show that $y^2 = 4x$ and then find $\frac{dy}{dx}$ in terms of $y$.

Compare your answer with part 1(a).

### Solution

(a) $x = t^2$, $y = 2t$

$$\frac{dy}{dx} = \frac{\frac{dy}{dt}}{\frac{dx}{dt}}$$

$$= \frac{2}{2t}$$

$$= \frac{1}{t} \quad (t \neq 0)$$

(b) $x = t^2$, $y = 2t$ $\qquad y^2 = (2t)^2 = 4t^2 = 4x$

$$y^2 = 4x$$

Rearrange to get $x = \frac{y^2}{4}$

$\frac{dx}{dy} = \frac{2y}{4} = \frac{y}{2}$

Implicit differentiation (w.r.t. $x$)

$$2y\frac{dy}{dx} = 4$$

$$\frac{dy}{dx} = \frac{4}{2y} = \frac{2}{y}$$

Differentiate w.r.t. $y$

$$2y = 4\frac{dx}{dy}$$

$$\frac{y}{2} = \frac{dx}{dy}$$

$$\text{But } \frac{dx}{dy} = \frac{1}{\frac{dy}{dx}} \text{ so } \frac{dy}{dx} = \frac{2}{y}$$

[We know that $y = 2t$ so $\frac{dy}{dx} = \frac{2}{2t} = \frac{1}{t}$ which is the same as in 1(a)]

## Example 2

If $(x + 1)^2 + (y + 6)^2 = 25$ then find the value of $\frac{dy}{dx}$ when $x = -5$ and $y = -9$

**Solution**

$$(x + 1)^2 + (y + 6)^2 = 25$$

$$x^2 + 2x + 1 + y^2 + 12y + 36 = 25$$

$$x^2 + y^2 + 2x + 12y + 11 = 0$$

Differentiate w.r.t. $x$

$$2x + 2y\frac{dy}{dx} + 2 + 12\frac{dy}{dx} = 0$$

Implicit differentiation

Divide by 2

$$x + y\frac{dy}{dx} + 1 + 6\frac{dy}{dx} = 0$$

When $x = -5$ and $y = -9$ $\quad -5 - 9\frac{dy}{dx} + 1 + 6\frac{dy}{dx} = 0$

$$-4 - 3\frac{dy}{dx} = 0$$

$$-3\frac{dy}{dx} = 4$$

$$\frac{dy}{dx} = -\frac{4}{3}$$

## Exercise 8.5

**A1** Use parametric differentiation to find $\frac{dy}{dx}$ in terms of $t$ if $x = 3t^3 - 1$, $y = 1 - 2t$.

**A2** Find $\frac{dy}{dx}$ in terms of $t$ if $x = t^3 + 3t$, $y = 6t^2 + 3t$. Simplify your answer as far as possible.

**A3** If $x = 3 + 2\sin t$ and $y = 2 - 3\cos t$ find $\frac{dy}{dx}$ in terms of $t$.

**A4** Use implicit differentiation to find an expression for $\frac{dy}{dx}$ in terms of $x$ and $y$ if

(a) $x^2 + y^2 = 1$

(b) $x^2 + y^2 - 2x + 6y + 3 = 0$

**A5** Find the value of $\frac{dy}{dx}$ at the point with parameter $t = -3$ on the curve whose parametric equations are $x = t^3$, $y = t^2$.

## Exercise 8.5 *continued*

**A6** If $x = 1 - \cos t$ and $y = 3\sin t$ find $\frac{dy}{dx}$ when $t = \frac{\pi}{3}$.

**A7** If $x^2 + y^2 = 25$ find the value of $\frac{dy}{dx}$ where $x = -4$ and $y$ is positive

**A8** If $2x^2 + 3y^2 = 12$ find $\frac{dy}{dx}$ in terms of $x$ and $y$

**A9** Use parametric differentiation to find $\frac{dy}{dx}$ in terms of $t$ if

(a) $x - 1 + t$, $y = t^2$

(b) $x = 3t^2 - 5$, $y = 1 - t^3$

(c) $x = 3\cos t$, $y = 4\sin t$

**A10** Find $\frac{dy}{dx}$ in terms of $x$ and $y$ when $xy - 2y - 3x + 2 = 0$

**B1** When $y = 4t + \frac{4}{t}$ and $x = 2t - \frac{2}{t}$ find $\frac{dy}{dx}$ in terms of $t$ in its simplest form and verify that $\frac{dy}{dx} = 1.2$ when $t = 2$.

**B2** If $(x - 4)^2 + (y - 3)^2 = 16$ show that the value of $\frac{dy}{dx}$ is zero when $x = 4$ and $y = -1$

**B3** Show that the points given by $x = 2 - t$ and $y = t^2 + 3$ lie on the curve $y = x^2 - 4x + 7$.

Find the value of the parameter $t$ at the two points where the line $y = 7$ intersects the curve, and the value of $\frac{dy}{dx}$ at these two points.

**B4** Find an expression for $\frac{dz}{dy}$ if $z^3 + 3y^2 = z$

**B5** (a) If $y = t^3$ and $x = t^2$ where $t$ is positive find $\frac{dy}{dx}$ in terms of $t$ in its simplest form.

(b) Show that $y^2 = x^3$

(c) Find $\frac{dy}{dx}$ in terms of $x$ and $y$ and by substituting the $t$ values for $x$ and $y$ in this result show that your two answers for $\frac{dy}{dx}$ are consistent.

**B6** If $x = 3t^2 + 2t + 3$ and $y = 2t^2 - 3t + 1$, find $\frac{dy}{dx}$ in terms of $t$. Find the value of $t$ when $\frac{dy}{dx} = \frac{1}{8}$ and state the corresponding values of $x$ and $y$.

**B7** If $x^2 + y^2 + 6x - 8y = 0$ find $\frac{dy}{dx}$ in terms of $x$ and $y$. Find $x$ when $\frac{dy}{dx} = 0$ and also find the corresponding values of $y$.

**B8** If $y^3 - 4y^2 + x^3 = 0$ find the value of $\frac{dy}{dx}$ when $y = 2$

**B9** (a) If $x = 2t - \cos t$ and $y = 4\sin t - \frac{1}{2}\cos 2t$ show that $\frac{dy}{dt}$ may be written in the form $4\cos t + 2\sin t\cos t$.

(b) Now find $\frac{dy}{dx}$ in the form $k\cos t$ where $k$ is to be found.

(c) Find the values of $t$ when $0 \le t \le 2\pi$ for which $\frac{dy}{dx} = 1$.

**B10** If $x = \cos^3 t$ and $y = \sin^3 t$, $0 < t < \dfrac{\pi}{2}$, show that $\dfrac{dy}{dx} = -\tan t$.

If $\dfrac{dy}{dx} = -\sqrt{3}$ find $x$ and $y$ **exactly**.

## 8.6 Inverse trigonometrical functions

### Key points

$$\frac{d}{dx}(\sin^{-1}x) = \frac{1}{\sqrt{1-x^2}} \qquad \frac{d}{dx}(\tan^{-1}x) = \frac{1}{1+x^2}$$

### Example 1

Find $\dfrac{d}{dx}(\sin^{-1}3x)$

use the chain rule

**Solution**

Let $y = \sin^{-1}3x$ Let $z = 3x$

then $y = \sin^{-1}z$ $\dfrac{dz}{dx} = 3$

$$\frac{dy}{dz} = \frac{1}{\sqrt{1-z^2}}$$

key fact

$$\frac{dy}{dx} = \frac{dy}{dz} \times \frac{dz}{dx}$$

$$= \frac{1}{\sqrt{1-z^2}} \times 3$$

$$= \frac{3}{\sqrt{1-9x^2}}$$

## Example 2

Find $\dfrac{d}{dx}\left(\tan^{-1}\dfrac{x}{2}\right)$

**Solution**

Let $y = \tan^{-1}\dfrac{x}{2}$, and let $z = \dfrac{x}{2}$

Use the chain rule

so $y = \tan^{-1}z$, and $\dfrac{dz}{dx} = \dfrac{1}{2}$

$$\frac{dy}{dz} = \frac{1}{1 + z^2}$$

key point

$$\frac{dy}{dx} = \frac{dy}{dz} \times \frac{dz}{dx}$$

$$= \frac{1}{1 + z^2} \times \frac{1}{2}$$

$$= \frac{1}{1 + \frac{x^2}{4}} \times \frac{1}{2}$$

Now multiply numerator and denominator by 4

$$= \frac{4}{4 + x^2} \times \frac{1}{2}$$

$$= \frac{2}{4 + x^2}$$

## Exercise 8.6

In questions **A1** to **A6** use the given substitution $z = f(x)$ together with the chain rule

**A1** $y = \sin^{-1}4x$, $z = 4x$. Find $\dfrac{dy}{dx}$

**A2** $y = \tan^{-1}3x$, $z = 3x$. Find $\dfrac{dy}{dx}$

**A3** Find $\dfrac{d}{dx}\left(\sin^{-1}\dfrac{x}{2}\right)$, $z = \dfrac{x}{2}$.

**A4** Find $\dfrac{d}{dx}\left(\tan^{-1}\dfrac{x}{4}\right)$, $z = \dfrac{x}{4}$.

**A5** $f(x) = \sin^{-1}\dfrac{3x}{4}$, $z = \dfrac{3x}{4}$. Find $f'(x)$.

**A6** $f(x) = \tan^{-1}\dfrac{5x}{3}$, $z = \dfrac{5x}{3}$. Find $f'(x)$.

Attempt to simplify your answers by 'clearing fractions from fractions'.

e.g. (a) $\dfrac{1}{1 + \frac{9x^2}{4}} = \dfrac{4}{4 + 9x^2}$ if you multiply top and bottom by 4

(b) $\dfrac{1}{\sqrt{1 - \frac{4x^2}{9}}} = \dfrac{1}{\sqrt{\frac{9 - 4x^2}{9}}} = \dfrac{1}{\frac{1}{3}\sqrt{9 - 4x^2}} = \dfrac{3}{\sqrt{9 - 4x^2}}$

multiply top and bottom by 3 here

**B1** If $z = \dfrac{1}{x}$ write down the value of $\dfrac{dz}{dx}$. Use the chain rule to find $\dfrac{dy}{dx}$ when $y = \tan^{-1}\left(\dfrac{1}{x}\right)$. Simplify your answer.

**B2** If $f(x) = \dfrac{1}{2}\ln(1 + x^2) + \tan^{-1}x$ find and simplify $f'(x)$. Hence find the value of $f(x)$ when $f'(x) = 0$

**B3** Find the derivative of $\sqrt{1 - x^2}$ $(|x| < 1)$

Now use the product rule to find $\dfrac{d}{dx}(x\sqrt{1 - x^2})$

**B4** By letting $z = x^2$ and using the chain rule find

(a) $\dfrac{d}{dx}\tan^{-1}(x^2)$

(b) $\dfrac{d}{dx}\sin^{-1}(x^2)$

## Chapter 8: A level questions

**C1** If $x^2 - 2xy + 3y^2 = 9$ find the possible values of $y$ when $x = 3$.

Find $\dfrac{dy}{dx}$ in terms of $x$ and $y$ and then find the value of $\dfrac{dy}{dx}$ when $x = 3$ and $y$ is positive.

**C2** If $y = \dfrac{x}{1 - x}$ $(x \neq 1)$ find $\dfrac{dy}{dx}$ and show that $\dfrac{dy}{dx} - y^2 = \dfrac{1 + x}{1 - x}$

**C3** If $y = \ln(1 + \cos x)$ use the substitution $u = 1 + \cos x$ to find $\dfrac{dy}{dx}$ and then show that $\dfrac{d^2y}{dx^2} = -\dfrac{1}{1 + \cos x}$

By writing $1 + \cos x$ in terms of $y$ show that $\dfrac{d^2y}{dx^2} + e^{-y} = 0$ and explain why $\dfrac{d^2y}{dx^2}$ is always negative.

**C4** (a) If $x = 3e^t\cos t$ and $y = 3e^t\sin t$ show that $x^2 + y^2 = 9e^{2t}$.

(b) Show that $\dfrac{dx}{dt} = 3e^t(\cos t - \sin t)$ and obtain a similar expression for $\dfrac{dy}{dt}$

(c) Simplify $\left(\dfrac{dx}{dt}\right)^2$

(d) Show that

$$\left(\frac{dx}{dt}\right)^2 + \left(\frac{dy}{dt}\right)^2 = 2(x^2 + y^2).$$

**C5** (a) If $y = 5 + 3e^{-2t}$ find $\dfrac{dy}{dt}$ in terms of (i) $t$ (ii) $y$.

(b) If $f(x) = \sin(x^2 - 4)$ use a suitable substitution to find $f'(x)$ and then find $f'(2)$.

(c) Obtain the derivative of $\sqrt{x}$. If $g(x) = e^{\sqrt{x}}$ find $g'(x)$ and show that $\dfrac{g(x)}{g'(x)} = 2\sqrt{x}$.

## Chapter8: A level questions *continued*

**C6** If $y^2x = 2$ find

(a) $y$ when $x = 2$

(b) $x$ when $y = 2$

Show that $\frac{dy}{dx} = -\frac{y}{2x}$ and find the value of $\frac{dy}{dx}$ when $y = -1$.

**C7** If $x = t - \frac{1}{t}$ and $y = t + \frac{1}{t}$ show that

$y^2 - x^2 = 4$.

(a) Obtain expressions for $\frac{dx}{dt}$ and $\frac{dy}{dt}$ and hence $\frac{dy}{dx}$ in terms of $t$.

(b) Use $y^2 - x^2 = 4$ to find $\frac{dy}{dx}$ in terms of $x$ and $y$.

(c) Show that the results of (a) and (b) are equivalent.

(d) Find $t$ when $\frac{dy}{dx} = 0$.

(e) Show that when $\frac{dy}{dx} = \frac{1}{2}$ then $t = \pm\sqrt{3}$

**C8** (a) If $x = \cos^4 t$ use the substitution $z = \cos t$ to find $\frac{dx}{dt}$

(b) If $y = \sin^4 t$ find $\frac{dy}{dt}$

(c) Show that $\frac{dy}{dt} = -\tan^2 t \left(0 < t < \frac{\pi}{2}\right)$

(d) Give exact values of $x$, $y$ and $\frac{dy}{dx}$ when $t = \frac{\pi}{6}$ and when $t = \frac{\pi}{4}$.

**C9** If $g(x) = x^2e^{4x}$ find $g'(x)$ and factorise it. State the two values of $x$, $x_1$ and $x_2$ with $x_1 > x_2$ for which $g'(x) = 0$ and find $g(x_1)$ and $g(x_2)$.

**C10** If $f(x) = \frac{3x - 6}{x^2 + x - 2}$ show that $f(x)$ may be written in the form

$\frac{A}{x-1} + \frac{B}{x+2}$ where $A$ and $B$ are integers whose values are to be found.

Using this, find $f'(x)$ in the form $\frac{a}{(x-1)^2} + \frac{b}{(x+2)^2}$.

Show that $f'(0) = 0$ and find the other value of $x$ for which $f'(x) = 0$.

# Chapter 9

## DIFFERENTIATION 2

## 9.1 Increasing and decreasing functions

### Key points

- (a) $\frac{dy}{dx}$ is the 'gradient function' which is a measure of how $y$ is changing relative to $x$.
- (b) When the gradient $\frac{dy}{dx}$ is positive then the function is called an **increasing** function.

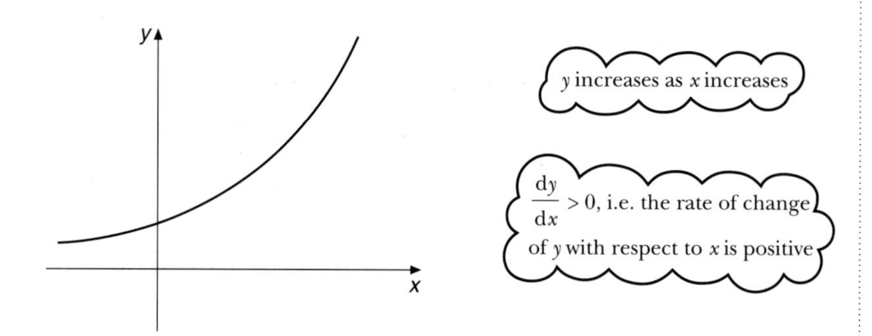


- (c) When the gradient $\frac{dy}{dx}$ is negative then the function is called a **decreasing** function.

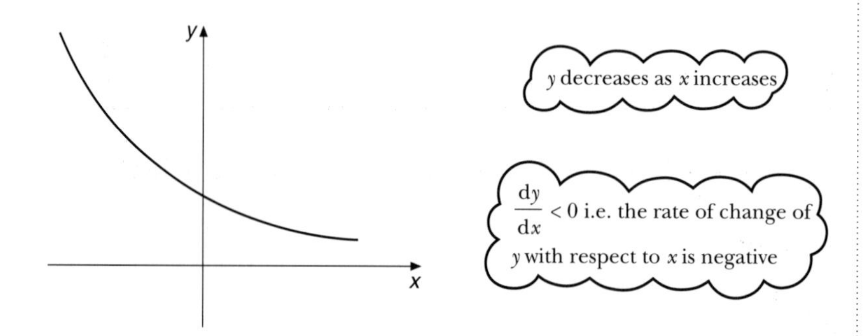

- (d) If $\frac{dy}{dx} = 0$ for some value of $x$ then the function is neither increasing or decreasing and is said to be **stationary** at that value.

## Example 1

State the set of values of $x$ for which $g(x) = x^3 - 4x^2 + 4x - 1$ is (a) increasing (b) decreasing (c) stationary.

### Solution

$$g(x) = x^3 - 4x^2 + 4x - 1$$
$$g'(x) = 3x^2 - 8x + 4$$
$$= (3x - 2)(x - 2)$$

It will now help to look at the graph of $y = g'(x)$

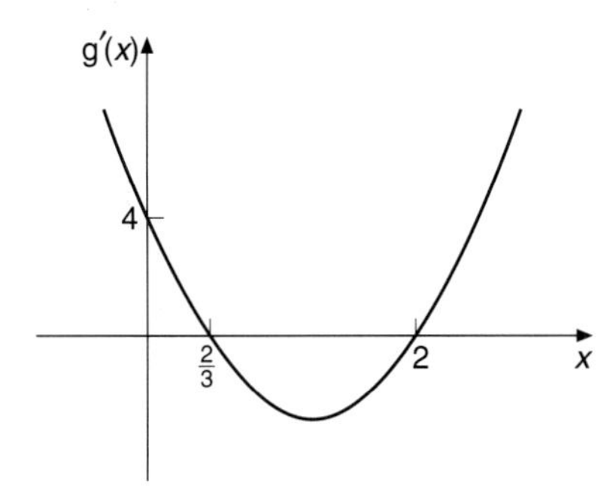


(a) $g(x)$ is increasing when $g'(x) > 0$ i.e. when $x < \frac{2}{3}$ or $x > 2$

(b) $g(x)$ is decreasing when $g'(x) < 0$ i.e. when $\frac{2}{3} < x < 2$

(c) $g(x)$ is stationary when $g'(x) = 0$ i.e. when $x = \frac{2}{3}$ or $x = 2$.

## Example 2

If $y = \frac{2 + x}{1 + x}$ $(x \neq -1)$ show that $y$ is a decreasing function.

### Solution

$$y = \frac{2 + x}{1 + x}$$

Use the quotient rule here to get $\frac{dy}{dx} = \frac{1(1 + x) - 1(2 + x)}{(1 + x)^2}$

$= \frac{-1}{(1 + x)^2}$

You know that $(1 + x)^2$ is always positive and so $\frac{-1}{(1 + x)^2}$ is always negative

remember $x \neq -1$ is given in the question

Hence $y$ is a decreasing function as $\frac{dy}{dx} < 0$ for all $x$ except $x = -1$

## Exercise 9.1

**A1** Given that $f(x) \equiv 4x - x^2$ for $x < 2$ and $g(x) \equiv 3x^2 + 6x + 3$ for $x > -1$

show that both f and g are increasing functions.

**A2** Show that the functions f, g, F and G are each decreasing functions if

(a) $f : x \rightarrow 2e^{-\frac{1}{2}x}, x \in R$

(b) $g : x \rightarrow 3\cos 2x, 0 < x < \frac{\pi}{2}$

(c) $F : x \rightarrow \ln\left(\frac{3}{x}\right), x > 0$

(d) $G : x \rightarrow \frac{4}{\sqrt{x}}, x > 0$

**A3** Solve the inequality $3x^2 + 4x - 4 > 0$.

If $y = x^3 + 2x^2 - 4x - 8$ find the set of values of $x$ for which

(a) $y$ increases as $x$ increases

(b) $y$ decreases as $x$ increases.

**A4** (a) Write $z = \frac{3x - 8}{x - 2}$ $(x \neq 2)$ in the form $A - \frac{B}{x - 2}$

(b) Find $\frac{dz}{dx}$ and hence show that $z$ is an increasing function of $x$.

**A5** (a) Sketch the graph of $y = (x + 2)x(x - 2)$ and use your graph to state the values of $x$ for which (a) $y > 0$ (b) $y < 0$

(b) If $f(x) \equiv x^4 - 8x^2 + 7$ find and factorise $f'(x)$. Now state the values of $x$ for which $f(x)$ is a decreasing function.

**A6** If $y = (x + 1)^2 e^{-x}$ find an expression for $\frac{dy}{dx}$ and then factorise it fully. Show that $y$ increases with $x$ only when $|x| < 1$.

**A7** The functions f, g and h given below are each defined on the domain $0 < x < \frac{\pi}{2}$.

Which of them is an increasing function and which is a decreasing function?

(a) $f(x) \equiv \ln(\cos x)$

(b) $g(x) \equiv e^{\tan x}$

(c) $h(x) \equiv \ln\left(\frac{1}{\sin x}\right)$

[Hints: $\frac{d}{dx}(\tan x) = \sec^2 x$, $\ln\left(\frac{a}{b}\right) = \ln a - \ln b$]

## Exercise 9.1 *continued*

**A8** (a) Find and factorise fully the derivatives of (i) $x^2 \ln x$ (ii) $x^3 \ln x$

(b) The functions f and g are defined as follows

$f: x \to x^2 \ln x \ (x > 0)$, $g: x \to x^3 \ln x \ (x > 0)$

Show that when f is increasing with $x$, then $\ln x > -\frac{1}{2}$ and make $x$ the subject of this inequality.

Show that g increases with $x$ only when $x > e^a$ where $a$ is a rational number to be found.

## 9.2 Tangents and normals; the importance of equal scales

### Key points

- Using the gradient function $\frac{dy}{dx}$ you can find the gradient of the curve at any given point. This is the gradient of the tangent at that point.
- The normal to a curve at a point is a line at right angles to the curve at that point.
- The product of the gradients of the tangent and of the normal is $-1$
- Only with equal scales on the axes will the tangent and the normal appear at right angles on your diagram.

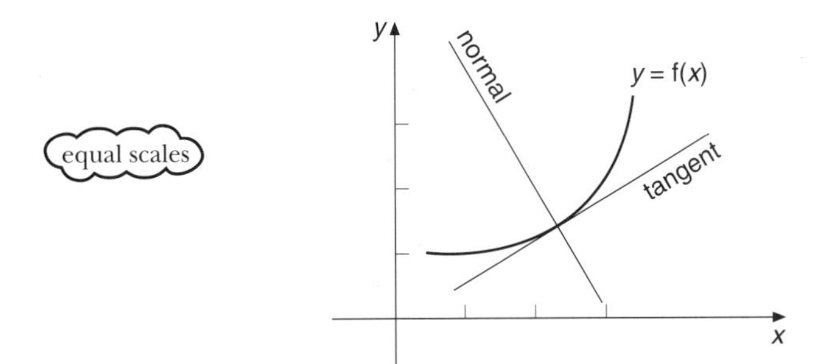


### Example 1

Find the equations of the tangent and the normal to the curve $y = x^2 + 2$ at $P(2,6)$. If the tangent meets the $x$ axis at $A$ and the normal meets the $x$ axis at $B$ then find the area of triangle $APB$

**Solution**

$$y = x^2 + 2$$

$$\frac{dy}{dx} = 2x$$

$\therefore$ gradient of tangent at P (when $x = 2$) is 4

and the gradient of the normal is $-\dfrac{1}{4}$

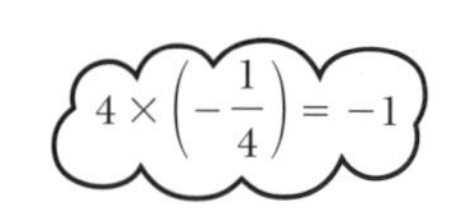


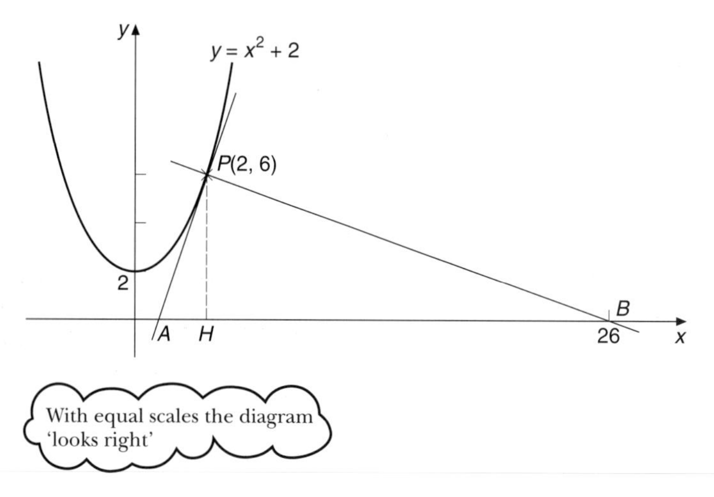


With equal scales the diagram 'looks right'

At $P(2,6)$ the equation of the tangent is

$y - 6 = 4(x - 2)$

i.e. $y = 4x - 2$

The tangent meets the $x$ axis when $y = 0$

i.e. when $x = \frac{1}{2}$

$\therefore$ $A$ is the point $(\frac{1}{2},0)$

At $P(2,6)$ the equation of the normal is $y - 6 = -\frac{1}{4}(x - 2)$

$$4y - 24 = -x + 2$$

$$4y + x = 26$$

The normal meets the $x$ axis when $x = 26$

$\therefore$ $B$ is the point $(26,0)$

Area of triangle $APB = \frac{1}{2}(AB) \times PH = \frac{1}{2}(25\frac{1}{2}) \times 6$

$= 76\frac{1}{2}$ square units

## Example 2

Find the equation of the normal at $P(1,4)$ to the graph $xy = 4$ and then find the coordinates of the point where the normal cuts the curve again.

**Solution**

$xy = 4$

$y = \dfrac{4}{x} = 4x^{-1}$

$$\therefore \frac{dy}{dx} = -4x^{-2} = \frac{-4}{x^2}$$

At $P$ (where $x = 1$) $\frac{dy}{dx} = -4 \therefore$ the gradient of the normal is $\frac{1}{4}$

$\therefore$ the equation of the normal is $y - 4 = \frac{1}{4}(x - 1)$

$$4y - 16 = x - 1$$

$$4y = x + 15$$

$$(\text{or } 4y - 15 = x)$$

You can substitute this value of $x$ into $xy = 4$ to find where the normal cuts the curve again.

or you could have substituted $x = \frac{4}{y}$ into the line

So

$$(4y - 15)y = 4$$

$$4y^2 - 15y - 4 = 0$$

$$(4y + 1)(y - 4) = 0$$

$$\downarrow \qquad\qquad \downarrow$$

$$\therefore y = -\tfrac{1}{4} \quad \text{and} \quad y = 4 \quad (\text{at } P)$$

When $y = -\frac{1}{4}$ (substituting in $xy = 4$) you get $x = -16$.

$\therefore (-16, -\frac{1}{4})$ is the point you are looking for.

## Exercise 9.2

In questions **A1–A8** find the equations of the tangent and the normal to the curve at the given points on that curve.

**A1** $y = (x - 3)^2$ at $(1,4)$

**A2** $y = \frac{1}{x} + 1$ at $\left(3, \frac{4}{3}\right)$

**A3** $y = x^3 - x^2 + x + 3$ when $x = -1$

**A4** $y = \sin x$ at $\left(\frac{\pi}{3}, \frac{\sqrt{3}}{2}\right)$

**A5** $y = e^x$ when $x = 2$

**A6** $y = x^2 - 1$ at $(3,8)$

**A7** $y = \ln x$ at $(1,0)$

**A8** $y = \cos 2x$ when $x = \frac{\pi}{6}$

**A9** Find the equations of the tangents to the curve $y = \frac{1}{x}$ which are parallel to the line $x + 4y = 8$

**A10** The graph of $y = e^{-x} + 2$ crosses the $y$ axis at $A$ and the normal to the curve at $A$ meets the $x$ axis at $B$ as shown in the following diagram.

Find the coordinates of the points $A$ and $B$ and show that the distance $AB = 3\sqrt{2}$

## Exercise 9.2 *continued*

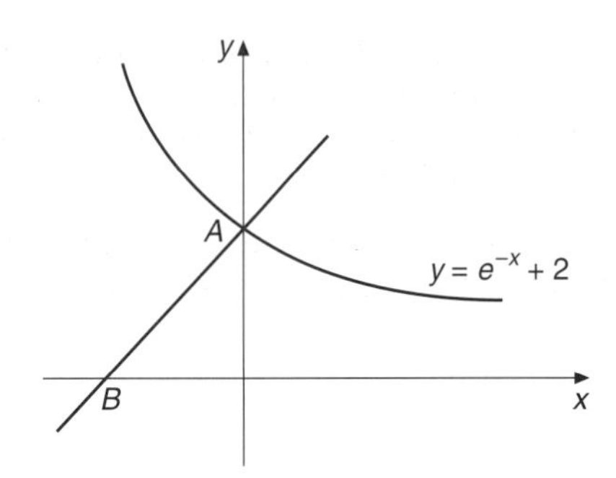


**B1** Show that the tangent at (3,9) to the curve $y = x^2$ meets the normal at (1,1) to that curve at the point $\left(\frac{21}{13}, \frac{9}{13}\right)$.

**B2** Show that the tangents to the curve $y = x^2 - 2x$ at the points (3,3) and (−3,15) meet on the $y$ axis.

**B3** The tangent to the curve $y = (2x - 1)^2$ at the point (2,9) meets the $x$ axis at $P$ and the $y$ axis at $Q$. Find the coordinates of $P$ and $Q$ and show that the length of $PQ$ is $\frac{5\sqrt{145}}{4}$.

**B4** If the curve $y = ax^2 + bx + 3$ passes through $A(1,6)$ and $B(-1,2)$ find the values of $a$ and $b$.

Find the equation of the tangent to the curve that is parallel to $AB$.

**B5** A curve has equation of the form $y = a + \frac{b}{x}$ and passes through the points $P(1,3)$ and $Q(-1,5)$

(a) find the values of $a$ and $b$

(b) find the equations of the tangents at $P$ and $Q$

(c) show that these tangents are both perpendicular to line $PQ$.

**B6** Sketch the graph of $y = 2\sqrt{x}$ for $0 \le x \le 8$. The point $A$ on the graph has $x$ coordinate 4. Find the gradient of the curve at $A$ and obtain the equation of

(a) the tangent

(b) the normal to the curve at $A$.

If the tangent and normal meet the $x$ axis at $T$ and $N$ respectively write down the distance $TN$, find the area of triangle $ATN$ and show that the midpoint of $AT$ lies on the $y$ axis.

**B7** The point $A$ lies on the graph of $y = e^{2x} - e^{-2x} + 3$ and also lies on the $y$ axis. Write down the coordinates of $A$. Obtain $\frac{dy}{dx}$ and find the equation of the tangent to the graph at $A$. If this line crosses the $x$ axis at $B$ find the length of $AB$.

**B8**

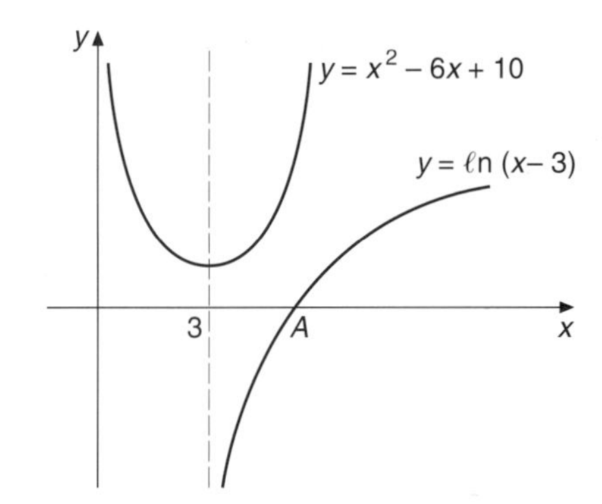


The diagram shows the graphs of $y = \ln(x - 3)$ and $y = x^2 - 6x + 10$. The normal to the graph of $y = \ln(x - 3)$ at $A$, the point of intersection with the $x$ axis, meets the graph of $y = x^2 - 6x + 10$ at $B$ and $C$

(a) By writing $y = x^2 - 6x + 10$ in the form $y = (x - \mathrm{a})^2 + \mathrm{b}$ obtain the coordinates of the vertex of the parabola

(b) Find the coordinates of $B$ and $C$ and show that one of these points lies on the axis of symmetry of the parabola.

**B9** The function $f(x) \equiv 2x - \ln x$ is defined on the domain $x > 0$. The point $A$ lies on the graph of $y = f(x)$ at the point where $x = 1$.

## Exercise 9.2 *continued*

Find the equations of the tangent and normal at $A$. If the tangent meets the $x$ axis at $B$, and the normal meets the $x$ axis at $C$, show that triangle $ABC$ is isosceles.

**B10** On the graph of $y = \ln x$ ($x > 0$) the point $A$ has $x$ coordinate $e^2$. Find the equation of the tangent to the curve at $A$ and show that it passes through the point $B(0,1)$. Find the coordinates of the point $C$ where the tangent meets the $x$ axis. Show that $B$ is the midpoint of $AC$.

Sketch the situation showing clearly the curve, the tangent and the points $A$, $B$ and $C$.

## 9.3 Stationary points and their applications

### Key points

A stationary point on a curve is the point at which the gradient is zero.

$$\frac{dy}{dx} = f'(x) = 0$$

There are three types of stationary point

- (1)

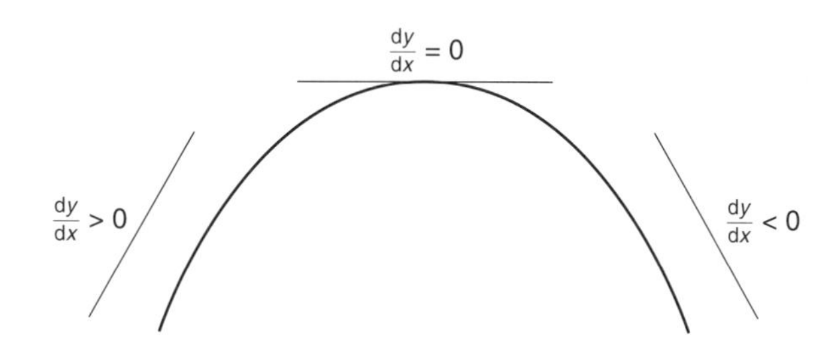


MAXIMUM

If $\dfrac{dy}{dx} = 0$ and $\dfrac{d^2y}{dx^2} < 0$ for some value $x = a$ then there is a 'local maximum' at $x = a$

- (2)

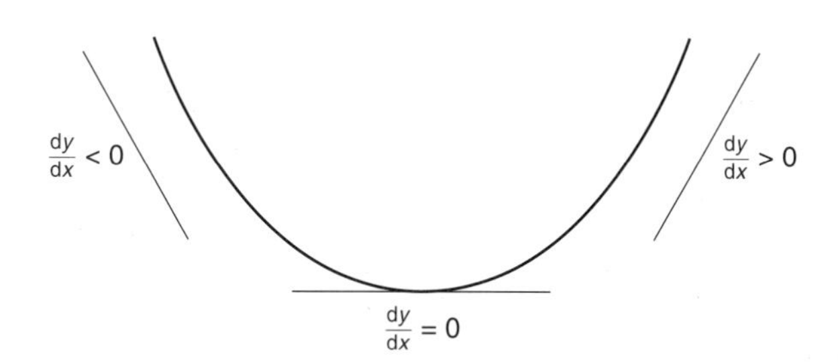


MINIMUM

If $\dfrac{dy}{dx} = 0$ and $\dfrac{d^2y}{dx^2} > 0$ for some value $x = a$ then there is a 'local minimum' at $x = a$

- (3)

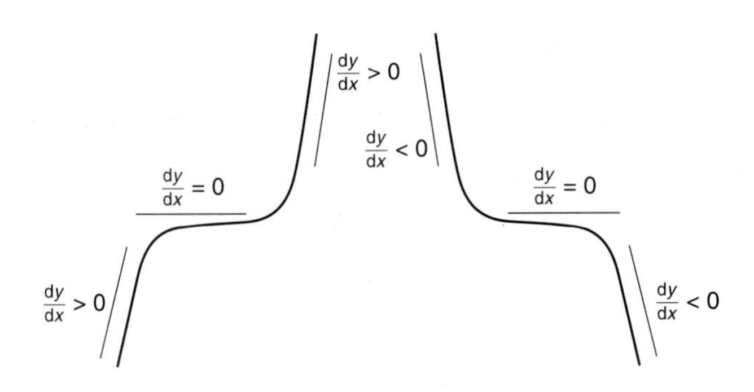


## POINT OF INFLEXION WITH ZERO GRADIENT

If $\dfrac{dy}{dx} = 0$ and $\dfrac{d^2y}{dx^2} = 0$ for some value of $x = a$ then be very careful!

If $\dfrac{d^2y}{dx^2} = 0$ look at the gradient on either side of $x = a$ to check if it is a point of inflexion or a maximum or a minimum

## Example 1

If $y = x^4 - 8x^2$ find the coordinates of the stationary points and determine if they are maximum or minimum. Sketch the curve, marking the coordinates of the turning points and the intersections with the axes.

**Solution**

$y = x^4 - 8x^2$

$$\frac{dy}{dx} = 4x^3 - 16x = 4x(x^2 - 4)$$

$$= 4x(x-2)(x+2)$$

$$\downarrow \quad \downarrow \quad \searrow$$

$\dfrac{dy}{dx} = 0$ when $x = 0 \quad x = 2 \quad x = -2$

$\dfrac{d^2y}{dx^2} = 12x^2 - 16$ When $x = 0$ $\dfrac{d^2y}{dx^2} = -16$ so $\dfrac{d^2y}{dx^2} < 0$

$\therefore$ maximum turning point

When $x = 2$ $\quad \dfrac{d^2y}{dx^2} = 48 - 16 = 32 \quad$ so $\dfrac{d^2y}{dx^2} > 0$

$\therefore$ minimum

When $x = -2$ $\quad \dfrac{d^2y}{dx^2} = 48 - 16 = 32 \quad$ so $\dfrac{d^2y}{dx^2} > 0$

$\therefore$ minimum.

$\therefore$ (0,0), (2,−16), (−2,−16) are the coordinates of the stationary points.

The curve cuts the $x$ axis when $y = 0$

$$\text{i.e. } 0 = x^4 - 8x^2$$
$$0 = x^2(x^2 - 8)$$

$x = 0$ (repeated) $\qquad x = \pm\sqrt{8} = \pm 2\sqrt{2}$

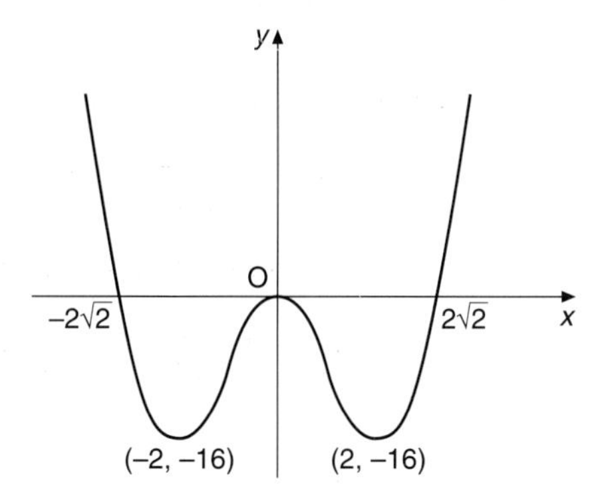


## Example 2

A cylindrical open can (i.e. no lid) has a surface area of $300\pi\ \text{cm}^2$. Find the maximum volume of the can giving reasons to justify the maximum.

**Solution**

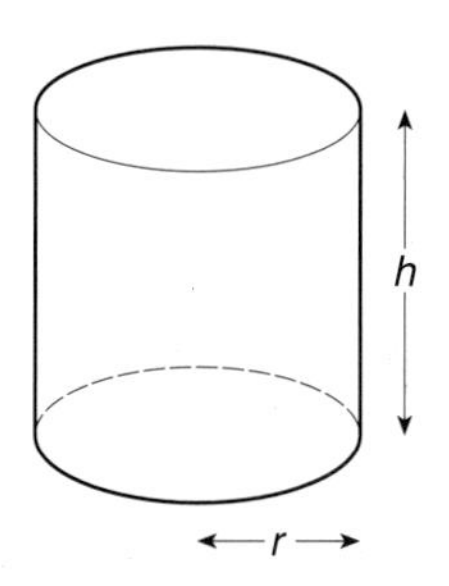

The surface area ($S\,\text{cm}^2$) is given by $S = \pi r^2 + 2\pi rh$

So we have

$$300\pi = \pi r^2 + 2\pi rh$$

$$\text{i.e. } 300 = r^2 + 2rh$$

$$\frac{300 - r^2}{2r} = h$$

The volume ($V\,\text{cm}^3$) of the can is given by $V = \pi r^2 h$

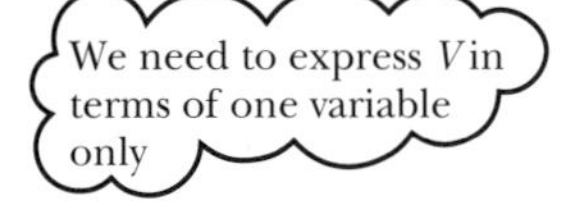


You know that

$$\frac{300 - r^2}{2r} = h$$

so you can write $V$ in terms of $r$ only and then differentiate $V$ with respect to $r$

$$V = \pi r^2\left(\frac{300 - r^2}{2r}\right) = \frac{\pi}{2}(300r - r^3)$$

$$\therefore \frac{dV}{dr} = \frac{\pi}{2}(300 - 3r^2)$$

$$= \frac{3\pi}{2}(100 - r^2)$$

For a stationary point, $\frac{dV}{dr} = 0$

$$\text{i.e. } \frac{3\pi}{2}(100 - r^2) = 0$$

$$r^2 = 100$$

$$r = 10$$

$r > 0$, so no negative square root

When $r < 10$, $100 - r^2 > 0$

$$\therefore \frac{dV}{dr} > 0$$

When $r > 10$, $100 - r^2 < 0$

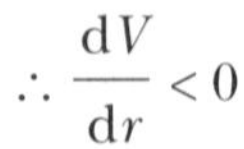

$$\therefore \frac{dV}{dr} < 0$$

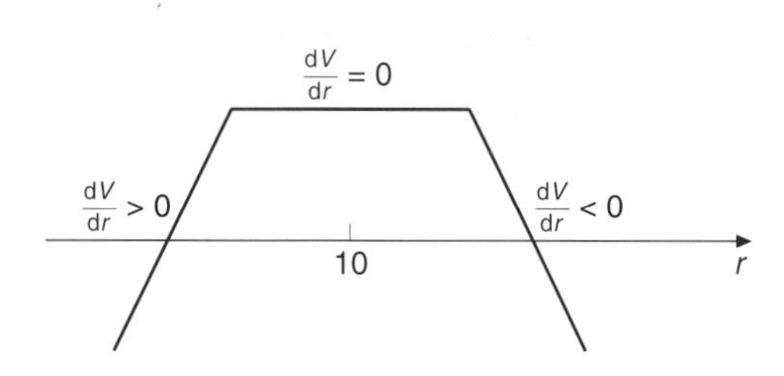


$\therefore$ Maximum volume when $r = 10$.

You know that $V = \frac{\pi}{2}(300r - r^3)$

so when $r = 10$ $\quad V = \frac{\pi}{2}(3000 - 1000) = 1000\pi$

This means that the maximum possible volume of the can is $1000\pi$ cm$^3$.

## Exercise 9.3

**A1** Find the coordinates of any stationary points of the curves

(a) $y = x^3 + 2x^2 + x$

(b) $y = x^3 - 6x^2 + 12x - 8$

(c) $y = x^3 + 3x$

**A2** Investigate the nature of the stationary points of the curve $y = x(x - 1)^2$ and sketch the curve, marking clearly the points of intersection with the axes and the coordinates of the turning points.

**A3** Find the $x$ coordinate of the stationary point on the graph of $y = 4\ln x - x^2$ $(x > 0)$. Prove that $y \leq 2(\ln 2 - 1)$.

**A4** Show that the function $h(x) \equiv 2x + \frac{8}{x}$

$(x > 0)$ has a stationary point

which is a minimum and find its coordinates.

**A5** If $f(x) \equiv x^3 - 6x^2 + 12x - 4$ find $f'(x)$ and factorise it fully. Hence show that $f'(x)$ is zero for just one value of $x$ but is otherwise positive. What can be deduced about the stationary point on the graph of $y = f(x)$? Sketch the graph.

**A6** Find the coordinates of the two stationary points on the graph of $y = x^3 - 6x^2 + 5$. Establish, with reasons, whether each point is a maximum or a minimum or neither. Confirm that the midpoint of the line joining these stationary points lies on the graph.

**A7** Prove that the maximum value of $3x - e^x$ is $3(\ln 3 - 1)$.

**A8** The function $f(x) \equiv 3x - \ln x$ is defined on the domain $x > 0$. Use calculus to prove that $f(x) \geqslant 1 + \ln 3$.

**A9** Given that $y = e^{-x} + 4e^x$ write down expressions for $\frac{dy}{dx}$ and $\frac{d^2y}{dx^2}$. Show that $\frac{dy}{dx} = 0$ only when $e^x = \frac{1}{2}$.

Hence show that the graph of $y$ has a minimum point at $(-\ln 2, 4)$.

## Exercise 9.3 *continued*

**A10** If $y = e^x(\sin x + \cos x)$ show that $\frac{dy}{dx} = 2e^x\cos x$. Given that $0 \leq x \leq \pi$ show that the graph of $y$ has just one stationary point. Find its coordinates and determine its nature.

**B1** A farmer builds a rectangular enclosure for his sheep shearing. The enclosure has one side which is the side of a barn and the farmer uses 70 metres of fencing for the other three sides. Find the dimensions of the pen to give the largest area for the sheep.

**B2** An open (i.e. topless!) rectangular water tank of capacity $13\frac{1}{2}$ m$^3$ is to be made with a square horizontal base and 4 vertical rectangular sides using thin sheet metal (ignoring 'seams', 'overlaps' and the possibility of leaks!).

By writing the length of the base as $x$ m, the height $h$ m and the area of metal $z$ m$^2$ show that $z = x^2 + 4xh$ and hence that $z = x^2 + \frac{54}{x}$.

Find the least possible area of metal.

**B3** (a) A variable rectangle has a fixed perimeter of 30 cm. If the length is $x$ cm write down its width and then an expression for its area $y$ cm$^2$ in terms of $x$. Find the maximum area of the rectangle.

(b) A variable rectangle has a fixed perimeter of $2p$ cm. If the length is $x$ cm write down its width and hence an expression for its area $z$ cm$^2$ in terms of $x$ and $p$. Find the maximum area of the rectangle in terms of $p$.

**B4** (a) A variable rectangle has a fixed area of 200 cm$^2$. If the length is $x$ cm find an expression for the perimeter $p$ cm in terms of $x$. Show that the minimum length of the perimeter is $40\sqrt{2}$ cm.

(b) Another variable rectangle has a fixed area of $A$ cm$^2$. Again by writing the length as $x$ cm show that the perimeter $z$ cm is given by $z = 2x + \frac{2A}{x}$ and establish that the minimum perimeter is $4\sqrt{A}$ cm.

**B5** A rectangular piece of paper measures 20 cm by 12 cm. A square of side $x$ cm is cut from each of the four corners and then the paper is folded and glued to form an open tray with a rectangular base and height $x$ cm. Three students in a class used different values for their $x$ each hoping to get the maximum possible volume for the tray. One chose 2.3 cm, another 2.4 cm and another 2.5 cm. Who was closest and, using your calculated value of $x$ to 4 decimal places, find the maximum possible volume to two decimal places and the percentage error in $x$ to 1 decimal place for the student with the best guess.

**B6** A closed metal oil tank has a square box of side $x$ metres and vertical rectangular sides of height $h$ metres. If the surface area of metal used to make the tank is $A$ m$^2$ show that the volume $V$ m$^3$ is given by $V = \frac{1}{4}(Ax - 2x^3)$. If 54 m$^2$ of metal is used show that the maximum volume possible is when the tank is a cube.

**B7** An earring is made up of 18 cm of platinum wire bent around two squares of gold and including the hanging wire. Prove that the area of the gold surface is least when the squares are equal.

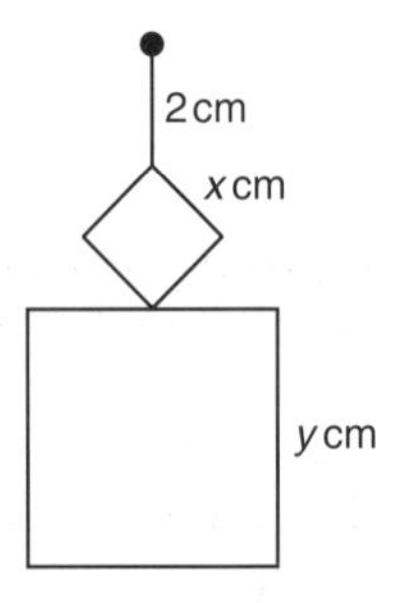

## Exercise 9.3 *continued*

**B8**

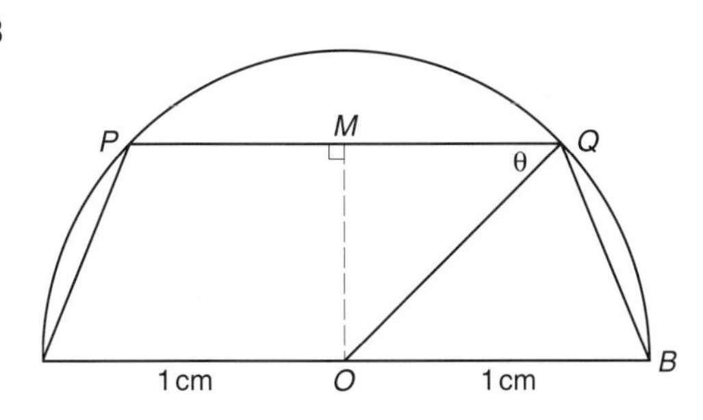


The diagram shows a semi-circle centre $O$, radius 1 cm and diameter $AB$. The line $PQ$ is always parallel to $AB$ but changes its position as angle $PQO = \theta$ radians varies between 0 and $\frac{\pi}{2}$ $\left(0 < \theta < \frac{\pi}{2}\right)$. $M$ is the midpoint of $PQ$.

(a) By finding the lengths of $PQ$ and $OM$ show that the area $z$ cm$^2$ of the trapezium $APQB$ is given by $z = (1 + \cos\theta)\sin\theta$

(b) Obtain an expression for $\frac{dz}{d\theta}$ and hence find the value of $\theta$ which gives the maximum area of the trapezium.

(c) Justify that this area is a maximum and find its exact value.

**B9**

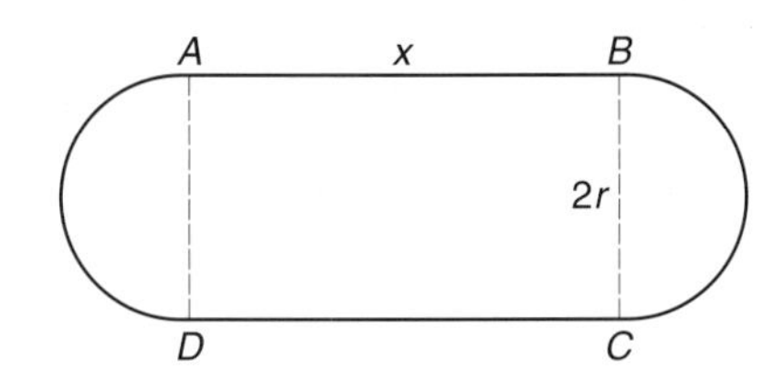


The diagram represents the 'inside' of the 'inside lane' of a 400 m athletics track.

$ABCD$ is a rectangle and each curve is a semi-circle. If $AB = x$m and $BC = 2r$m show that $2x + 2\pi r = 400$.

(a) Find the length of the 'straight' and the length of an 'inside bend' when the area of the rectangle is as large as possible

(b) How much longer is a circuit of the 'outside' of the 'outside lane' if the track is 10 m wide?

**B10**

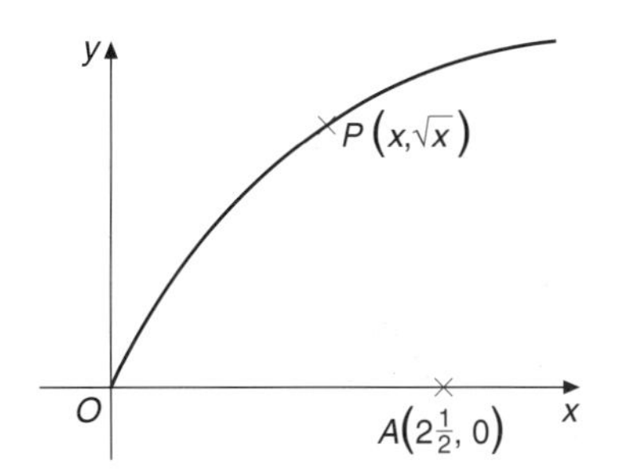


The diagram shows the variable point $P(x,\sqrt{x})$ on the graph of $y = \sqrt{x}$ where $x \geqslant 0$.

The point $A$ is fixed at $(2\frac{1}{2},0)$

(a) Show that $AP^2 = x^2 - 4x + \frac{25}{4}$

(b) Show that $B(2,\sqrt{2})$ is the point on the curve nearest to $A$

(c) Show that $AB$ is normal to the curve at $B$.

## 9.4 Applications of implicit and parametric differentiation

The following examples will help you understand some of the geometrical problems the examiners can set using either parametric or implicit differentiation.

## Example 1

A curve is represented by $x = 4t^2$ and $y = 8t$ where $t$ is a non-zero parameter. Find the equation of the normal to this curve at the point $A$ with parameter $t = \frac{1}{2}$. Show that the normal meets the curve again at the point $(81, -36)$

**Solution**

$x = 4t^2, \quad y = 8t$

$\frac{dx}{dt} = 8t, \frac{dy}{dt} = 8 \quad \therefore$ the gradient function $\frac{dy}{dx} = \frac{\frac{dy}{dt}}{\frac{dx}{dt}} = \frac{8}{8t} = \frac{1}{t}$

The normal to the curve at any point, parameter $t$ will have gradient $-t$

because $\frac{1}{t} \times (-t) = -1$ for perpendicular lines

At $A$, $t = \frac{1}{2}$ so $A$ is the point where $x = 4 \times \frac{1}{4} = 1$

and $y = 8 \times \frac{1}{2} = 4$.

The normal at $A(1,4)$ has gradient $-t = -\frac{1}{2}$

$\therefore$ the equation of the normal at $A$ is

$y - 4 = -\frac{1}{2}(x - 1)$

$2y - 8 = -x + 1$

$2y + x = 9$

To find where this normal meets the curve again you substitute the parametric values for $x$ and $y$ into the equation. This gives

$2(8t) + 4t^2 = 9$

$4t^2 + 16t - 9 = 0$

$(2t - 1)(2t + 9) = 0$

$t = \frac{1}{2}$ (i.e. point $A$) and $t = -\frac{9}{2}$ which gives $x = 4 \times (-\frac{9}{2})^2 = 81$

$y = 8(-\frac{9}{2}) = -36.$

## Example 2

The diagram shows the point $A(2,1)$ on the curve $4x^2 + 9y^2 = 25$

Find

(a) the gradient of the curve at $A$

(b) the equation of the tangent at $A$

(c) the equation of the normal at $A$

(d) If the tangent meets the $x$-axis at $T$ and the normal meets the $x$ axis at

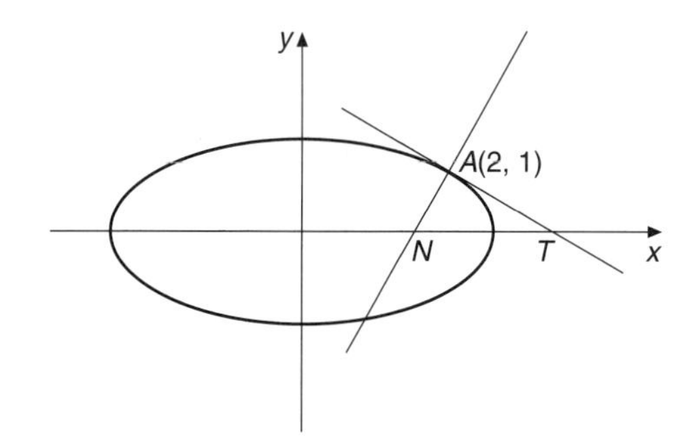


$N$ show that the area of triangle $ANT$ is approximately one square unit.

**Solution**

(a) $4x^2 + 9y^2 = 25$

Differentiate both sides with respect to $x$

$$8x + 18y\frac{dy}{dx} = 0$$

At $A$, $x = 2$ and $y = 1$ so $\quad 16 + 18\frac{dy}{dx} = 0 \Rightarrow \frac{dy}{dx} = -\frac{16}{18} = -\frac{8}{9}$

$\therefore$ the gradient of the tangent at $A$ is $-\frac{8}{9}$

(b) the equation of the tangent at $A$ is given by

$$y - 1 = -\frac{8}{9}(x - 2)$$

$$9y - 9 = -8x + 16$$

$$9y + 8x = 25.$$

(c) The gradient of the normal is $\frac{9}{8}$

$-\frac{8}{9} \times \frac{9}{8} = 1$

$\therefore$ the equation of the normal is

$$y - 1 = \frac{9}{8}(x - 2)$$

$$8y - 8 = 9x - 18$$

$$8y = 9x - 10$$

(d) $9y + 8x = 25$ meets the $x$ axis when $8x = 25$

$y = 0$

i.e. $x = \frac{25}{8}$

$8y = 9x - 10$ meets the $x$ axis when $0 = 9x - 10$ 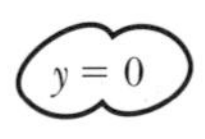


$$\frac{10}{9} = x$$

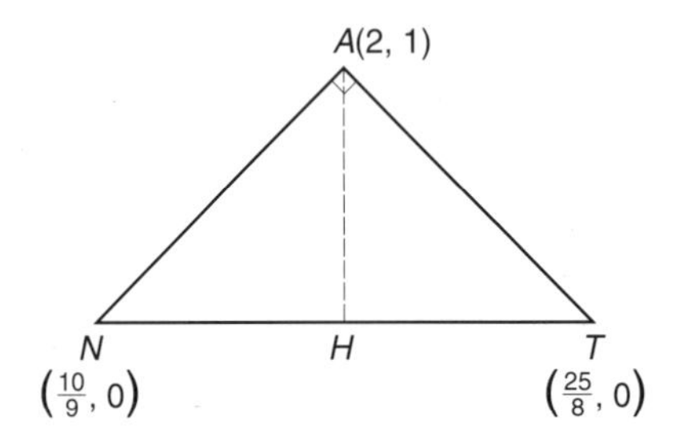


So the area of triangle $ANT$ is given by $\frac{1}{2} \times NT \times AH$

$$= \frac{1}{2} \times \left(\frac{25}{8} - \frac{10}{9}\right) \times 1$$

$$= \frac{1}{2} \times \left(\frac{225}{72} - \frac{80}{72}\right)$$

$$= \frac{1}{2} \times \left(\frac{145}{72}\right)$$

$$\simeq \frac{1}{2} \times 2 = 1$$

So the area of $\Delta ANT$ is approximately one square unit.

## Exercise 9.4

**A1** A curve is defined parametrically by $x = \frac{t}{2}$, $y = t^2 - 4$. Prove that the tangent to the curve at the point with parameter $t = 4$ can be written in the form $y = \lambda(4x - 5)$ and state the value of $\lambda$.

**A2** Find the equations of the tangent and normal to the circle $x^2 + y^2 = 100$ at the point on the curve where $x = 6$ and $y$ is negative.

**A3** A curve is defined parametrically by $x = 2\cos\theta$ and $y = 3\sin\theta$. Show that the equation of the normal at the point with parameter $t = \frac{\pi}{4}$ is given by $3\sqrt{2}y = 2\sqrt{2}x + 5$

**A4** If $9x^2 - 4y^2 = 32$ find $\frac{dy}{dx}$ in terms of $x$ and $y$. Show that the point $A(-2,1)$ lies on the curve $9x^2 - 4y^2 = 32$ and find the equation of the tangent to the curve at $A$. This tangent meets the $x$ axis at $B$ and the $y$ axis at $C$. Find the area of triangle $BOC$ where $O$ is the origin.

## Exercise 9.4 *continued*

**A5** A curve is defined parametrically by $x = t^3$, $y = t^2$

(a) find $\frac{dy}{dx}$ in terms of $t$

(b) If $P$ is the point $(p^3, p^2)$ on the curve find the equation of the tangent at $P$.

(c) Show that $Q$, the point on the curve with parameter $t = -\frac{p}{2}$ lies on the tangent at $P$.

**B1** The normal drawn to the curve $x^3 + y^3 = 28$ at the point (3,1) on the curve meets the line $y = 5x$ at the point $B$. Find the coordinates of $B$.

**B2** On the curve defined parametrically by $x = 3t^2$, $y = 2t^3$ the points $A$, $B$ have parameters $t = 2$ and $t = -1$ respectively.

(a) Write down the coordinates of $A$ and $B$.

(b) Show that the tangent to the curve at $A$ meets the curve again at $B$.

**B3** (a) Show that $\frac{d}{dx}(\ln y) = \frac{1}{y}\frac{dy}{dx}$

(b) If $y = 2^x$ show that $\ln y = x\ln 2$ and hence that $\frac{dy}{dx} = 2^x \ln 2$

(c) Find the equation of the tangent to the curve $y = 2^x$ at the point where the curve crosses the $y$ axis. Also find the equation of the normal to the curve at this point.

(d) The tangent and normal meet the $x$ axis at $A$ and $B$ respectively. Find the coordinates of $A$ and $B$ and show that the distance $AB$ is

$$\ln 2 + \frac{1}{\ln 2}$$

**B4** The curve $C$ is given by parametric equations $x = 2t$, $y = \frac{2}{t}$ and the point $A$ on the curve has parameter $t = \frac{1}{2}$.

(a) Find $\frac{dy}{dx}$ in terms of $t$

(b) Find the equations of the tangent and normal to the curve at $A$

(c) If the tangent and normal meet the $x$ axis at $D$ and $E$ respectively find the length of $DE$ and the area of triangle $ADE$.

**B5** The parametric equations of a curve are $y = 3\cos 2t$, $x = 4\cos t$

(a) Show that $\frac{dy}{dx} = 3\cos t$

(b) At $A$, $t = \frac{\pi}{3}$ and at $B$, $t = 0$.

Show that the equation of the tangent at $A$ is $2y - 3x + 9 = 0$ and find the equation of the tangent at $B$

(c) If the tangents meet at $D$ show that $D$ lies on the $x$ axis and that $D$ is nearer to the origin than it is to $B$.

**B6** A curve is defined parametrically by $x = t^2$, $y = 2t$. $(t \geqslant 0)$

(a) Show that the distance $AP$ between the point $A(11,0)$ and the point $P(t^2,2t)$ on the curve is such that $AP^2 = t^4 - 18t^2 + 121$

(b) Taking $f(t) \equiv t^4 - 18t^2 + 121$ find the positive value of $t$ for which $f'(t) = 0$

(c) Hence find the minimum distance from the point $A$ to the curve, showing that your answer is a minimum, and of the form $k\sqrt{10}$ where $k$ is an integer.

## 9.5 Maclaurin's series

### Key points

You are sometimes asked to find a series for functions such as $\sin x$, $e^x$, $\ln(1 + x)$ etc. To do this you use Maclaurin's series which states that, under certain conditions,

$$f(x) = f(0) + xf'(0) + \frac{x^2}{2!}f''(0) + \frac{x^3}{3!}f'''(0) + \ldots\ldots$$

The following examples should help.

### Example 1

Use Maclaurin's Theorem to find a series for $\sin x$.

**Solution**

$$\begin{array}{ll} f(x) = \sin x & f(0) = 0 \\ f'(x) = \cos x & f'(0) = 1 \\ f''(x) = -\sin x & f''(0) = 0 \\ f'''(x) = -\cos x & f'''(0) = -1 \\ f^4(x) = \sin x & f^4(0) = 0 \end{array}$$

$$\therefore \sin x = 0 + x(1) + \frac{x^2}{2}(0) + \frac{x^3}{3!}(-1) + \frac{x^4}{4!}(0) + \ldots$$

$$= x - \frac{x^3}{3!} + \ldots$$

This is true for all $x$.

### Example 2

Show that, if $x$ is small enough for powers of $x^4$ and above to be neglected, then $\ln(1 + 2x) = 2x - 2x^2 + \frac{8x^3}{3}$

**Solution**

$$f(x) = \ln(1 + 2x) \qquad f(0) = 0$$

$$f'(x) = \frac{2}{1 + 2x} \qquad f'(0) = 2$$

$$f''(x) = \frac{-4}{(1 + 2x)^2} \qquad f''(0) = -4$$

$$f'''(x) = \frac{16}{(1 + 2x)^3} \qquad f'''(0) = 16$$

$$\therefore \ln(1 + 2x) = 0 + x(2) + \frac{x^2}{2!}(-4) + \frac{x^3}{3!}(16)$$

$$= 2x - 2x^2 + \frac{8x^3}{3}$$

which is the required result.

## Exercise 9.5

**A1** Find the Maclaurin expansion of $\ln(3 + x)$ up to the term in $x^2$.

**A2** Find the Maclaurin expansions of $e^x$ and $\cos x$ each up to the term in $x^2$. Hence write down the expansion of $e^{2x}$ and $\cos 2x$ and then work out the first two terms of the expansion of $e^{2x}\cos 2x$.

**A3** (a) If $f(x) = \sin^2 x$ find the expansion of $f(x)$ up to the term in $x^4$ using the Maclaurin series for $\sin x$ and squaring it.

(b) Find the Maclaurin expansion for $\cos 2x$ up to the term in $x^4$.

(c) Verify that the equation $\cos 2x = 1 - 2\sin^2 x$ is satisfied by your expansions found in parts (a) and (b).

**A4** (a) Use the Maclaurin expansion to show that

$$\ln(1 + x) = x - \frac{x^2}{2} + \frac{x^3}{3} - \ldots.$$

(b) Show that

$$\ln(3 + x) = \ln 3 + \ln\left(1 + \frac{x}{3}\right) \text{ and}$$

hence find the expansion of $\ln(3 + x)$ up to the term in $x^2$. (Check your answer against question **A1**).

**A5** If $f(x) = e^{-2x}$ use the Maclaurin expansion to establish the first three terms of the series for $f(x)$.

**A6** Given that $\ln(1 + x) = x - \dfrac{x^2}{2} + \dfrac{x^3}{3} - \ldots.$

for small $x$ write down the series for

(a) $\ln(1 - x)$

(b) $\ln\left(\dfrac{1 + x}{1 - x}\right)$ up to the term in $x^3$.

## Chapter 9: A level questions

**C1** Find the equation of the tangent to $y = x^3$ at the point $A(-2,-8)$ on the curve. If this tangent meets the curve again at the point $B$ show that the $x$ coordinate at $B$ is a root of the equation $x^3 - 12x - 16 = 0$. Using the factor theorem, or otherwise, solve this equation and find the coordinates of $B$.

**C2** Prove that the function $g(x) \equiv 2\sin x + \cos 2x$, $(0 \leq x \leq \pi)$, has three stationary values, one of which is at the point with $x$ coordinate $\dfrac{5\pi}{6}$. Find the coordinates of each of these points and determine its nature.

**C3** (a) Given that $y = \dfrac{a}{x} + \ln x$ where both $x$ and $a$ are positive and $a$ is constant, find $\dfrac{dy}{dx}$ and $\dfrac{d^2y}{dx^2}$.

(b) Show that $y$ has a minimum value when $x = a$ and find this value.

(c) Find the set of values of $a$ for which this minimum is always positive.

## Chapter 9: A level questions *continued*

**C4** Given that $y = \sin^2 x$ and that $0 < x < \frac{\pi}{2}$ show that $y$ is an increasing function, but that over the same domain $z = \cos^2 x$ decreases as $x$ increases.

**C5** Given that $F(x) \equiv ax + \frac{b}{x}$ where $x > 0$ and $a$ and $b$ are constants show that $F(x)$ is an increasing function if $a > 0$ and $b < 0$.

If, however, $a = 2$ and $b = 8$ show that $F(x)$ decreases as $x$ increases when $0 < x < 2$.

**C6** A curve has equation $y = \dfrac{14 - 3x}{(x-3)(x+2)}$

(a) Express $\dfrac{14 - 3x}{(x-3)(x+2)}$ in partial fractions.

(b) Show that $\dfrac{dy}{dx} = \dfrac{4}{(x+2)^2} - \dfrac{1}{(x-3)^2}$ and that at the point when $x = 8$ there is a stationary point on the curve.

(c) Find the $x$ coordinate of the other stationary point of the curve and by considering $\dfrac{d^2y}{dx^2}$, or otherwise, determine the nature of both stationary points.

**C7** A large open rectangular container of capacity 1000 $m^3$ is to be constructed with a horizontal rectangular base whose length is double its width and with vertical sides. The material for construction of the base costs £30 per $m^2$ and that of the sides costs £40 per $m^2$. Show that the minimum possible cost is £18 000 and state the dimensions of the container in this case.

(Let the base be $2x$ by $x$, the height $h$ and set up a formula for the cost £$y$ in terms of $x$)

**C8** A curve has parametric equations $x = t^2 + 1$, $y = 2t$.

(a) Write down the coordinates of the points $P$ and $Q$ whose parameters are $t = 1$ and $t = 3$ respectively.

(b) Obtain the equations of the tangents to the curve at $P$ and $Q$.

(c) If the tangents intersect at $R$ find the coordinates of $R$.

(d) Find $M$, the midpoint of $PQ$ and show that $RM$ is parallel to the $x$ axis. What is the distance $RM$?

**C9** A curve $C$ has parametric equations $x = 8t$, $y = 4t^2$.

(a) Write down the coordinates of the points $A$ and $B$ which have parameters $t = 2$ and $t = -\frac{1}{2}$ respectively.

Find the equation of $AB$ and show that this line crosses the $y$ axis at $(0,4)$.

(b) Find $\dfrac{dy}{dx}$ in terms of $t$ and hence show that the tangent to $C$ at $A$ is at right angles to the tangent to $C$ at $B$.

(c) Obtain the equation of the tangents at $A$ and $B$ and show that they intersect on the line $y = -4$. Find the $x$ coordinate of their point of intersection.

**C10** (a) Use the Maclaurin expansion to establish that the first three terms of the expansion of $e^x$ are

$$1 + x + \frac{1}{2}x^2 \ldots$$

(b) Find the error in using this expansion when $x = -\frac{1}{2}$

(c) Write down the first three terms of the expansion of $e^{-2x}$.

# Chapter 10

## INTEGRATION I

## 10.1 Simple differential equations; integration as the reverse of differentiation

### Key points

- 

| $\frac{dy}{dx}$ | $y$ | Notes |
|---|---|---|
| $x^n$ | $\frac{x^{n+1}}{n+1} + c$ | $\frac{d}{dx}(x^{n+1}) = (n+1)x^n$ |
| $k$ | $kx + c$ | $\frac{d}{dx}(kx) = k$ |
| $\frac{1}{x}$ | $\ln\lvert x\rvert + c$ | $\frac{d}{dx}(\ln\lvert x\rvert) = \frac{1}{x}$ |
| $e^{ax}$ | $\frac{1}{a}e^{ax} + c$ | $\frac{d}{dx}(e^{ax}) = ae^{ax}$ |
| $\sin ax$ | $-\frac{1}{a}\cos ax + c$ | $\frac{d}{dx}(\cos ax) = -a\sin ax$ |
| $\cos ax$ | $\frac{1}{a}\sin ax + c$ | $\frac{d}{dx}(\sin ax) = a\cos ax$ |
| $\sec^2 ax$ | $\frac{1}{a}\tan ax + c$ | $\frac{d}{dx}(\tan ax) = a\sec^2 ax$ |

- Notation: If $\frac{dy}{dx} = f(x)$ then $y$ can be written as $\int f(x)dx$
- Note: You are often asked to find the value of c when you solve a differential equation and so you will be given enough information in the question about particular values of the variables to be able to find c.

### Example 1

(a) If $\frac{dy}{dx} = 2x + 3$ find $y$  (b) If $f'(x) = 2e^{3x} - \sin 2x$ find $f(x)$

**Solution**

(a) $y = 2\left(\dfrac{x^2}{2}\right) + 3x + c$

$y = x^2 + 3x + c$

(b) $f(x) = 2\left(\dfrac{1}{3}e^{3x}\right) + \dfrac{1}{2}\cos 2x + c$

$f(x) = \dfrac{2}{3}e^{3x} + \dfrac{1}{2}\cos 2x + c$

## Example 2

If $\dfrac{d^2x}{dt^2} = 12t - 4$ and when $t = 0$, $\dfrac{dx}{dt} = 3$ and $x = 2$, find $x$ in terms of $t$.

**Solution**

$$\frac{dx}{dt} = 12\left(\frac{t^2}{2}\right) - 4t + c = 6t^2 - 4t + c$$

When $t = 0$, $\dfrac{dx}{dt} = 3$ so $3 = 0 - 0 + c$

Hence $\dfrac{dx}{dt} = 6t^2 - 4t + 3$ and so $x = 6\left(\dfrac{t^3}{3}\right) - 4\left(\dfrac{t^2}{2}\right) + 3t + k$

When $t = 0$, $x = 2$

$2 = 0 - 0 + 0 + k$

$\therefore x = 2t^3 - 2t^2 + 3t + 2$

## Exercise 10.1

Using the reverse of differentiation solve the following differential equations

**A1** (a) $\dfrac{dy}{dx} = x(2x - 3)$

(b) $\dfrac{dy}{dx} = (3x - 1)^2$

(c) $\dfrac{dy}{dx} = \sqrt{x} + \dfrac{2}{\sqrt{x}}$

**A2** (a) $f'(x) = (2x - 3)^2$

(b) $f'(x) = (1 + 2x)(3x - 4)$

(c) $f'(x) = x^3(x - 1)$

**A3** (a) $\dfrac{dy}{dx} = \cos x$

(b) $\dfrac{dy}{dx} = \cos 2x$

(c) $\dfrac{dy}{dx} = \sec^2 x$

**A4** (a) $f'(x) = x + \dfrac{1}{x}$

(b) $f'(x) = \dfrac{1 - x^2}{x}$

**A5** (a) $\dfrac{dy}{dx} = e^{2x}$

(b) $\dfrac{dy}{dx} = e^x + e^{-3x}$

(c) $\dfrac{dy}{dx} = \dfrac{e^{3x} - e^{-x}}{e^{2x}}$

**A6** If $\dfrac{ds}{dt} = 36t^2 - 24t + 13$ find $s$.

## Exercise 10.1 *continued*

**A7** Find $\int \left(t^2 - \frac{3t}{2} + 4\right) dt$

**A8** If $\frac{dv}{dt} = 3 + \frac{2}{t}$ find $v$.

**A9** Find

(a) $\int x^3(5 - x)\,dx$

(b) $\int \frac{5 - x}{x^3}\,dx$

**A10** If $\frac{d^2y}{dx^2} = 4x + 3$ find

(a) $\frac{dy}{dx}$

(b) $y$

In **B1** to **B5** find an expression for $y$ from the following differential equations.

**B1** (a) $\frac{dy}{dx} = \left(x + \frac{1}{x}\right)^2$

(b) $\frac{dy}{dx} = \left(\sqrt{x} + \frac{1}{\sqrt{x}}\right)^2$

**B2** (a) $\frac{dy}{dx} = \left(x - \frac{1}{\sqrt{x}}\right)^2$

(b) $\frac{dy}{dx} = \left(2\sqrt{x} - \frac{3}{x}\right)^2$

**B3** $\frac{dy}{dx} = \frac{(x + 3)^2}{x^2}$

**B4** $\frac{dy}{dx} = 2\sin 2x + \sin\frac{1}{2}x$

**B5** $\frac{dy}{dx} = (\sin x + \cos x)^2$ (Remember: $\sin 2x = 2\sin x\cos x$)

**B6** If $\frac{dy}{dx} = x^2 + 3x - 2$ and $y = 5$ when $x = 0$ find $y$.

**B7** If $\frac{dx}{dt} = 4\cos 2t + 9\sin 3t$ find $x$ if $x = 2$ when $t = 0$.

**B8** If $\frac{dA}{dx} = 2x + 5$ find $A$ if

(a) $A = 0$ when $x = 0$

(b) $A = 0$ when $x = -2$.

**B9** If $\frac{d^2y}{dx^2} = 6x - 4$ and if $y = -2$ and $\frac{dy}{dx} = 1$ when $x = 0$, show that $y = (x^2 + 1)(x - 2)$.

**B10** Given that $s = 0$ and $\frac{ds}{dt} = 4$ when $t = 0$, find $s$ if

(a) $\frac{d^2s}{dt^2} = 4$

(b) $\frac{d^2s}{dt^2} = 2t + 1$.

## 10.2 Routine limit work; working out definite integrals

### Key points

$$\int_a^b f(x)\,dx = \left[g(x)\right]_a^b = g(b) - g(a)$$

If $g'(x) = f(x)$, differentiate g to get f

## Example 1

Find the values of

(a) $\left[x^2 + 3x + 2\right]_1^4$

(b) $\left[x^2 + 3x + c\right]_1^4$

**Solution**

(a) $\left[x^2 + 3x + 2\right]_1^4$

$= (16 + 12 + 2) - (1 + 3 + 2)$
$= 30 - 6$
$= 24$

(b) $\left[x^2 + 3x + c\right]_1^4$

$= (16 + 12 + c) - (1 + 3 + c)$
$= (28 + c) - (4 + c)$
$= 28 + c - 4 - c$
$= 24$

The constant term in the question does not affect the answer.

## Example 2

Evaluate

(a) $\int_1^5 (1 - x)(x - 5)\mathrm{d}x$

(b) $\int_{\pi/6}^{\pi/2} (1 + \cos x)\mathrm{d}x$

**Solution**

(a) $\int_1^5 (1 - x)(x - 5)\mathrm{d}x$

$$= \int_1^5 (-x^2 + 6x - 5)\mathrm{d}x$$

$$= \left[\frac{-x^3}{3} + 3x^2 - 5x\right]_1^5$$

$$= \left(-\frac{125}{3} + 75 - 25\right) - \left(-\frac{1}{3} + 3 - 5\right)$$

$$= 10\frac{2}{3}$$

(b) $\int_{\pi/6}^{\pi/2} (1 + \cos x)\mathrm{d}x$

$$= \left[x + \sin x\right]_{\pi/6}^{\pi/2}$$

$$= \left(\frac{\pi}{2} + 1\right) - \left(\frac{\pi}{6} + \frac{1}{2}\right) = \frac{\pi}{3} + \frac{1}{2}$$

## Exercise 10.2

**A1** Find

(a) $\left[x^2 + 2x\right]_1^3$

(b) $\left[x^2 + 2x + k\right]_1^3$

**A2** Find

(a) $\left[2x + 5\right]_1^4$

(b) $\left[2x + 5\right]_{-4}^{-1}$

**A3** Find

(a) $\left[2x - \frac{3}{x}\right]_2^5$

(b) $\left[2x - \frac{3}{x}\right]_{-4}^{-2}$

Evaluate

**A4** (a) $\int_2^3 (2x + 1)\,dx$

(b) $\int_0^2 (x - 1)(x + 1)\,dx$

**A5** (a) $\int_2^6 \frac{1}{x}\,dx$

(b) $\int_{-6}^{-2} \frac{1}{x}\,dx$

**A6** $\int_0^1 e^{2x}\,dx$ (leave your answer in terms of e)

**A7** $\int_0^{\pi/4} (\sin x + \cos x)\,dx$

**A8** Show that $\int_1^6 (4x - 3)\,dx =$

$\int_4^6 (4x - 3)\,dx + \int_1^4 (4x - 3)\,dx$

**A9** If $I_1 = \int_3^6 x^2\,dx$ and $I_2 = \int_3^6 (4x + 3)\,dx$,

evaluate $I_1$ and $I_2$.

Show that $\int_3^6 (x^2 + 4x + 3)\,dx = I_1 + I_2$.

**A10** If $I_1 = \int_0^3 (x^3 - 9x)\,dx$ and

$I_2 = \int_{-3}^0 (x^3 - 9x)\,dx$, show that $I_1 = -I_2$.

**B1** Find $\frac{d}{dx}(xe^x)$ using the product rule.

Hence evaluate $\int_1^2 e^x(1 + x)\,dx$

(a) in terms of e

(b) to 2 decimal places.

**B2** Find $\frac{d}{dx}(\sqrt{1 + 2x})$ using the chain rule.

Hence find the exact value of

$\int_0^1 \frac{1}{\sqrt{1 + 2x}}\,dx$

**B3** Find $\frac{d}{dx}(\cos 4x)$ and then show that

$\int_0^{\pi/8} \sin 4x\,dx = \frac{1}{4}$.

**B4** Use the chain rule to find $\frac{d}{dx}\left(\frac{1}{(2x + 1)^3}\right)$.

Now evaluate $\int_0^1 \frac{1}{(2x + 1)^4}\,dx$.

## Exercise 10.2 *continued*

**B5** Find the value of $\int_{-1}^{0} (3x - 1)^5 \mathrm{d}x$

$\left(\frac{\mathrm{d}}{\mathrm{d}x}(3x-1)^6 \text{ may help}\right)$.

In **B6–B10** try to find some function which, when differentiated, gives some multiple of your integral. You may get only a 'half hint'.

**B6** Find the value of

$\int_{3}^{6} \frac{1}{\sqrt{x-2}}\mathrm{d}x \rightarrow$ try (something)$^{\frac{1}{2}}$

**B7** Evaluate $\int_{-1}^{3} \sqrt{2x+3}\,\mathrm{d}x \rightarrow$ try (something)$^{\frac{3}{2}}$

**B8** Find the value of $\int_{0}^{\pi/6} (\cos 3x + \sin 2x)\,\mathrm{d}x$

**B9** Evaluate

$\int_{1\frac{1}{2}}^{2\frac{1}{2}} (2x-3)^4 \mathrm{d}x \rightarrow$ try (something)$^{\text{to some power}}$

**B10** Evaluate

$\int_{3}^{4} \frac{1}{(x-2)^3}\mathrm{d}x \rightarrow$ you are on your own here.

(We call this integration by inspection or, more often, 'informed guesswork'.)

If you find these last five questions awkward then don't worry – another method, 'integration by substitution', explained in 10.5 will boost your confidence for this type of integral.

## 10.3 Integrating algebraic fractions

### Key points

$$\int \frac{f'(x)}{f(x)}\mathrm{d}x = \ln|f(x)| + c$$

$\ln x$ is only defined for $x > 0$ so we need the modulus sign

When you are integrating a fraction always check to see if the numerator is the derivative of the denominator.

Note: Functions of the type $\frac{3}{(2x+1)(x-1)}$ need to be split into partial fractions first and then integrated

### Example 1

Find (a) $\int \frac{2}{3+2x}\mathrm{d}x$

(b) $\int_{0}^{1} \frac{x}{x^2+5}\mathrm{d}x$

**Solution**

(a) $\int \frac{2}{3 + 2x} dx = \ln|3 + 2x| + c$

modulus sign essential

(b) $\int_0^1 \frac{x}{x^2 + 5} dx$

You would prefer the numerator to be $2x$ here to have a straightforward 'ln' integral, so re-write the question as

$$\frac{1}{2}\int_0^1 \frac{2x}{x^2 + 5} dx = \frac{1}{2}\left[\ln(x^2 + 5)\right]_0^1$$

modulus signs omitted here as $x^2 + 5$ is always positive

$$= \frac{1}{2}(\ln 6 - \ln 5)$$

$$= \frac{1}{2}\ln\frac{6}{5}$$

$\ln a - \ln b = \ln\frac{a}{b}$

## Example 2

Show that $\int_1^2 \frac{2x + 13}{(2x - 1)(x + 3)} dx = \ln\left(\frac{36}{5}\right)$

**Solution**

First split into partial fractions.

$$\frac{2x + 13}{(2x - 1)(x + 3)} \equiv \frac{4}{2x - 1} - \frac{1}{x + 3}$$

Now the integral is much easier to deal with.

$$I = \int_1^2 \left(\frac{4}{2x - 1} - \frac{1}{x + 3}\right) dx = [2\ln|2x - 1| - \ln|x + 3|]_1^2$$

$$= (2\ln 3 - \ln 5) - (2\ln 1 - \ln 4)$$

$\ln 1 = 0$ remember

$$= 2\ln 3 - \ln 5 + \ln 4$$

$$= \ln 9 - \ln 5 + \ln 4$$

$$= \ln\frac{36}{5}$$

rules for logs here $a\ln x = \ln x^a$
$\ln a + \ln b = \ln ab$
$\ln a - \ln b = \ln\frac{a}{b}$

## Exercise 10.3

Remember, with fractions, always check to see if the numerator is the derivative of the denominator or is a multiple of that derivative.

**A1** Find $\int \frac{2}{2x + 3} dx$ (don't forget the mod sign)

## Exercise 10.3 *continued*

Now write down $\int \frac{72}{2x+3}dx$, $\int \frac{1}{2x+3}dx$, $\int \frac{6}{5(2x+3)}dx$.

**A2** Work out $\int \frac{3}{1-x}dx$ (be careful with the signs)

**A3** Find $\int \left(\frac{2}{x+3} - \frac{4}{1-x}\right)dx$

**A4** Find $\int \frac{2x+3}{x^2+3x+4}dx$

**A5** Find $\int \left(\frac{1}{3x-1} + \frac{3}{x-1}\right)dx$

Evaluate the following

**A6** (a) $\int_0^4 \frac{2}{x+3}dx$

(b) $\int_{-5}^{-2} \frac{3}{x+1}dx$

**A7** (a) $\int_1^3 \frac{5}{4-x}dx$

(b) $\int_3^6 \frac{3}{2-x}dx$

**A8** $\int_0^2 \frac{x}{x^2+4}dx$

**A9** $\int_{-1}^2 \frac{x^2}{x^3+4}dx$

**A10** $\int_0^2 \frac{6x^2+4x}{x^3+x^2+4}dx$

**B1** By writing $\frac{4}{4-x^2}$ in the form $\frac{A}{2+x} + \frac{B}{2-x}$ show that $\int_{-1}^1 \frac{4}{4-x^2}dx = 2\ln 3$ and write down the value of $\int_{-1}^1 \frac{1}{4-x^2}dx$.

**B2** Show that $\int_0^1 \frac{x}{4-x^2}dx = \frac{1}{2}\ln\frac{4}{3}$.

**B3** Split $\frac{5x+2}{x(x+1)}$ into partial fractions and then work out the values of $a$ and $b$ if $\int_2^3 \frac{5x+2}{x(x+1)} = \ln\frac{a}{b}$.

**B4** Show that $\int_0^1 \frac{1}{x^2+5x+6}dx = \ln\frac{9}{8}$ .

**B5** If $\int_a^b \frac{3}{2x-1}dx = \frac{3}{2}\ln 5$ and $b = 3a$ find the values of $a$.

**B6** If $\frac{x}{x+1} = A + \frac{B}{x+1}$ find $A$ and $B$ and then show that $\int_1^3 \frac{x}{x+1}dx = 2 - \ln 2$.

**B7** Evaluate $\int_2^3 \frac{2x+1}{x^2+x-3}dx$.

**B8** Find $\int_0^2 \frac{2x}{9-x^2}dx$ and $\int_0^2 \frac{3}{9-x^2}dx$.

Hence write down the value of $\int_0^2 \frac{2x+3}{9-x^2}dx$.

**B9** Show that $\frac{2x+3}{9-x^2}$ may be written in the

## Exercise 10.3 *continued*

form $\frac{1}{2}\left(\frac{A}{3-x} - \frac{B}{3+x}\right)$ where $A$ and $B$ are positive integers. Hence find

$$\int_0^2 \frac{2x+3}{9-x^2}\,dx.$$

**B10** Express $\frac{x^3+3x}{1+x^2}$ in the form $Ax + \frac{Bx}{1+x^2}$ and hence evaluate $\int_0^2 \frac{x^3+3x}{1+x^2}\,dx.$

## 10.4 Integration by parts

### Key points

$$\int u\frac{dv}{dx}\,dx = uv - \int v\frac{du}{dx}\,dx$$

this integral needs to be simpler than the one you started with

one part is differentiated and the other integrated

- You need to recognise the type of integral which leads to using 'parts'.
  $\int xe^x dx$, $\int x\sin x\,dx$, $\int x\ln x\,dx$, $\int x^2e^{2x}dx$, $\int x^2\cos x\,dx$ etc.
  Also $\int \ln x\,dx$, surprisingly.

More often than not the part differentiated is the term $x$ or $x^2$.

$\int x\ln x\,dx$ is an exception to this.

### Example 1

Find $\int xe^{2x}dx$

**Solution**

$\int xe^{2x}dx$ Let $u = x$ $\quad \frac{dv}{dx} = e^{2x}$

$\frac{du}{dx} = 1 \quad v = \frac{1}{2}e^{2x}$

the simplest value of $v$ when $c = 0$

Use the formula now

$$I = \int x\,e^{2x}dx = x\left(\frac{1}{2}e^{2x}\right) - \int\left(\frac{1}{2}e^{2x}\right)(1)\,dx$$

$$= \frac{1}{2}xe^{2x} - \frac{1}{2}\int e^{2x}dx$$

Always simplify the integral by taking constants outside

$$= \frac{1}{2}xe^{2x} - \frac{1}{4}e^{2x} + c$$

$$= \frac{1}{4}e^{2x}(2x-1) + c$$

## Example 2

Evaluate $\int_0^{\pi/2} x^2 \cos x \, dx$

**Solution**

Let $u = x^2 \qquad \Rightarrow \frac{du}{dx} = 2x$

Let $\frac{dv}{dx} = \cos x \qquad \Rightarrow v = \sin x$

So $I = \int_0^{\pi/2} x^2 \cos x \, dx$

$$= \left[x^2 \sin x\right]_0^{\pi/2} - \int_0^{\pi/2} (\sin x)(2x) \, dx$$

$$I = \left[\frac{\pi^2}{4}(1) - 0\right] - 2\int_0^{\pi/2} x \sin x \, dx$$

You have to use 'parts' for a second time to evaluate $\int x \sin x \, dx$.

Let $u = x \qquad \Rightarrow \frac{du}{dx} = 1$

Let $\frac{dv}{dx} = \sin x \qquad \Rightarrow v = -\cos x$

So $\int_0^{\pi/2} x \sin x \, dx = \left[x(-\cos x)\right]_0^{\pi/2} - \int_0^{\pi/2} (-\cos x)(1) \, dx$

$$= (0 - 0) + \left[\sin x\right]_0^{\pi/2}$$

$$= 0 + (1 - 0)$$

$$= 1$$

So $I = \frac{\pi^2}{4} - 2$.

## Exercise 10.4

Integrate the following

**A1** $\int x e^{-2x} dx$

**A2** $\int x \ln x \, dx$

**A3** $\int \frac{x}{e^x} dx$

**A4** $\int x^4 \ln x \, dx$

**A5** $\int x \sin x \, dx$

**A6** $\int (x + 2) e^x dx$

**A7** $\int x e^{x+2} dx$

## Exercise 10.4 *continued*

Evaluate

**A8** $\int_0^1 xe^x dx$

**A9** $\int_0^{\pi/2} x\cos x dx$

**A10** $\int_1^e x^2 \ln x dx$

Find

**B1** $\int x\sin 2x dx$

**B2** $\int x\cos 2x dx$

**B3** $\int 3xe^{3x} dx$

**B4** $\int x^2 e^x dx$ (you will have to use 'parts' twice here)

**B5** If $I = \int e^x \sin x dx$ use 'parts' twice to find an expression for $2I$ and hence $I$.

Evaluate

**B6** $\int_1^{e^2} (1)\ln x dx$

**B7** $\int_1^e \frac{1}{x^3}\ln x dx$ $\left(\text{hint: } \frac{d}{dx}(x^{-2}) = ?\right)$

**B8** $\int_0^{\pi/3} x^2 \sin x dx$

**B9** $\int x(x-2)^3 dx$

(Hint: $\frac{d}{dx}(x-2)^4$ may help you.)

**B10** $\int_0^3 x(x-3)^4 dx$

## 10.5 Integration by substitution

The examiners will usually tell you when an integration requires the method of substitution by giving you a sensible substitution to use.

This substitution will change what appears to be a very difficult or awkward integral into a much more simple one.

Integrals will usually be of the type

$$\int (x+4)^6 dx,\ \int \frac{1}{(x+4)^6} dx,\ \int x\sqrt{x^2+4} dx,\ \int \frac{x}{\sqrt{x^2+4}} dx,\ \int \frac{x+1}{x-1} dx,$$
$$\int \frac{x}{(4x+1)^2} dx$$

### Key points

The substitution changes $\int_{x \text{ limits}} f(x)dx$ into $\int_{u \text{ limits}} g(u)du$

where a relation between $u$ and $x$ has been given.

## Example 1

(a) Integrate $\int \frac{1}{(x+2)^3}\,\mathrm{d}x$

(b) Evaluate $\int_{x=2}^{x=3} (2x-3)^5\,\mathrm{d}x$

### Solution

(a) Let $u = x + 2$

$$\frac{\mathrm{d}u}{\mathrm{d}x} = 1$$

'$\mathrm{d}u = \mathrm{d}x$'

So the integral becomes

$$\int \frac{1}{u^3}\,\mathrm{d}u = \frac{u^{-2}}{-2} + c = -\frac{1}{2u^2} + c$$

$$= -\frac{1}{2(x+2)^2} + c$$

You must substitute back into $x$ terms

(b) Let $u = 2x - 3$

$$\frac{\mathrm{d}u}{\mathrm{d}x} = 2$$

So '$\frac{1}{2}\mathrm{d}u = \mathrm{d}x$'

When $x = 2$, $u = 1$,
$x = 3$, $u = 3$

The integral becomes

$$\int_{u=1}^{u=3} u^5\left(\frac{1}{2}\mathrm{d}u\right) = \frac{1}{2}\int_1^3 u^5\mathrm{d}u$$

$$= \frac{1}{2}\left[\frac{u^6}{6}\right]_1^3$$

$$= \frac{1}{2}\left[\frac{3^6}{6} - \frac{1}{6}\right]$$

$$= 60\tfrac{2}{3}$$

## Example 2(a)

Evaluate $I = \int_0^2 \frac{x}{x+3}\,\mathrm{d}x$

### Solution

Let $u = x + 3$

$$\frac{\mathrm{d}u}{\mathrm{d}x} = 1 \Rightarrow \text{'}\mathrm{d}u = \mathrm{d}x\text{'}$$

When $x = 0$, $u = 3$

$x = 2$, $u = 5$

$$\text{So } I = \int_{u=3}^{u=5} \frac{u-3}{u}\,\mathrm{d}u$$

$$= \int_3^5 \left(1 - \frac{3}{u}\right)\mathrm{d}u$$

$$= \left[u - 3\ln|u|\right]_3^5$$
$$= (5 - 3\ln5) - (3 - 3\ln3)$$
$$= 2 - 3\ln5 + 3\ln3$$
$$= 2 + 3(\ln3 - \ln5)$$
$$= 2 + 3\ln\frac{3}{5}\left(\text{or } 2 - 3\ln\frac{5}{3}\right)$$

## Example 2(b)

Show that $\int_0^1 \frac{x}{\sqrt{2 - x^2}}dx = \sqrt{2} - 1$

### Solution

We need to make the integral more simple so let $u = 2 - x^2$

$$\frac{du}{dx} = -2x$$

'$du = -2xdx$'

$-\frac{1}{2}du = xdx$

When $x = 0$, $u = 2$

$x = 1$, $u = 1$

So the integral becomes

$$\int_{u=2}^{u=1} \frac{-\frac{1}{2}du}{\sqrt{u}} = -\frac{1}{2}\int_2^1 u^{-\frac{1}{2}}du = -\frac{1}{2}\left[2u^{\frac{1}{2}}\right]_2^1 = -\frac{1}{2}\left[2 - 2\sqrt{2}\right]$$

this could also be written as $+\frac{1}{2}\int_1^2 u^{-\frac{1}{2}}du$

$$= -1 + \sqrt{2}$$

which is the required result.

**Sometimes the substitutions you have to use are given in parametric form**

If $x = f(t)$ and $y = g(t)$

as $\frac{dx}{dt} = f'(t)$ so '$dx = f'(t)dt$'

then $\int_{x=x_1}^{x=x_2} ydx = \int_{t=t_1}^{t=t_2} g(t)f'(t)dt$ where $x_1 = f(t_1)$ and $x_2 = f(t_2)$

## Example 3

If $y = 2t$ and $x = t^2$ $(t > 0)$ find $I = \int_{x=0}^{x=4} ydx$

**Solution**

$\frac{dx}{dt} = 2t$ i.e. '$dx = 2tdt$'

When $x = 0$, $t = 0$

When $x = 4$, $t = 2$ as $t > 0$

$$\text{Hence } I = \int_{t=0}^{t=2} 2t(2tdt) = 4\int_0^2 t^2dt$$

$$= 4\left[\frac{t^3}{3}\right]_0^2 = \frac{32}{3}$$

## Exercise 10.5

Integrate the following using the given substitutions

In **A3–A5** try to check your answers by differentiation using the chain rule if necessary.

**A1** $\int \frac{x}{x+3}dx$ (let $u = x + 3$)

**A2** $\int \frac{x}{2x+3}dx$ (let $u = 2x + 3$)

**A3** $\int (3x+1)^5dx$ (let $z = 3x + 1$)

**A4** $\int \sqrt{2x-1}dx$ (let $z = 2x - 1$)

**A5** $\int \frac{1}{\sqrt{2x-1}}dx$ (let $z = 2x - 1$)

Evaluate the following integrals

**B1** $\int_0^1 (4x+1)^4dx$ (let $u = 4x + 1$)

**B2** $\int_0^1 x(x^2+3)dx$ (let $z = x^2 + 3$)

**B3** $\int_0^{\pi/2} \sin^2x\cos x dx$ (let $z = \sin x$)

**B4** $\int_0^{1/2} \frac{x}{\sqrt{1-x^2}}dx$ (let $u = 1 - x^2$)

**B5** $\int_{e^2}^{e^3} \frac{1}{x\ln x}dx$ (let $z = \ln x$)

**B6** If $y = t^3$ and $x = \frac{1}{t}$ find $\int_{x=1}^{x=2} ydx$

**B7** If $y = 3t^2$ and $x = 2t$ find $\int_{x=2}^{x=4} y^2dx$

In the examination it is likely that you will be given a suitable substitution to use. These next five questions are to help you in case the examiners are particularly mean!

Evaluate

**B8** $\int_0^1 \frac{x}{(1+x^2)^3}dx$

**B9** $\int_0^4 x\sqrt{x^2+9}dx$

**B10** $\int_0^1 x(x-1)^4dx$

**B11** $\int_0^2 \frac{x}{(2x+1)^3}dx$

**B12** $\int_0^2 \frac{x^2}{\sqrt{1+x^3}}dx$

## 10.6 More difficult integrals using trigonometrical functions

In this section you will be challenged to work out integrals of the more difficult trigonometrical functions using familiar trigonometrical identities and the techniques of integration covered so far.

### Key points

You need to be familiar with these formulae

$$\cos 2x = 2\cos^2 x - 1 \qquad \cos^2 x = \frac{1}{2}(1 + \cos 2x)$$

$$= 1 - 2\sin^2 x$$

$$\sin 2x = 2\sin x\cos x \qquad \sin^2 x = \frac{1}{2}(1 - \cos 2x)$$

Also remember that $\sin^2 x + \cos^2 x = 1$ and $\sec^2 x = 1 + \tan^2 x$

### Example 1

Find $\int \sin x \cos x \, dx$

**Solution**

*Method 1*

$$\int \sin x \cos x \, dx = \frac{1}{2}\int \sin 2x \, dx$$

$$= \frac{1}{2}\left(-\frac{1}{2}\cos 2x\right) + c$$

$$= -\frac{1}{4}\cos 2x + c$$

(This is the easier method if you can spot it.)

You could try to solve this integral using 'integration by parts' if you wanted a challenge!

*Method 2* Substitution.

$$\int \sin x \cos x \, dx \qquad \text{Let } u = \sin x$$

$$= \int \sin x(\cos x \, dx) \qquad \frac{du}{dx} = \cos x$$

$$= \int u \, du \qquad \text{“}du = \cos x \, dx\text{”}$$

$$= \frac{u^2}{2} + c$$

$$= \frac{\sin^2 x}{2} + c$$

$= \frac{1}{4}(1 - \cos 2x) + c$

$= -\frac{1}{4}\cos 2x + k$

to be in the same form as method 1

### Example 2

Find (a) $\int \frac{\cos x}{2 + \sin x} dx$ (b) $\int \cos^3 x \, dx$

**Solution**

(a) $I = \int \frac{\cos x}{2 + \sin x} dx$

Let $u = 2 + \sin x$

$\frac{du}{dx} = \cos x$

'$du = \cos x dx$'

$I = \int \frac{(\cos x dx)}{2 + \sin x}$

$= \int \frac{du}{u} = \ln|u| + c$

$= \ln|2 + \sin x| + c$

You may have spotted this as $\int \frac{f'(x)}{f(x)} dx$ which gives a simpler solution

(b) $I = \int \cos^3 x dx$

$= \int \cos^2 x \cos x dx$

$= \int (1 - \sin^2 x)\cos x dx$

If $u = \sin x$
'$du = \cos x dx$'

$I = \int (1 - u^2) du$

$= u - \frac{u^3}{3} + c$

$= \cos x - \frac{1}{3}\cos^3 x + c$

## Exercise 10.6

**B1** Find $\int_0^{\pi/2} \frac{\cos x}{(1 + \sin x)^2} dx$ (The substitution $z = 1 + \sin x$ may help)

**B2** Find $\int_0^{\pi/3} \frac{\sin x}{3 - 2\cos x} dx$

**B3** Express $\tan^2 x$ in terms of $\sec x$.

Hence find $\int_0^{\pi/4} \tan^2 x dx$

**B4** (a) Find $\int_0^{\pi/4} \frac{\sin x}{\cos x} dx$

(b) Find $\int_0^{\pi/3} \tan x dx$

(c) $\int_{\pi/6}^{\pi/2} \cot x dx$

**B5** (a) Find $\frac{d}{dx}(\sin^2 x)$ (use the product rule)

(b) Find $\int_0^{\pi/2} \frac{\sin x \cos x}{1 + \sin^2 x} dx$ (part (a) should help)

**B6** Use the substitution $x = \tan z$ to calculate $\int_0^1 \frac{1}{1 + x^2} dx$

**B7** Use the substitution $x = \sin z$ to calculate $\int_0^{\frac{1}{2}} \frac{1}{\sqrt{1 - x^2}} dx$

**B8** Use the substitution $z = \sin x$ to find

$\int_0^{\pi/6} \sin^4 x \cos x dx$

Now use an appropriate substitution to find

$\int_0^{\pi/3} \cos^5 x \sin x dx$

**B9** If $z = \sin x + \cos x$ write down the value of $\frac{dz}{dx}$

## Exercise 10.6 *continued*

Find

(a) $\int_0^{\pi/4} \frac{\cos x - \sin x}{\sin x + \cos x} dx$

(b) $\int_0^{\pi/2} \frac{\cos x - \sin x}{(\sin x + \cos x)^2} dx$

**B10** Use the facts that (a) $\sin^2 x + \cos^2 x = 1$ and (b) $\cos^2 x - \sin^2 x = \cos 2x$ to write $\sin^2 x$ in terms of $\cos 2x$.

Hence find $\int_0^{\pi/2} \sin^2 x dx$

Find also $\int_0^{\pi/2} (\sin^2 x + \cos^2 x) dx$ and hence obtain the value of $\int_0^{\pi/2} \cos^2 x dx$.

## Chapter 10: A level questions

**C1** (a) Show that $\frac{x^2}{x^2 - 4} = A + \frac{B}{x^2 - 4}$ where $A$ and $B$ are to be found.

(b) Write $\frac{B}{x^2 - 4}$, with your value of $B$, in partial fractions.

(c) Show that

$$\int_3^4 \frac{x^2}{x^2 - 4} dx = 1 + \ln\frac{5}{3} = \ln\frac{5e}{3}$$

**C2** (a) Use the 'quotient' rule to show that

$$\frac{d}{dx}(\cot x) = -\operatorname{cosec}^2 x$$

(b) Find $\int_{\pi/6}^{\pi/3} \operatorname{cosec}^2 x dx$

**C3** (a) Use the formula $\cos(A + B) = \cos A \cos B - \sin A \sin B$ to find an expression for $\cos 2x$ and use the formula $\sin(A + B) = \sin A \cos B + \sin B \cos A$ to find an expression for $\sin 2x$.

(b) By writing $\cos 3x$ as $\cos(2x + x)$ show that $\cos 3x = 4\cos^3 x - 3\cos x$

(c) Find $\int_0^{\pi/6} \cos 3x \sin x dx$ by using a suitable substitution.

**C4** Use the substitution $x = \sin z$ to evaluate

$$\int_0^{\frac{1}{2}} \frac{x^2}{\sqrt{1 - x^2}} dx$$

**C5** Find $\int_{\pi/6}^{\pi/4} \frac{\sin x \cos x}{1 - \cos^2 x} dx$

**C6** (a) Use the formula $\sin(A + B) = \sin A \cos B + \sin B \cos A$ to find an expression for $\sin 2x$.

(b) Evaluate the integral $\int_0^{\pi/4} x \sin x \cos x dx$ using the method of integration by 'parts'.

**C7** (a) By using the substitution $z = \ln x$, or otherwise, find $\frac{d}{dx}(\ln x)^2$

(b) Find $\int_1^{e^2} \frac{1}{x} \ln x dx$

(c) Write $\frac{1}{x} \ln\left(\frac{1}{x}\right)$ in terms of $x$ and $\ln x$ and then write down, or obtain, the value of $\int_1^{e^2} \frac{1}{x} \ln\left(\frac{1}{x}\right) dx$

## Chapter 10: A level questions *continued*

**C8** Find

(a) $\int_1^3 10x^{\frac{3}{2}}\,dx$ (b) $\int_3^4 \left(\frac{2}{\sqrt{x}} + 3\sqrt{x}\right)dx$

and in both cases give your answer in the form $a + b\sqrt{3}$ where $a$ and $b$ are integers to be stated.

**C9** (a) Use the formula for $\cos(A + B)$ to show that $\cos 2x = 2\cos^2 x - 1$

(b) Find $\int \cos^2 x\,dx$

(c) Show that $\int_0^{\pi/2} x\cos^2 x\,dx = \frac{1}{16}(\pi^2 - 4)$

by using integration by parts.

**C10** (a) Use the substitution $z = ax^2 + b$ to find the derivative of $\ln(ax^2 + b)$ where $a$, $b$ are constants.

(b) Show that $\frac{2x^3 + 20x}{x^4 + 2x^2 - 8}$ can be written in the form $\frac{Ax}{x^2 - 2} - \frac{Bx}{x^2+4}$

where $A$ and $B$ are positive integers whose values should be stated.

(c) Show that

$$2\int_2^3 \frac{x^3 + 10x}{x^4 + 2x^2 - 8}\,dx = \ln\left(\frac{98}{13}\right)$$

# Chapter 11

## INTEGRATION 2

### 11.1 Areas

**Key points**

(a) In the diagram if $y \geqslant 0$ and $y$ is a function of $x$ then $A = \int_{x=a}^{x=b} y\,\mathrm{d}x$

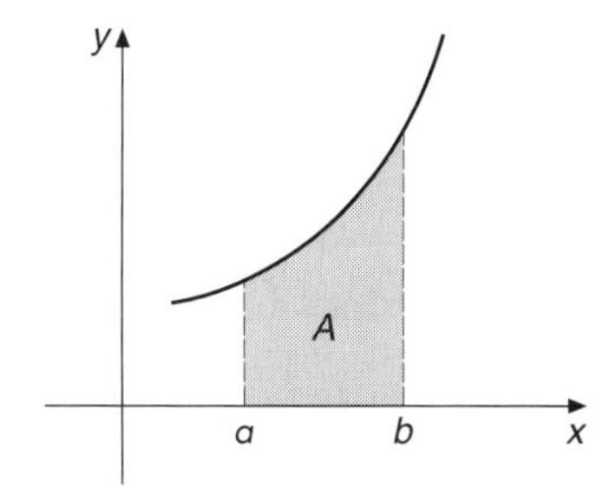


(b) In the diagram if $y \leqslant 0$ and $y$ is a function of $x$ then $A = -\int_{x=c}^{x=d} y\,\mathrm{d}x$

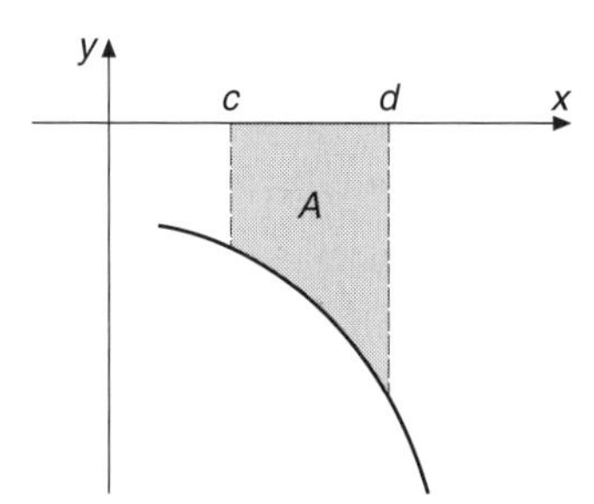


(c) In the diagram if $x \geqslant 0$ and $x$ is a function of $y$ then $A = \int_{y=y_1}^{y=y_2} x\,\mathrm{d}y$

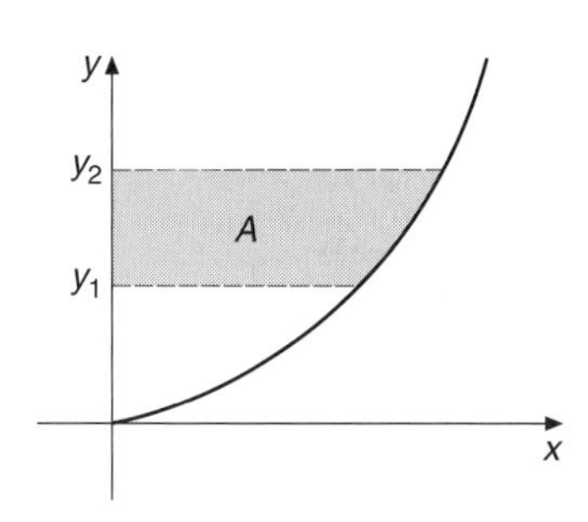

## Example 1

Find the area enclosed by the curve $y = (1 - x)(x - 4)$ and the $x$ axis.

**Solution**

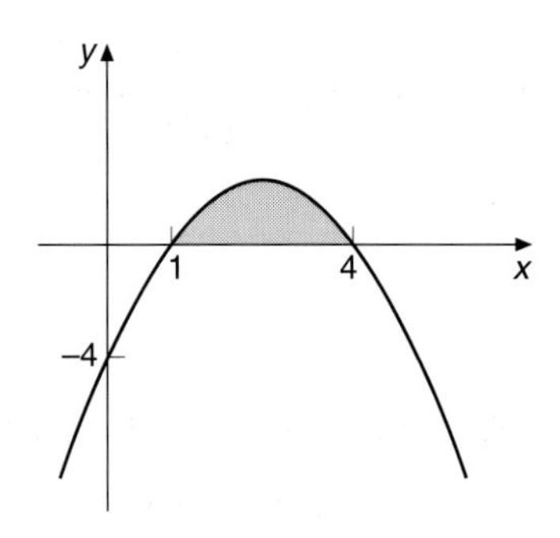


$$\text{The shaded area} = \int_{x=1}^{x=4} (1 - x)(x - 4)\,dx$$

$$= \int_1^4 (-4 + 5x - x^2)\,dx$$

$$= \left[-4x + \frac{5x^2}{2} - \frac{x^3}{3}\right]_1^4 = \left(2\frac{2}{3}\right) - \left(-1\frac{5}{6}\right) = 4\frac{1}{2}$$

## Example 2

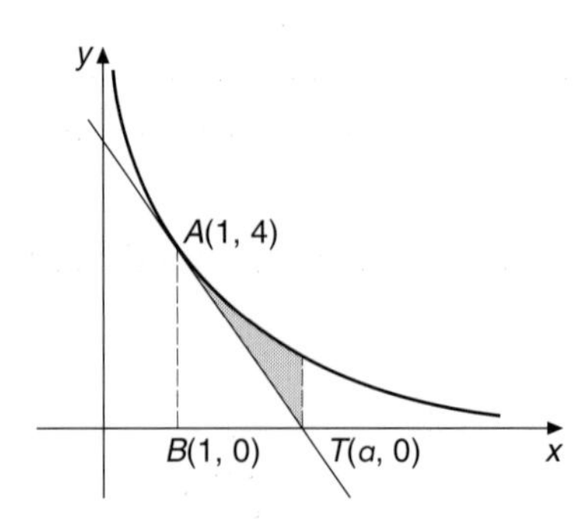


The diagram shows the tangent to the curve $y = \dfrac{4}{x}$ at the point $A(1,4)$.

The tangent meets the $x$ axis at $T(a,0)$.

Find the area bounded by the tangent, the curve and the line $x = a$.

**Solution**

$$y = \frac{4}{x}$$

$$\frac{dy}{dx} = \frac{-4}{x^2}$$

The gradient of the tangent at $A(1,4)$ is $\dfrac{-4}{(1)^2} = -4$

So the equation of the tangent is

$$y - 4 = -4(x - 1)$$

$$y = -4x + 8$$

The tangent meets the $x$ axis when $y = 0$ i.e. when $x = 2$.

The required shaded area is given by the area under the curve between $x = 1$ and $x = 2$ minus the area of $\Delta ABT$

$$\text{So Area} = \int_{x=1}^{x=2} y\,dx - \text{area } \Delta ABT$$

$$= \int_1^2 \frac{4}{x}dx - \frac{1}{2}(BT)(AB)$$

alternatively the area of $\Delta ABT = \int_1^2 (-4x + 8)dx$

$$= \Big[4\ln|x|\Big]_1^2 - \frac{1}{2}(1)(4)$$

$$= 4\ln2 - 4\ln1 - 2$$

$$= 4\ln2 - 2$$

$$= 2(2\ln2 - 1)$$

## Example 3

The diagram shows a sketch of the curve $x = 2t$, $y = t^2 + 1$ where $t$ is a parameter.

Points $A(2,2)$ and $B(6,10)$ lie on the curve. Find the shaded area.

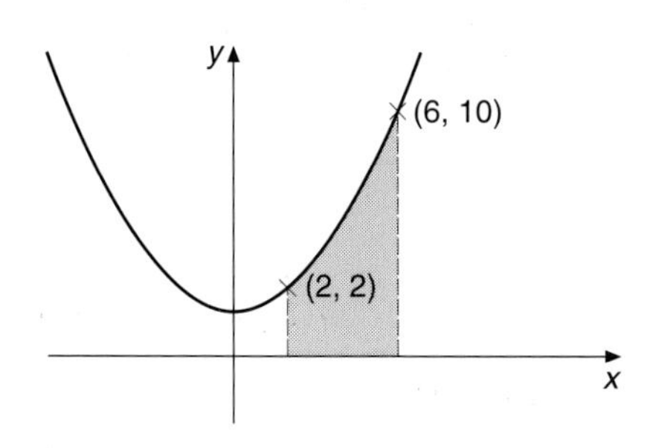

**Solution**

At (2,2), $t = 1$
At (6,10), $t = 3$

We need $A = \int_{x=2}^{x=6} y\,\mathrm{d}x$

But $y = t^2 + 1$ and $x = 2t$

so $\frac{\mathrm{d}x}{\mathrm{d}t} = 2$, '$\mathrm{d}x = 2\mathrm{d}t$'

When $x = 2$, $t = 1$, when $x = 6$, $t = 3$

$$\therefore A = \int_{t=1}^{t=3} (t^2 + 1)2\mathrm{d}t = \left[\frac{2t^3}{3} + 2t\right]_1^3$$

$$= (24) - (2\tfrac{2}{3})$$

$$= 21\tfrac{1}{3}$$

N.B. When a question is given using parameters it is usually better to work with these parameters rather than converting to the Cartesian equation of the curve.

The integration uses the method of 'substitution'.

In this particular example, conversion to the Cartesian equation is quicker. You have $t = \frac{x}{2}$ which gives $y = \frac{x^2}{4} + 1$.

$$\text{Hence the required area} = \int_{x=2}^{x=6} \left(\frac{x^2}{4} + 1\right)\mathrm{d}x$$

$$= \left[\frac{x^3}{12} + x\right]_2^6$$

$$= (18 + 6) - (\tfrac{2}{3} + 2)$$

$$= 24 - 2\tfrac{2}{3}$$

$$= 21\tfrac{1}{3}$$

## Exercise 11.1

**A1** Find the area enclosed by the curve, the $x$ axis and the given lines

(a) $y = x^2 + 2x,\ x, = 1,\ x = 3$

(b) $y = (3x - 2)^2,\ x, = 0,\ x = \frac{2}{3}$

(c) $y = x^3 + 4x,\ x = 2,\ x = 4$

(d) $y = \frac{4}{x},\ x = \frac{1}{2},\ x = 2$

(e) $y = 3\sin x,\ x = \frac{\pi}{6},\ x = \frac{5\pi}{6}$

## Exercise 11.1 *continued*

**A2** Find the area enclosed by the curve, the $y$ axis and the given lines

(a) $x = y^2 + 2y, \quad y = 1, y = 3$

(b) $x = (y + 2)^2, \quad y = 0, y = 1$

(c) $x = 2 + \cos y, \quad y = 0, y = \pi$

**A3** Obtain the $x$ coordinates of the points of intersection of the graph of $y = 4x - x^2$ with the $x$ axis. Sketch the curve and then find the area enclosed between the curve and the $x$ axis.

**A4** Calculate the area

(a) between the curve $y = \sqrt{x}$, the $x$ axis and the lines $x = 1$ and $x = 9$

(b) between the curve $y = \dfrac{1}{\sqrt{x}}$, the $x$ axis and the lines $x = 1$ and $x = 9$

(c) Write down the value of

$$\int_1^9 \left(\sqrt{x} - \frac{1}{\sqrt{x}}\right) dx$$

**A5** Find the coordinates of the points of intersection of the line $y = 5x$ and the curve $y = x^2$. Sketch the situation and find the area of the region between the line and the curve.

**A6** (a) Find $\displaystyle\int_0^{\pi/2} \sin x \, dx$ and illustrate this area on a graph for domain $0 \leqslant x \leqslant \dfrac{\pi}{2}$

(b) Find the value of $\alpha \left(0 \leqslant \alpha \leqslant \dfrac{\pi}{2}\right)$ such that the area enclosed by $y = \sin x$ and the lines $y = 0, x = \alpha, x = \dfrac{\pi}{2}$ is half the area found in (i).

**A7** Sketch the curve $y = (x + 2)(x - 1)^2$ and find the area of the finite region bounded by the axes and the curve when

(a) $x$ is negative

(b) $x$ is positive

**A8**

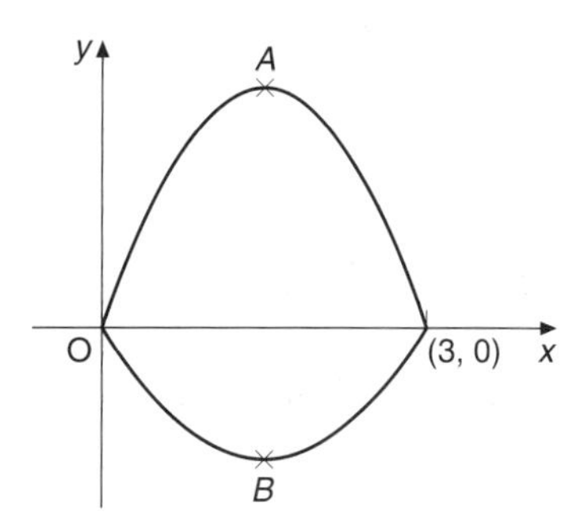


The sketch shows the graphs of $y = x^2 - 3x$ and $y = 6x - 2x^2$ for $0 \leqslant x \leqslant 3$

(a) Write down the coordinates of $A$ and $B$

(b) Find the area between the graphs.

**A9**

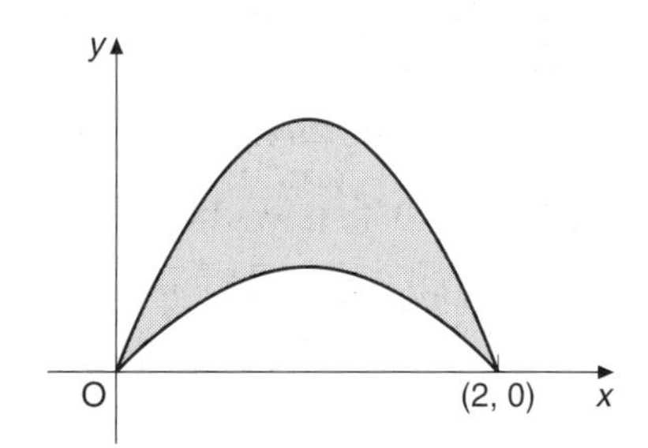


The sketch shows parts of the graphs of $y = 2x - x^2$ and $y = 4x - x^3$.

(a) Which is the 'upper' curve?

(b) Calculate the shaded area.

**A10**

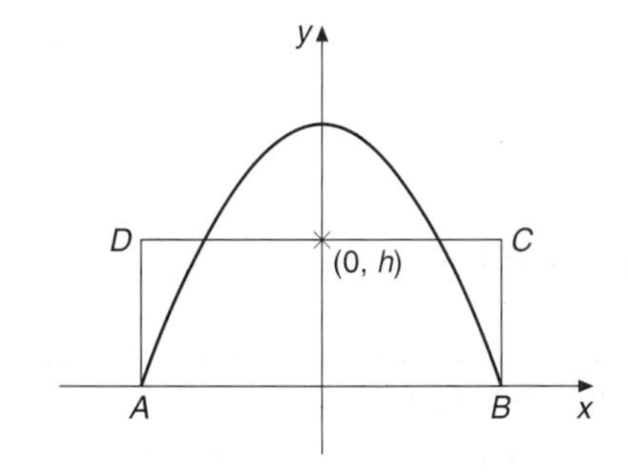

## Exercise 11.1 *continued*

The graph of $y = 9 - x^2$ intersects the $x$ axis at $A$ and $B$ and ABCD is a rectangle, height $h$, as shown in the diagram.

Find

(a) the coordinates of the points $A$ and $B$

(b) the area of the region bounded by the curve and the $x$ axis

(c) the value of $h$ if the area of the rectangle is equal to the area of the region found in part (ii).

**B1** The line $y = 2x$ divides the area enclosed by the curve $y = 4x - x^2$ and the $x$ axis into two parts. Find the ratio of the smaller area to the larger area.

**B2** Show that the line $2y = x + 1$ is a tangent to the curve $y = \sqrt{x}$ at the point (1,1). Sketch the situation and shade the area enclosed by the line, the curve and the $x$ axis. Find this shaded area.

**B3** (a) Obtain the derivative of $x\ln x$ $(x > 0)$ and hence find $\int \ln x \, dx$

(b) Sketch the graph of $y = \ln x$ $(x > 0)$

(c) Show that the area bounded by the curve $y = \ln x$, the $x$ axis and the lines $x = 2$, $x = 4$ may be written as $6\ln 2 - 2$

(d) Find the area between the curve $y = \ln x$, the $x$ axis and the line $x = \frac{1}{2}$.

**B4**

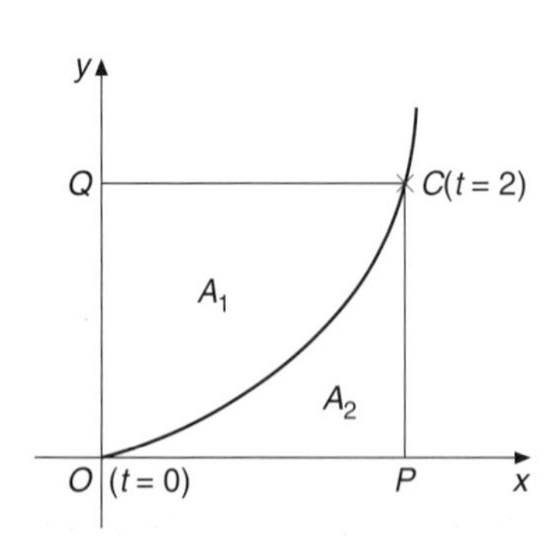


The diagram is a sketch of part of the curve given parametrically by $x = t^2$, $y = t^3$. Points $O$ and $C$ on the curve have parameters $t = 0$ and $t = 2$. $OPCQ$ is a rectangle.

Show that area $A_1$ is 12.8 and that $A_2 = \dfrac{3}{2}A_1$.

**B5** Find $\int_0^2 e^x dx$ giving an exact answer in terms of e.

State the geometrical transformations needed to obtain the graphs of

(a) $y = e^x - 1$

(b) $y = e^{x-2}$

from the graph of $y = e^x$.

Hence, or otherwise, obtain $\int_0^2 (e^x - 1)dx$ and $\int_2^4 e^{x-2}dx$.

**B6** The equation of a curve is $x = 3t^2$, $y = 6t$ where $t$ is a parameter. At point $A$, $t = 1$ and at point $B$, $t = 3$.

(a) Use parametric integration to find the area of the region bounded by the curve, the $x$ axis and lines parallel to the $y$ axis through $A$ and $B$.

(b) Find the area of the region bounded by the curve, the $y$ axis and lines parallel to the $x$ axis through $A$ and $B$.

(c) Show that the ratio of the areas is 2 : 1

**B7** A curve $E$ has equation $x = 2\cos\theta$, $y = \sin\theta$ where $\theta$ is a parameter with $0 \leqslant \theta \leqslant \dfrac{\pi}{2}$.

Show that the shaded area is $\int_{\pi/2}^{0} -2\sin^2\theta \, d\theta$

and establish that this area is $\dfrac{\pi}{2}$.

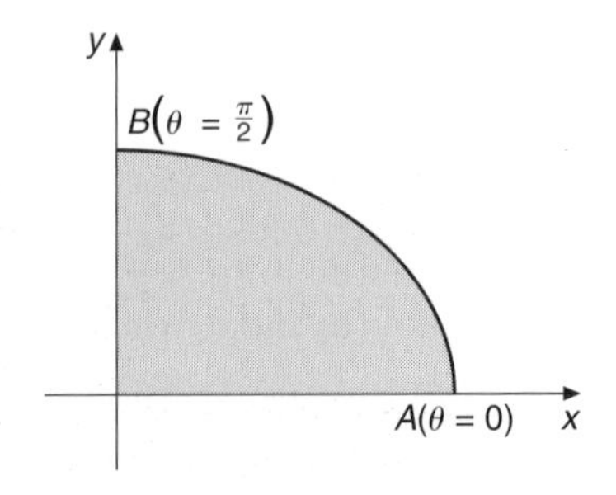

## Exercise 11.1 *continued*

**B8**

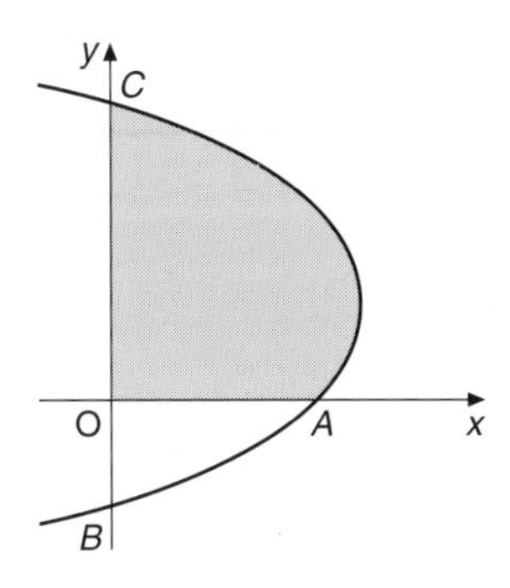


The diagram shows a sketch of $x = (4 - y)(1 + y)$

(a) Write down the coordinates of $A$, $B$ and $C$

(b) Find the shaded area

**B9** (a) Find the coordinates of the points of intersection of the curves $y = x^2 - 3x$ and $y = 5x - x^2$

(b) Sketch the curves on the same axes

(c) Calculate the area of the region between the curves.

**B10**

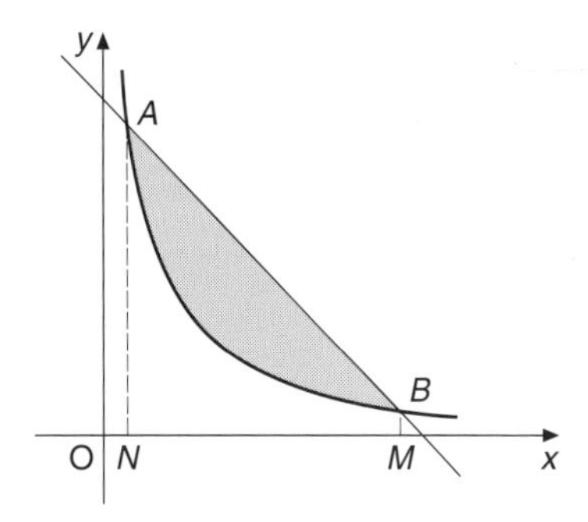


The diagram shows a sketch of the line $y = 5 - 2x$ and the curve $y = \frac{2}{x}$ with points of intersection at $A$ and $B$.

(a) Show that the $x$ coordinate of $B$ is 2 and hence find the coordinates of both $A$ and $B$

(b) Show that the area of trapezium $NMBA$ is $\frac{15}{4}$

(c) Calculate the shaded area.

## 11.2 Volumes of revolution

### Key points

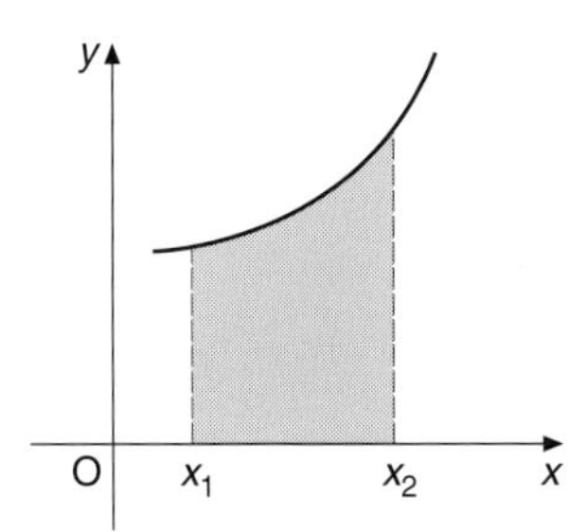


If $y$ is a function of $x$ then if the shaded area is rotated 360° about the $x$ axis, the volume generated is given by

$$V = \pi \int_{x=x_1}^{x=x_2} y^2 \mathrm{d}x$$

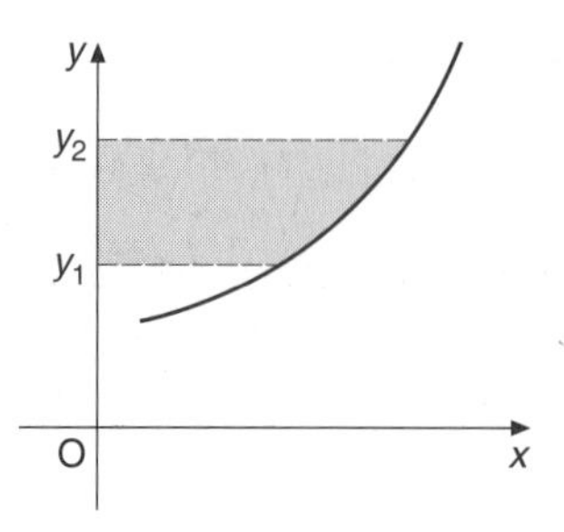


Similarly if the shaded area is rotated about the $y$ axis then

$$V = \pi \int_{y=y_1}^{y=y_2} x^2 \, dy$$

## Example 1

The diagram shows the graph of $y = e^{2x} + 1$. Find the volume generated when the shaded area is rotated through 360° about the $x$ axis.

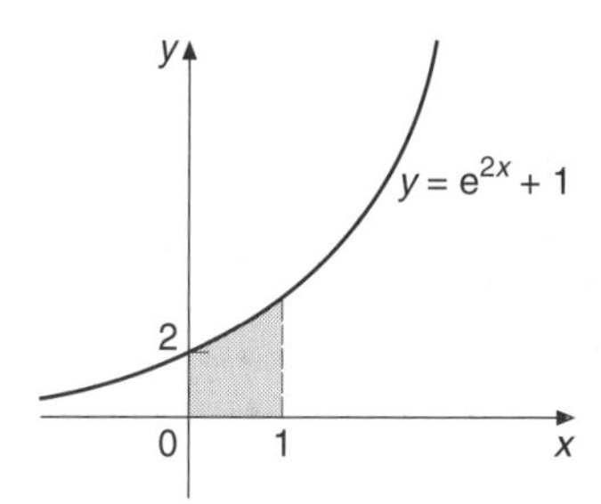


### Solution

$$V = \pi \int_{x=0}^{x=1} y^2 dx$$

$$V = \pi \int_0^1 (e^{2x} + 1)^2 dx$$

$$= \pi \int_0^1 (e^{4x} + 2e^{2x} + 1) dx$$

$$= \left[\frac{1}{4}e^{4x} + e^{2x} + x\right]_0^1$$

$$= \left(\frac{1}{4}e^4 + e^2 + 1\right) - \left(\frac{1}{4} + 1\right)$$

$$= \frac{1}{4}e^4 + e^2 - \frac{1}{4}$$

## Example 2

The diagram shows the curve given by $x = 2t$, $y = \dfrac{2}{t}$ where $t$ is a parameter. The area between the curve, the $x$ axis and the lines $x = 1$ and $x = 4$ is shaded on the diagram. If this area is rotated through $2\pi$ radians about the $x$ axis find the volume of the solid formed.

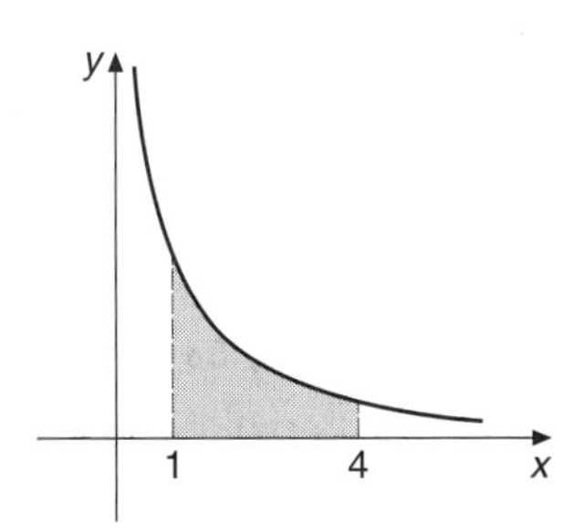


### Solution

$$V = \pi \int_{x=1}^{x=4} y^2 \mathrm{d}x$$

$x = 2t$
'$\mathrm{d}x = 2\mathrm{d}t$'

$$V = \pi \int_{t=\frac{1}{2}}^{t=2} \left(\frac{2}{t}\right)^2 2\mathrm{d}t$$

don't forget to change the limits

$$V = 8\pi \int_{\frac{1}{2}}^{2} \frac{1}{t^2} \mathrm{d}t$$

$$= 8\pi \int_{\frac{1}{2}}^{2} t^{-2} \mathrm{d}t$$

$$= 8\pi \left[-\frac{1}{t}\right]_{\frac{1}{2}}^{2}$$

$$= 8\pi \left[\left(-\frac{1}{2}\right) - (-2)\right]$$

$$= 8\pi \left(\frac{3}{2}\right)$$

$$= 12\pi$$

## Exercise 11.2

**A1** Find the volume generated when the region bounded by the given curve, the $x$ axis and the two lines is rotated through 360° about the $x$ axis.

(a) $y = 2\sqrt{x}$, $x = 2$, $x = 5$

(b) $y = 4 - \sqrt{x}$, $x = 1$, $x = 4$

(c) $y = x^2$, $x = 1$, $x = 2$

## Exercise 11.2 *continued*

(d) $y = x + \dfrac{2}{x}$, $x = 1$, $x = 3$

(e) $y = 2 - e^{-x}$, $x = 0$, $x = 1$

**A2** Find the volume generated when the region bounded by the given curve, the $y$ axis and the two lines is rotated through a full turn about the $y$ axis

(a) $x = 2\sqrt{y}$, $y = 2$, $y = 5$

(b) $y = 2\sqrt{x}$, $y = 1$, $y = 2$

(c) $y = \ln x$, $y = 0$, $y = 2$.

**A3** (a) Show that $2\sin^2 x = 1 - \cos 2x$ using the formula for $\cos(A + B)$

(b) The region bounded by the curve $y = 2\sin x$, $0 \leqslant x \leqslant \pi$ and the $x$ axis is rotated through 360° about the $x$ axis. Show that the volume generated is $2\pi^2$.

**A4** The area between the graph of $y = x^2 - 1$ and the $x$ axis is rotated through $2\pi$ radians about the $x$ axis. Show that the solid formed has a volume equal to that of a sphere of radius $\left(\dfrac{4}{5}\right)^{\frac{1}{3}}$.

$\left(\text{Hint: the volume of a sphere is } \dfrac{4}{3}\pi r^3\right)$

**A5** By considering rotating an appropriate area between the line $4y = 3x$ and the $x$ axis establish the volume of a cone, base radius 3 and height 4.

**B1**

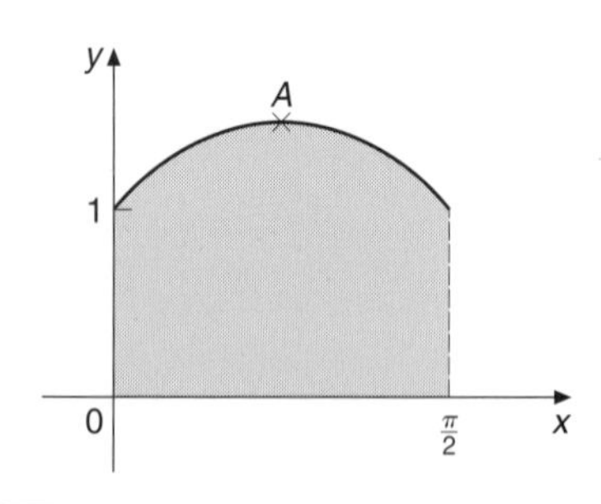


The diagram is a sketch of $y = \sin x + \cos x$, $0 \leqslant x \leqslant \dfrac{\pi}{2}$

(a) At $A$, $x = \dfrac{\pi}{4}$. Confirm that $A$ is a maximum point

(b) Calculate the shaded area

(c) Calculate the volume of revolution when this area $\left(\text{bounded by } y = \sin x + \cos x, \text{ the axes and the line } x = \dfrac{\pi}{2}\right)$ is rotated through 360° about the $x$ axis.

**B2**

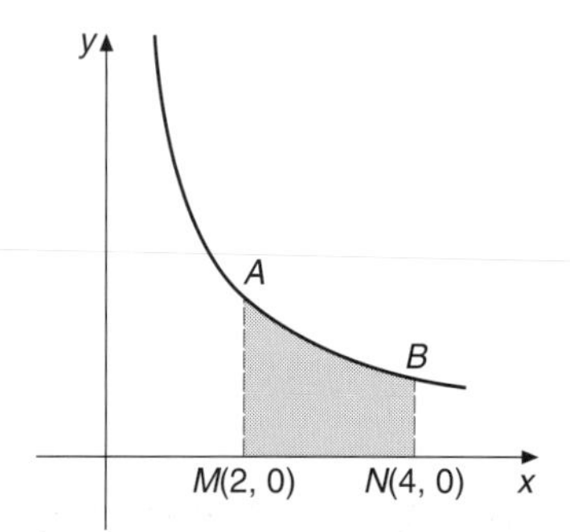


The sketch shows part of the graph of $y = \dfrac{2}{2x - 3}$.

If the area $ABNM$ is rotated through 360° about the $x$ axis show that the volume of the solid formed is $\dfrac{8\pi}{5}$.

**B3**

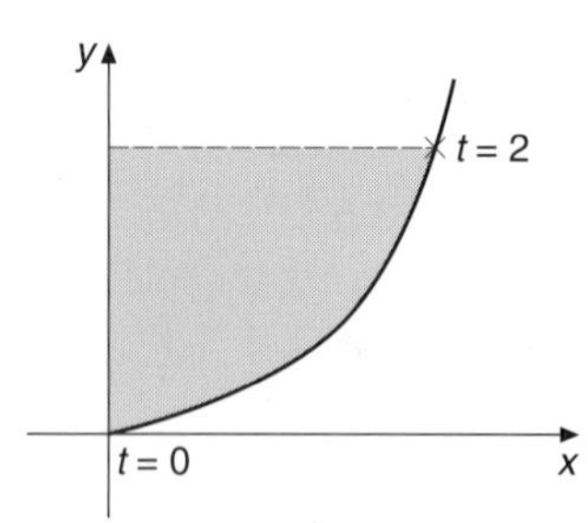


A graph with parametric equations $x = t^2$, $y = t^3$ is shown in the diagram.

The shaded area is rotated through $2\pi$ radians about the $y$ axis.

Show that the volume of the solid formed is $\dfrac{384\pi}{7}$.

## Exercise 11.2 *continued*

**B4** A curve is given in terms of parameter $t$ by $x = 2t^2$, $y = 4t$. The points $A$ and $B$ have parameters $t = 1$ and $t = 2$ respectively. Find the volume formed when the area bounded by the curve, the $x$ axis and lines through $A$ and $B$ parallel to the $y$ axis is rotated a full turn about the $x$ axis.

**B5**

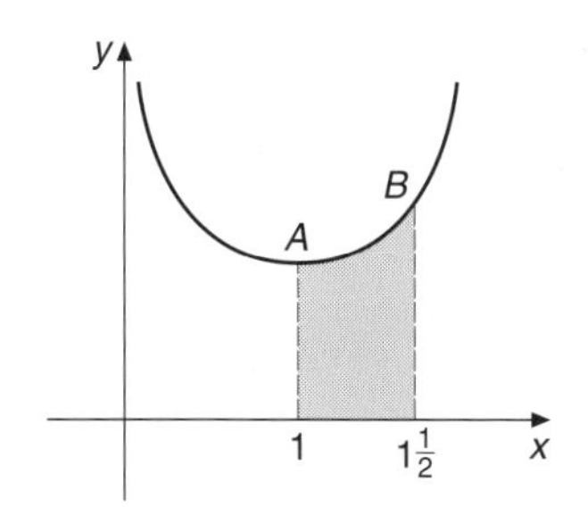


The curve $y = \sqrt{x} + \dfrac{1}{\sqrt{x}}$ is sketched in the diagram. $A$ and $B$ on the curve have $x$ coordinates 1 and $1\frac{1}{2}$ respectively.

(a) Find the shaded area correct to 1 decimal place

(b) Find the volume of the solid formed (to 1 decimal place) when the area is rotated through 360° about the $x$ axis

(c) Verify that $A$ is a stationary point on the curve.

## 11.3 Separating the variables and then integrating

### Key points

If $\dfrac{dy}{dx} = f(x)g(y)$ then $\dfrac{1}{g(y)}\dfrac{dy}{dx} = f(x)$

Integrating with respect to $x$ gives

$$\int \frac{1}{g(y)}\frac{dy}{dx}dx = \int \frac{1}{g(y)}dy = \int f(x)dx$$

The following examples should make the method seem quite simple.

A gentle reminder:
If $\dfrac{dy}{dx} = f(x)$ then $y = \int f(x)dx$

### Example 1

Solve the differential equation $\dfrac{dy}{dx} = 2y$ $(y > 0)$ given that $y = 1$ when $x = 2$.

#### Solution

$$\frac{dy}{dx} = 2y$$

If we are going to integrate both sides with respect to $x$ then we cannot have $y$ on the right hand side.

So we change the equation around by dividing by $y$ to obtain

$$\frac{1}{y}\frac{dy}{dx} = 2$$

Now integrate w.r.t. $x$.

w.r.t. means 'with respect to'

$$\int \frac{1}{y}\frac{dy}{dx}dx = \int \frac{1}{y}dy = \int 2dx$$

we are given $y > 0$ so no modulus sign is needed

$$\ln y = 2x + c$$

When $y = 1$, $x = 2$

$$\ln 1 = 4 + c$$

$$0 = 4 + c$$

$$-4 = c$$

$$\therefore \ln y = 2x - 4$$

$$y = e^{2x-4}$$

## Example 2

Find an expression for $y$ if $\frac{dy}{dx} = e^{-y}\sin x$ and $y = 0$ when $x = \frac{\pi}{3}$. Show that $y = \ln 2$ when $x = \frac{2\pi}{3}$.

### Solution

$$\frac{dy}{dx} = e^{-y}\sin x.$$

Divide both sides by $e^{-y}$ to get

$$\frac{1}{e^{-y}}\frac{dy}{dx} = \sin x$$

so $e^{y}\frac{dy}{dx} = \sin x$

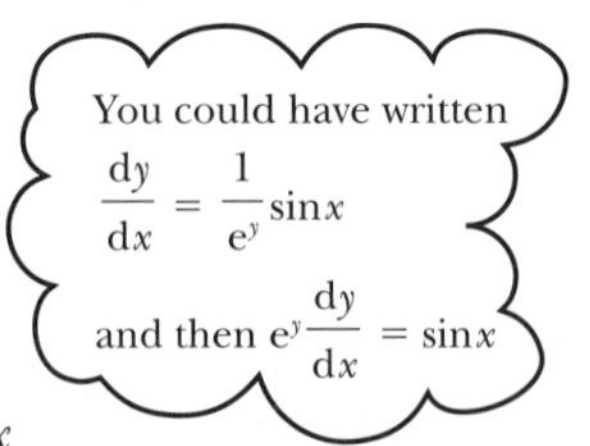


Now integrate both sides w.r.t. $x$

$$\int e^{y}\frac{dy}{dx}dx = \int e^{y}dy = \int \sin x dx$$

$$\Rightarrow e^{y} = -\cos x + c$$

$y = 0$ when $x = \frac{\pi}{3}$

So $e^{0} = -\cos\frac{\pi}{3} + c$

$$1 = -\frac{1}{2} + c$$

$$1\frac{1}{2} = c$$

So you get $e^y = -\cos x + \frac{3}{2}$

Hence $y = \ln\left(\frac{3}{2} - \cos x\right)$

$\left(\frac{3}{2} - \cos x\right)$ is always positive so no mod sign needed

When $x = \frac{2\pi}{3}$ $\quad y = \ln\left(\frac{3}{2} - \cos\frac{2\pi}{3}\right)$

$$= \ln\left(\frac{3}{2} - \left(-\frac{1}{2}\right)\right)$$

$$= \ln 2.$$

## Exercise 11.3

**A1** Find an expression for $y$ by solving the following differential equations

(a) $\frac{dy}{dx} = x$

(b) $\frac{dy}{dx} = y \; (y > 0)$

(c) $\frac{dy}{dx} = \frac{1}{x} \; (x > 0)$

(d) $\frac{dy}{dx} = \frac{1}{y}$

**A2** Find the solutions of the following, making $y$ the subject of the formula when possible

(a) $\frac{dy}{dx} = xy \; (y > 0)$

(b) $\frac{dy}{dx} = \frac{x}{y}$

(c) $\frac{dy}{dx} = \frac{y}{x} \; (x, y > 0)$

**A3** If $\frac{dy}{dx} = (y + 2)(2x + 3)$ and $y > -2$ find an expression for $y$ given that $y = -1$ when $x = 1$.

In questions **A4** to **A7** solve the differential equations.

**A4** $\frac{dy}{dx} = \frac{2x + 3}{3 - 4y}$ given $y = 1$ when $x = 0$

**A5** $\frac{dy}{dx} = \frac{e^{-x}}{\cos y}$ given $y = \frac{\pi}{6}$ when $x = 0$

**A6** $\left(\frac{y}{y^2 + 4}\right)\frac{dy}{dx} = \frac{1}{x^2}$ given that $y = 0$ when $x = 1$

**A7** $\frac{dy}{dx} = e^{2y - 3x}$ given that $y = 0$ when $x = 0$

**A8** If $\frac{dv}{dt} = 4v \; (v > 0)$ find $v$ when $t = \frac{1}{2}$ given that $v = 2$ when $t = 0$

## Exercise 11.3 *continued*

**A9** If $\frac{dm}{dt} = -km$ ($k$, $m > 0$ and $k$ is constant) and $m = A$ when $t = 0$ find $t$ in terms of $k$ when $m = \frac{A}{5}$.

**A10** If $v\frac{dv}{dx} = -4x$ ($v \geqslant 0$) and $v = 5$ when $x = 0$ find $v$ when

(a) $x = \frac{3}{2}$

(b) $x = \frac{5}{2}$

**B1** If $\frac{d\theta}{dt} = k(100 - \theta)$, where $k$ is a positive constant, and $\theta = 20$ when $t = 0$, show that $kt = \ln\left(\frac{80}{100 - \theta}\right)$.

If $\theta = 60$ when $t = 5$ find $t$ when $\theta = 80$.

**B2** A curve is such that at every point $(x,y)$ on it the gradient, $\frac{dy}{dx}$, satisfies the differential equation $y\frac{dy}{dx} = -2e^{2x-y}$.

Show that $e^{2x} = -\int ye^{y}dy$.

If the curve passes through the origin and $y < 1$, show, using integration by parts, that $e^{2x} = e^{y}(1 - y)$ and hence that

$x = \frac{1}{2}\left[y + \ln(1 - y)\right]$.

**B3** (a) Express $\frac{4}{4 - x^2}$ in partial fractions

(b) Solve the differential equation $\frac{dy}{dx} = \frac{8y}{4 - x^2}$ where $|x| < 2$ and $y > 0$ given that $y = 1$ when $x = 0$

(c) Show that $y = 9$ when $x = 1$ and find $y$ when $x = -1$.

**B4** If $\frac{dv}{dt} = \frac{2v}{t + 3}$, where $v > 0$ and $t \geqslant 0$ and $v = 9$ when $t = 0$, show that $v = (t + 3)^2$.

If further $v = \frac{dx}{dt}$ and $x = 15$ when $t = 0$, find $t$ when $x = 78$.

**B5** Given that $\frac{ds}{dt} = \frac{4}{3\sqrt{s}}$ ($s > 0$) and that $s = 1$ when $t = 0$, find

(a) $s$ when $t = 13$

(b) $t$ when $s = 25$

**B6** (a) Find $\frac{d}{dx}(x^2 - 9)^{\frac{1}{2}}$ and hence

$\int\frac{x}{\sqrt{x^2 - 9}}dx$

(b) Given that $x > 3$ and that $y = 9$ when $x = 5$ solve the differential equation $\sqrt{x^2 - 9}\frac{dy}{dx} = 2x\sqrt{y}$ by writing your answer as an expression for $\sqrt{y}$. Show that $y = 25$ when $x = 3\sqrt{5}$.

**B7** (a) If $\frac{dy}{dx} = \frac{y^2}{x^2}$ and $y = 1$ when $x = \frac{1}{2}$ show that $y = \frac{x}{1 - x}$

(b) If $\frac{dy}{dx} = \frac{x^2}{y^2}$ show that $y = (x^3 + A)^{\frac{1}{3}}$ where A is constant.

**B8** When a point moves along the positive $x$ axis with variable velocity $v$, its acceleration is $v\frac{dv}{dx}$ when it is a distance $x$ from the origin.

If the acceleration is $kx$, where $k$ is a positive constant and $v = 4$ when $x = 0$, show that $v^2 = 16 + kx^2$.

Given that $v = 5$ when $x = 3$ show that $x$ is nearly 7 when $v = 8$.

## 11.4 Uses of differential equations

The following examples will help you understand how to solve a practical problem involving differential equations. These questions often carry quite a lot of marks in an examination.

### Example 1

The gradient of the tangent at a general point $P(x,y)$ on a curve is double the gradient of the line $OP$, where $O$ is the origin. Given that the curve lies in the first quadrant (i.e. $x > 0$ and $y > 0$) form a differential equation and solve it to find the equation of the curve, given that the curve passes through the point (1,2).

**Solution**

The gradient of the tangent at $P(x,y)$ is $\dfrac{\mathrm{d}y}{\mathrm{d}x}$

The gradient of $OP$ is $\dfrac{y-0}{x-0} = \dfrac{y}{x}$ (using $\dfrac{y_2 - y_1}{x_2 - x_1}$)

So $\dfrac{\mathrm{d}y}{\mathrm{d}x} = 2\left(\dfrac{y}{x}\right)$ (expressing the first written statement of the question as an equation)

Now you have to solve this differential equation.

$$\frac{\mathrm{d}y}{\mathrm{d}x} = \frac{2y}{x}$$

Separate the variables

$$\frac{1}{y}\frac{\mathrm{d}y}{\mathrm{d}x} = \frac{2}{x}$$

Integrate w.r.t. $x$

$$\int \frac{1}{y}\,\mathrm{d}y = \int \frac{2}{x}\,\mathrm{d}x$$

($x > 0$ and $y > 0$ so no modulus signs needed)

$$\ln y = 2\ln x + c$$

so $\ln y = \ln x^2 + c$ (don't forget the constant)

The curve passes through (1,2) so when $x = 1$, $y = 2$.

Substitute these values into the equation to get

$$\ln 2 = \ln 1 + c$$

($\ln 1 = 0$)

i.e. $\ln 2 = c$

i.e. $\ln y = \ln x^2 + \ln 2 = \ln 2x^2$ (using $\ln a + \ln b = \ln ab$)

The required equation is $y = 2x^2$

## Example 2

According to Newton's law, the rate of cooling of a body in air is proportional to the difference between the temperature $\theta$ °C of the body and the temperature $\theta_0$ °C of the air. If the air temperature is kept constant at 18 °C and a liquid cools from 80 °C to 50 °C in 30 minutes, in what *further* time will the liquid cool to 30 °C?

### Solution

The rate of change of the temperature of liquid is $\dfrac{d\theta}{dt}$

and $\dfrac{d\theta}{dt}$ is proportional to $(\theta - 18)$

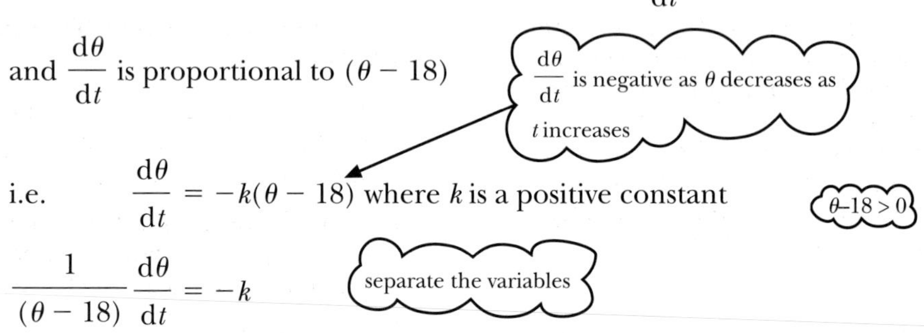


i.e. $\quad \dfrac{d\theta}{dt} = -k(\theta - 18)$ where $k$ is a positive constant

$$\frac{1}{(\theta - 18)}\frac{d\theta}{dt} = -k$$

Integrate both sides w.r.t. $t$ to get

$$\int \frac{1}{\theta - 18}\,d\theta = -\int k\,dt$$

$\theta > 18$ so $\ln(\theta - 18) = -kt + c$

When $t = 0$, $\theta = 80$

i.e. $\quad \ln 62 = c$

which gives $kt = \ln 62 - \ln(\theta - 18)$

When $t = 30$, $\theta = 50 \quad \therefore 30k = \ln 62 - \ln 32 = \ln\dfrac{62}{32} = \ln\dfrac{31}{16} \quad$ ①

When $t = T$, $\theta = 30 \quad kT = \ln 62 - \ln 12 = \ln\dfrac{62}{12} = \ln\dfrac{31}{6} \quad$ ②

You can divide ② by ① here to get $\dfrac{kT}{30k} = \dfrac{\ln\frac{31}{6}}{\ln\frac{31}{16}}$

$$\therefore T = 30\frac{\ln\frac{31}{6}}{\ln\frac{31}{16}} \approx 74.49$$

The further time needed to cool from 50 °C to 30 °C is $(74.49 - 30) \approx 44.5$ minutes.

## Exercise 11.4

**B1** A curve is such that the gradient of the normal at $P(x,y)$ is equal to the product of the gradients of the lines $AP$ and $BP$ where $A$ is $(-1,0)$ and $B$ is $(1,0)$.

Show that $\frac{dy}{dx} = \frac{1-x^2}{y^2}$ and then find the equation of the curve, given that it passes through the point $(0,1)$.

**B2** The gradient of the tangent drawn to the general point $P(x,y)$ of a curve is half the gradient of the line joining $P$ to the point $(0,1)$. Write down and then solve a differential equation to find the equation of the curve given that $x > 0$, $y > 1$ and that the curve passes through the point $(1,2)$. Verify that the point $(16,5)$ lies on the curve.

**B3** The growth of a population $P$ (where $P$ is treated as continuous) is assumed to be proportional to $P$. Write down this statement as a differential equation.

Given that the population was 500 in 1975 and 560 in 1985, what should it have been in 1995?

**B4** Insects are placed in a closed environment and their population is allowed to grow for a few days. After 4 days the number of insects is estimated as 2700 and after 5 days as 4050.

Model the population, $x$, as continuous and being such that the rate of increase of the population is proportional to the number of insects present at any time, $t$ days.

Establish a differential equation and solve it to find $x$ as a function of $t$. Estimate the initial population and the population after 2 days.

**B5** A warm object has temperature of $\theta°$ at time $t$ minutes $(\theta > 18)$. It is placed in a room of constant temperature 18 °C to cool. The rate of cooling of the object is modelled as being proportional to the quantity by which its temperature exceeds that of the room. Construct a differential equation connecting $\theta$ and $t$.

Given that the object's temperature was 78 °C when first placed in the room and that its temperature 10 minutes later was 63 °C, find

(a) its temperature after 30 minutes

(b) how long it takes to cool to 30 °C.

(Give answers to a reasonable degree of accuracy.)

**B6** Radium decays at a rate proportional to its mass. If the mass of a sample is $m$ gm at time $t$ yrs show that $m = Ae^{-kt}$.

The half life of this substance (i.e. the time taken for a given amount $M$ to be reduced to $\frac{1}{2}M$) is thought to be 1500 years.

(a) Calculate $k$

(b) If the initial mass is 100 gm find, to the nearest gm, the mass expected to remain after (a) 1000 years (b) 2000 years.

**B7** At a variable point $P(x,y)$ on a curve $C$ the tangent to $C$ is at right angles to the line $AP$ where $A$ is $(1,2)$. Express this statement as a differential equation and show that $\int(y-2)\,dy = \int(1-x)\,dx$.

Given that $C$ contains the point $B(-3,5)$, find its equation.

**B8** A model used to estimate the depreciation in value of a car is that its value, £$x$, when it is $t$ months old, decreases at a rate which is proportional to $x$. The car costs £15,000 when new.

Form and solve a differential equation to show that $x = 15\,000e^{-kt}$ where $k$ is a positive constant.

After 24 months the car is expected to be worth £10 000. Estimate

(a) its likely value after 60 months

(b) its likely age when it is worth half of its cost when new.

## Chapter 11: A level questions

**C1** (a) Show that $\cos 2x = 2\cos^2 x - 1$ by using the formula for $\cos(A + B)$

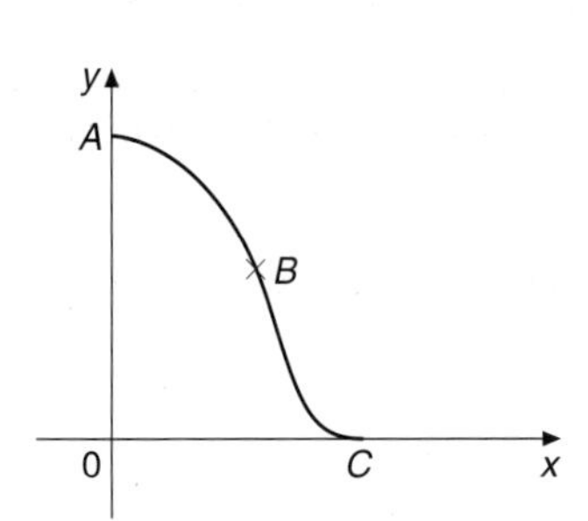


(b) The diagram shows a sketch of $y = \cos^2 x$ for $0 \leqslant x \leqslant \frac{\pi}{2}$. $A$ is $(0, y_1)$, $B$ is $\left(\frac{\pi}{4}, y_2\right)$ and $C$ is $\left(\frac{\pi}{2}, 0\right)$.

Find the values of $y_1$ and $y_2$ and show that points $A$, $B$ and $C$ lie on a straight line.

(c) Show that the area bounded by the curve $y = \cos^2 x$ and the axes is equal to the area of triangle $AOC$.

**C2**

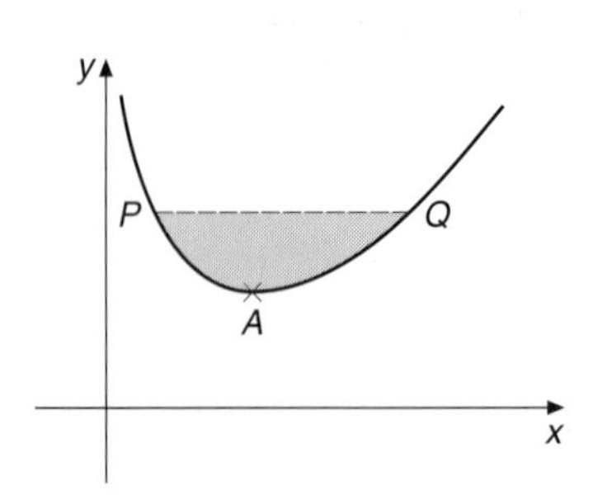


The diagram is a sketch of the graph of $y = x + \frac{1}{x}$ $(x > 0)$. The points $P$ and $Q$ have $x$ coordinates $\frac{1}{3}$ and 3 respectively.

(a) Show that $PQ$ is parallel to the $x$ axis.

(b) Show that the shaded area is $\frac{40}{9} - 2\ln 3$

(c) Establish that $A(1,2)$ is the minimum point on the graph.

**C3** (a) Use the substitution $u = x - 3$ to evaluate $\int_0^3 x(x - 3)^2 dx$

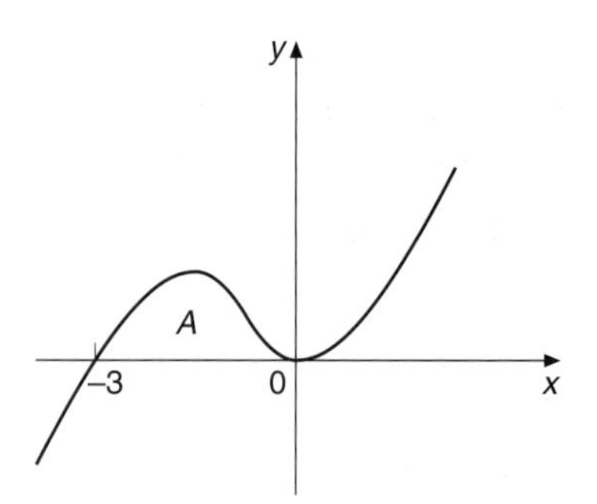


(b) The diagram shows a sketch of the graph of $y = (x + 3)x^2$. Show by integration that area $A$ is $\frac{27}{4}$.

(c) Explain your results of parts (a) and (b) geometrically.

**C4** (a) Expand and simplify $(e^x + e^{-x})^2$

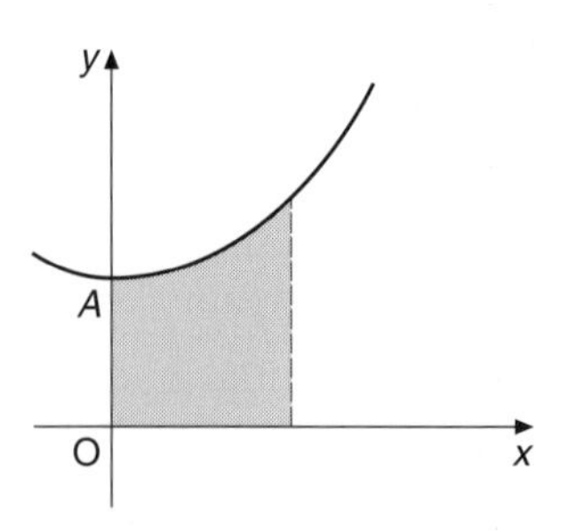


(b) The sketch shows part of the graph of $y = e^x + e^{-x}$ which crosses the $y$ axis at $A$

(i) Show that $A$ is a minimum point on the curve.

(ii) The shaded area bounded by the curve, the axes and the line $x = \ln 2$ is rotated through $2\pi$ radians about the $x$ axis. Show

## Chapter 11: A level questions

that the volume of the solid formed is $p + k\ln 2$ where

$$k = p + \frac{\pi}{8}$$

**C5** The area between the graph of $y = \tan x$, the $x$ axis and the lines $x = \frac{\pi}{6}$ and $x = \frac{\pi}{3}$ is rotated about the $x$ axis through a full turn. Calculate the volume of the solid formed and show that this may be written as $\frac{\pi}{6}(4\sqrt{3} - \pi)$.

**C6** Area $A$ is that bounded by the $x$ axis, the line $x = 1$ and the curve $y = 5x^{\frac{3}{2}}$.

Area $B$ is that bounded by the $x$ axis, the line $x = 1$ and the curve $y = 7x^{\frac{5}{2}}$.

(a) Show that area $A$ equals area $B$.

(b) Areas $A$ and $B$ are both rotated through 360° about the $x$ axis. Find the ratio of the volumes of the solids formed.

**C7** If $\frac{dz}{dt} = -k\sqrt{z}$ where $k$ is a positive constant and $z = 400$ when $t = 0$, show that $kt = 40 - 2\sqrt{z}$. Given that $z = 144$ when $t = 10$ find

(a) $t$ when $z = 49$

(b) $z$ when $t = 15$.

**C8** Find

(a) $\int xe^{-x}dx$

(b) $\int \cos 2y\,dy$

Hence find the general solution of the differential equation

$$(\cos^2 y - \sin^2 y)\frac{dy}{dx} = \frac{x}{e^x} \text{ if } -\frac{\pi}{4} < y < \frac{\pi}{4}$$

**C9** At time $t$ hrs the rate of decay of the mass of a radioactive substance is proportional to the mass $m$ gm of the substance at that time. The mass is $m_0$ at time $t = 0$.

Form and solve a differential equation to show that $m = m_0e^{-kt}$ where $k$ is a positive constant.

(a) If $m = \frac{1}{2}m_0$ when $t = 5$, find $m$ when $t = 10$

(b) Show that $t = \frac{5\ln 3}{\ln 2}$ when $m = \frac{1}{3}m_0$.

**C10** A liquid is removed from a fridge at 4 °C and placed in a warm room whose temperature is kept fixed at 20 °C. The temperature of the liquid $t$ minutes after removal from the fridge is $T$ °C. It is thought that the rate of increase of the temperature of the liquid is proportional to how far it is below room temperature. Set up a differential equation, solve it and show that $T = 20 - 16e^{-kt}$ where $k$ is a positive constant.

The temperature is measured at 8 °C after 30 minutes. What should it be after $1\frac{1}{2}$ hours and show that it reaches 15 °C in a little over two hours.

# Chapter 12

## ERRORS, ACCURACY AND ESTIMATION

### 12.1 Errors

**Key points**

The following examples should help you understand the ideas of

(a) greatest lower bound and least upper bound

(b) absolute, relative and percentage errors

**Example 1**

If a tall man says that his height is 182 cm (we normally state our height to the nearest whole number) then you know that he is at least 181.5 cm tall and not 182.5 cm tall.

If his height is $h$ cm then you can write $181.5 \leqslant h < 182.5$

notice the inequality signs are different

181.5 is the greatest lower bound
182.5 is the least upper bound

notice the different brackets
The square bracket denotes the '$\leqslant$' sign
The round bracket denotes the '<' sign

You can write this as '$h$ lies in the interval [181.5, 182.5)'

The error e in using 182 is $(h - 182)$ Now $181.5 \leqslant h < 182.5$

$$181.5 - 182 \leqslant h - 182 < 182.5 - 182$$

$$-0.5 \leqslant h - 182 < 0.5$$

$$-0.5 \leqslant \text{e} < 0.5$$

The absolute error is $|h - 182|$ so the maximum absolute error here is $|-0.5| = 0.5$

because of the $\leqslant$ sign

In this case the relative error

$$= \frac{\text{maximum absolute error in height}}{\text{given value in height}} = \frac{0.5}{182} \approx 0.0027$$

The percentage relative error is approximately $0.0027 \times 100$ i.e. 0.27%

**Example 2**

Given that $\frac{1}{f} = \frac{1}{u} + \frac{1}{v}$ and that $u = 15$ and $v = 20$, each correct to the nearest whole number, find the least possible value of $f$ giving your answer to 2 decimal places and show that the percentage relative error is approximately 3%.

**Solution**

Here, $u = 15$ and $v = 20$

so $\frac{1}{f} = \frac{1}{15} + \frac{1}{20} = \frac{7}{60}$

$\therefore f = \frac{60}{7} \approx 8.57142 = 8.5714$ (4 d.p.)

You have to be aware that if $f$ is large then $\frac{1}{f}$ is small, and if $f$ is small then $\frac{1}{f}$ is large. In this question you need $f$ to be as small as possible so $\frac{1}{f}$ has to be as large as possible. This means $\frac{1}{u} + \frac{1}{v}$ has to be as large as possible

i.e. $\frac{1}{u}$ large so $u$ small, $\frac{1}{v}$ large so $v$ small.

You are given that $14.5 \leqslant u < 15.5$ so the largest value of $\frac{1}{u} = \frac{1}{14.5}$

You are given that $19.5 \leqslant v < 20.5$ so the largest value of $\frac{1}{v} = \frac{1}{19.5}$

Hence the largest value of $\frac{1}{f} = \frac{1}{14.5} + \frac{1}{19.5}$

This means the least value of $f = 8.3162$ (4 d.p.)

The absolute error of this $f$ is $\approx (8.5714 - 8.3162) = 0.2552$

The relative error is $\approx \frac{0.2552}{8.5714} \approx 0.0298$

So the percentage relative error is $\approx 2.98$ i.e. approximately 3%.

## Exercise 12.1

**A1** A rectangle measures 2.3 cm wide and 4.2 cm long, both measurements correct to 2 significant figures.

Find the difference between

(a) the maximum and minimum possible areas

(b) the maximum and minimum possible perimeters.

**A2** A circle has a given radius of 20 cm (to the nearest whole number).

Find

(a) the greatest possible area

(b) the least possible circumference

giving your answers as multiples of $\pi$.

## Exercise 12.1 *continued*

**A3** A cube has side 3.4 cm to the nearest millimetre.

Find

(a) the minimum volume correct to the nearest cubic millimetre

(b) the maximum surface area correct to the nearest square millimetre.

**A4** Eight 'weights' each of mass marked 10 gm are used in an experiment. The 'weights' are guaranteed accurate to within 1%. Calculate the minimum and maximum mass of the total of the eight 'weights'.

**A5**

The diagram shows a right angled triangle *ABC* with *AB* measured as 63 mm and *BC* as 21 mm, each correct to the nearest whole number.

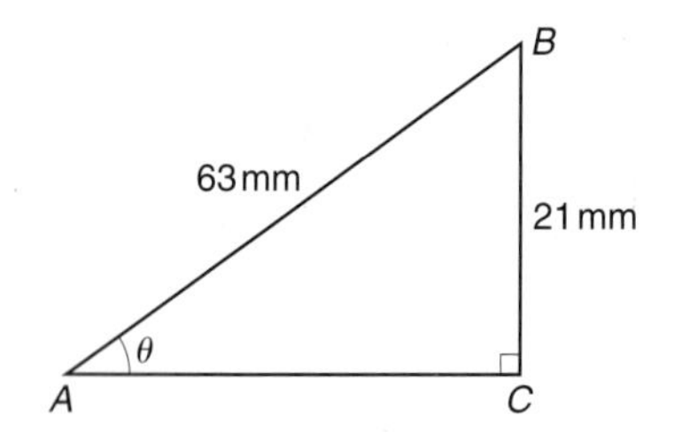


Find the greatest and least values of $\theta$ (both correct to 2 decimal places).

**A6** Triangle *PQR* has a right angle at *P*. The sides *QP* and *RP* are measured as 3.6 cm and 4.8 cm respectively, each correct to 1 decimal place.

(a) State the maximum absolute error and the maximum relative error in taking the length of *QP* as 3.6 cm.

(b) Find the greatest length of the hypotenuse *QR* giving your answer to 2 decimal places and find the percentage error in calculating *QR*.

**A7** The formula $S = 4\pi r^2$ is used to calculate the surface area of a sphere.

Given that $r = 3.6$ cm (correct to 1 decimal place) and that $\pi = 3.14$ (correct to two decimal places) find to 2 significant figures

(a) the maximum relative error in calculating $S$

(b) the maximum percentage error in calculating $S$.

**A8** The formula $V = \dfrac{4}{3}\pi r^3$ is used to calculate the volume of a sphere.

If $\pi = 3.14$ and $r = 2.48$, both correct to 2 decimal places, find, correct to 2 significant figures

(a) the maximum relative error in calculating $V$

(b) the maximum percentage error in calculating $V$.

## 12.2 Location of roots of f(x) = 0 by considering the change of sign of f(x) including interval bisection and decimal search

### Key points

Consider the continuous function $y = \mathrm{f}(x)$

If you work out the values of $\mathrm{f}(a)$ and $\mathrm{f}(b)$ and they turn out to have opposite signs, then this means that there is at least one root of the equation $\mathrm{f}(x) = 0$ in the interval between $x = a$ and $x = b$ (i.e. $a < x < b$).

It is usual to try successive integers for $a$ and $b$ and this interval can be written $(a, b)$ or, in particular, $(N, N+1)$.

if $f(a)$ turns out to be 0 you have found a root of the equation $f(x) = 0$ to be $x = a$

Interval bisection and decimal search are simple applications of this idea and are used in the examples.

## Example 1

(a) If $f(x) \equiv 6x^2 + 7x - 26$ show that $f(x) = 0$ has a root $\alpha$ in the interval $(1,2)$ and by interval bisection determine if $x = 1$ or $x = 2$ is closer to $\alpha$.

(b) Find the negative integer N such that the other root lies in the interval $(N, N+1)$

### Solution

a continuous function

(a) $f(x) \equiv 6x^2 + 7x - 26$

$f(1) = 6 + 7 - 26 = -13 < 0$

$f(2) = 24 + 14 - 26 = 12 > 0$

$f(x)$ changes sign in the interval $(1,2)$ and so $1 < \alpha < 2$

To bisect the interval we find $f(1.5) = 6(2.25) + 7(1.5) - 26$

$= 13.5 + 10.5 - 26 < 0$

$f(1.5) < 0$, $f(2) > 0$ so the root lies between 1.5 and 2 i.e. $1.5 < \alpha < 2$

Hence $\alpha$ is closer to $x = 2$.

(b) $f(x) \equiv 6x^2 + 7x - 26$

$f(0) = -26 < 0$

$f(-1) = 6 - 7 - 26 < 0$

$f(-2) = 24 - 14 - 26 < 0$

$f(-3) = 54 - 21 - 26 > 0$

So a second root lies in the interval $(-3, -2)$.

Comparing with $(N, N+1)$ you determine that $N = -3$.

[NB. As you know there are several other approaches to find the roots of the quadratic equation given in this example but the examiner may dictate this particular method be used.]

## Example 2

(a) If $f(x) \equiv 9 - x^2 - e^x$ show that the equation $f(x) = 0$ has a root $\alpha$ in the interval $(1.7, 1.8)$ and then by decimal search find $\alpha$ to 1 decimal place.

(b) If $x = \beta$ is another root then find the negative integer $n$ such that $n < \beta < n + 1$.

**Solution**

(a)
$$f(x) \equiv 9 - x^2 - e^x$$
$$f(1.7) = 9 - (1.7)^2 - e^{1.7} \approx 0.64 > 0$$
$$f(1.8) = 9 - (1.8)^2 - e^{1.8} \approx -0.29 < 0$$

$f(x)$ is continuous and $f(x)$ changes sign in the interval (1.7,1.8) so a root exists in this interval. i.e. $1.7 < \alpha < 1.8$.

For a decimal search you could look at f(1.71) then f(1.72) then f(1.73), etc., until the sign changes but a sensible start does save you some time.

You would 'guess' that $\alpha$ is closer to 1.8 from your values of f(1.7) and f(1.8) so perhaps start at f(1.76)

$f(1.76) \approx 0.09 > 0$

$f(1.77) \approx -0.004 < 0$

so $1.76 < \alpha < 1.77$ and hence $\alpha = 1.8$ (1 d.p.)

it is likely that 1.77 is an estimate of $\alpha$ to 2 d.p. here as f(1.77) is very close to zero

(b)
$$f(x) \equiv 9 - x^2 - e^x$$
$$f(0) = 9 - 1 = 8 > 0$$
$$f(-1) \approx 7.63 > 0$$
$$f(-2) \approx 4.86 > 0$$
$$f(-3) \approx -0.049 < 0$$

$\therefore$ a second root $\beta$ lies in the interval $(-3,-2)$ i.e. $-3 < \beta < -2$.

Comparing with $n < \beta < n + 1$ you determine that $n = -3$.

the root is very close to $-3$ as $f(-3)$ is close to zero

A challenge here could be to consider the graphs of $y = 9 - x^2$ and $y = e^x$ on your graphical calculators then trace to the points of intersections, compare with your solutions of $f(x) = 0$ and then justify why these values $x$ are the roots of $f(x) = 0$ and that there are no more roots

## Exercise 12.2

**A1** If $f(x) \equiv 4x^2 - 5x - 8$ show that $f(x) = 0$ has a root $\alpha$ in the interval (2,3) and by interval bisection determine if $x = 2$ or $x = 3$ is closer to $\alpha$.

**A2** If $g(x) \equiv 1 - 9x + 6x^2 - x^3$ show that $g(x) = 0$ has a root $\beta$ in the interval (0,1) and find the interval $(n,n + 1)$ for the second positive root $\alpha$ and the interval $(N,N + 1)$ for the third positive root $\gamma$.

**A3** If $h(x) \equiv 3x - x^2 + \ln x$ $(x > 0)$ show that the equation $h(x) = 0$ has a root in the interval (3,4) and then by decimal search and interval bisection find the root to 1 decimal place.

**A4** If $f(x) \equiv 2e^{-x} - \ln x$, $(x > 0)$, find the positive integer $N$ such that the root of $f(x) = 0$ lies in the interval $(N, N + 1)$ and then use a decimal search followed by interval bisection to find this root to 1 decimal place.

## Exercise 12.2 *continued*

**A5** Given that $g(x) \equiv x - \dfrac{8}{x}$, $(x > 0)$ then consider the equation $g(x) = 0$ and use a numerical method to estimate $\sqrt{8}$ to 1 decimal place.

**A6** (a) If $f(x) \equiv 2x - \tan x$, $-\dfrac{\pi}{2} < x < \dfrac{\pi}{2}$, show that a root of $f(x) = 0$ lies in the interval $[1,1.5]$.

(b) Show that $f(x)$ is an odd function.

(c) Find the negative root of $f(x) = 0$ (to 1 decimal place) by first finding an interval in which the root lies and then using the method of decimal search followed by interval bisection.

**A7** If $p(x) \equiv x - 3\sin^2 x$, $(x > 0)$

(a) show that the equation $p(x) = 0$ has a root in the interval $(0.3,0.4)$ and find this root correct to 1 decimal place.

(b) By finding two successive integer values of $x$ between which a second root lies, estimate this root correct to 1 decimal place by using the methods of decimal search and interval bisection.

**A8** Given that $f(x) \equiv x^4 - 16x^2 + 5$

(a) estimate the two positive roots of the equation $f(x) = 0$ each to 1 decimal place.

(b) Show that $f(x)$ is an even function.

(c) Write down the two negative roots of the equation $f(x) = 0$ each to 1 decimal place giving reasons for your answers.

(d) If $f(x)$ is written in the form $(x^2 - a)^2 - b$ find the values of $a$ and $b$ and confirm that if $f(x) = 0$ then $x^2 = a \pm \sqrt{b}$. Hence obtain the four roots of $f(x) = 0$ each correct to 3 decimal places.

## 12.3 Estimation of the roots of f(x) = 0 by iteration or by the Newton Raphson formula

### Key points

**A** To find an iterative formula for an equation $f(x) = 0$ you have to rearrange the equation into the form $x = g(x)$. There will be several possible arrangements – hopefully the examiner will give you an appropriate one which will converge rapidly to a root.

For example

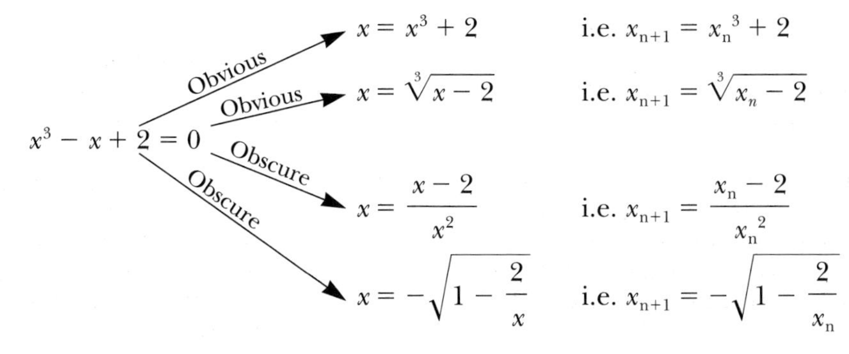

**B** The Newton Raphson formula

If $\alpha$ is an approximate root of $f(x) = 0$ then, in general,

$$\alpha - \frac{f(\alpha)}{f'(\alpha)}$$

gives a better root.

The general iterative formula is

$$x_{n+1} = x_n - \frac{f(x_n)}{f'(x_n)}$$

## Example 1

Show that $x_{n+1} = \ln(9 - x_n^2)$ is a possible iterative formula to find a solution of $9 - x^2 - e^x = 0$

Use this formula with $x_1 = 1.8$ (and your calculator!) to show that 1.77 seems a reasonable estimate of a root to two decimal places.

(N.B. You could compare this solution with example 2 of 12.2)

**Solution**

$9 - x^2 - e^x = 0$

$9 - x^2 = e^x$

$\ln(9 - x^2) = x$

Hence $x_{n+1} = \ln(9 - x_n^2)$ is a possible iterative formula.

$x_1 = 1.8$

$x_2 = \ln(9 - 1.8^2) \approx 1.7509 = 1.751$ (3 d.p.)

$x_3 = 1.781$

$x_4 = 1.763$

$x_5 = 1.774$

$x_6 = 1.767$

$x_7 = 1.771$

This appears to converge to 1.77 and so we can say that 1.77 is a reasonable estimate for a root of $9 - x^2 - e^x = 0$

## Example 2

(a) Show that $f(x) \equiv x^3 + 4x - 7$ is an increasing function.

(b) (i) Find consecutive positive integers between which the root of $f(x) = 0$ lies.

(ii) Use the method of decimal search followed by interval bisection to estimate the root to 1 d.p.

(iii) Estimate the root to one decimal place using two applications of the Newton Raphson formula.

**Solution**

(a) $f'(x) = 3x^2 + 4 \geqslant 4$ for all $x$ as $x^2 \geqslant 0$ for all $x$.

Hence $f(x)$ increases with $x$ i.e. $f(x)$ is an increasing function

(b) (i) $f(0) = -7 < 0$
$f(1) = 1 + 4 - 7 = -2 < 0$
$f(2) = 8 + 8 - 7 = 9 > 0$

$f(x)$ changes sign in the interval (1,2) so the root of the equation lies between $x = 1$ and $x = 2$.

(ii) It looks as if the root lies closer to 1 as $f(1) = -2$ and $f(2) = 9$ so a sensible start is nearer to 1

$f(1.1) = 1.1^3 + 4.4 - 7 < 0$

$f(1.2) < 0$

$f(1.3) > 0$

Now we know that this root, $\alpha$, say, lies between 1.2 and 1.3.

Using interval bisection we need to find $f(1.25)$ and from this we can determine if the root is closer to 1.2 or closer to 1.3.

$f(1.25) = 1.25^3 + 4(1.25) - 7 \approx -0.05 < 0$

So $f(x)$ changes sign between $x = 1.25$ and $x = 1.3$.

Hence $1.25 < \alpha < 1.3$

i.e. the root is closer to 1.3.

(iii) We know that the root lies in the interval (1,2) so either of these integers could be a sensible start for using the Newton Raphson formula.

Let us start with $x_1 = 1$, say, and we have $f(x) \equiv x^3 + 4x - 7$, $f'(x) \equiv 3x^2 + 4$

$$x_2 = x_1 - \frac{f(x_1)}{f'(x_1)} \quad \text{i.e. } x_2 = 1 - \frac{f(1)}{f'(1)} = 1 - \frac{(-2)}{7} \approx 1.286$$

$$x_3 = 1.286 - \frac{f(1.286)}{f'(1.286)} = 1.26 \text{ (2 d.p.)}$$

This gives an estimate of 1.26 for the root i.e. 1.3 (1 d.p.)

So $f(x)$ changes sign between $x = 1.25$ and $x = 1.3$.

Hence $1.25 < \alpha < 1.3$

i.e. the root is closer to 1.3.

## Exercise 12.3

**A1** Show that $x_{n+1} = \dfrac{1 - x_n^{\ 2}}{3}$ is a possible iterative formula for $x^2 + 3x - 1 = 0$.

Use this iteration starting with $x_1 = 1$ to write down the values of $x_2$, $x_3$, $x_4$ and $x_5$. Hence estimate this root to 2 decimal places.

**A2** Show that $x_{n+1} = \sqrt{\sqrt{\dfrac{30}{x_n}}}$ is a possible iterative formula for $x^5 = 30$.

Starting with $x_1 = 2$ find an approximation to $30^{\frac{1}{5}}$ to an appropriate degree of accuracy.

**A3** Show that $x_{n+1} = \sqrt{1 + \dfrac{5}{x_n}}$ is a possible iterative formula for $x^3 - x - 5 = 0$ and using $x_1 = 2$ write down $x_2$, $x_3$ and $x_4$ and find an approximate solution to this cubic equation to a suitable degree of accuracy.

**A4** Use one application of the Newton Raphson formula to estimate the root of $x - 2\sin x = 0$ to 1 decimal place, starting with $x = \dfrac{2\pi}{3}$.

**A5** (a) On the same axes and with equal scales, sketch the graphs of $y = 2x$ and $y = \cos x$ for $0 \leqslant x \leqslant \dfrac{\pi}{2}$

(b) Given that $x = 0.4$ is an approximation to the $x$ value at the point of intersection of the graphs in the given domain, use one application of the Newton Raphson formula to obtain a better solution.

**A6** Sketch the graphs $y = \ln x$ and $x + y = 3$ on the same axes and with equal scales. If $x = 2$ is a guess for the $x$ value at the point of intersection of the graphs use two applications of the Newton Raphson formula to estimate a closer $x$ value.

## 12.4 The use of the trapezium rule to estimate the value of an integral

### Key points

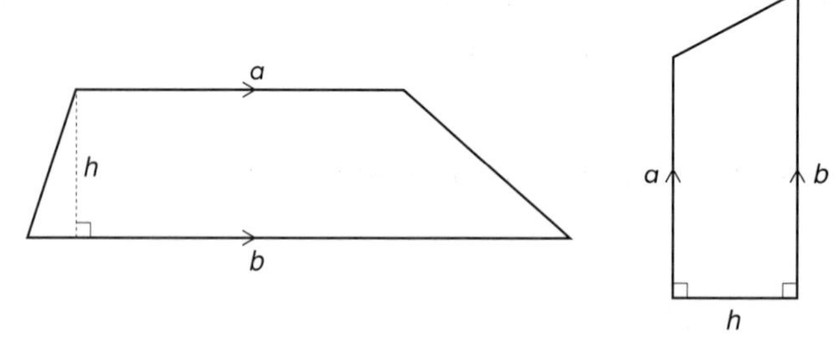


A gentle reminder: the area of a trapezium is $\frac{1}{2}(a + b)h$

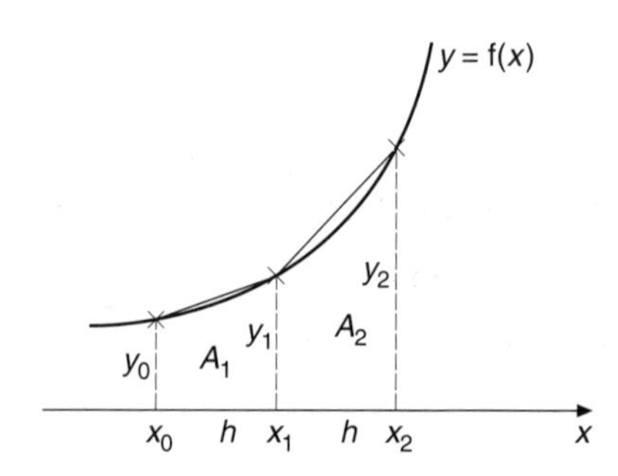

Area $A_1 \quad = \frac{1}{2}(y_0 + y_1)h$

Area $A_2 \quad = \frac{1}{2}(y_1 + y_2)h$

$A_1 + A_2 \quad = \frac{1}{2}(y_0 + 2y_1 + y_2)h$

$h = \frac{x_2 - x_0}{2}$

It is clear that this 'over-estimates' the area under the curve

In general

$$\int_{x_0}^{x_n} f(x)dx \approx \frac{1}{2}[y_0 + 2(y_1 + y_2 + \ldots + y_{n-1}) + y_n]h$$

$$\text{where } h = \frac{x_n - x_0}{n}$$

## Example I

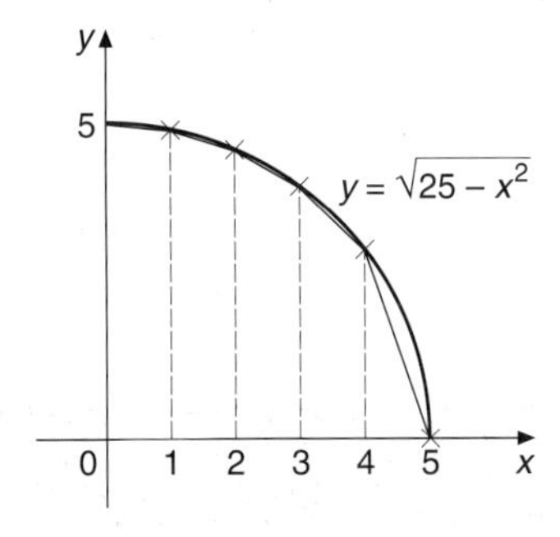


The diagram shows a quarter of a circle with radius 5 and centre (0,0)

Use the trapezium rule to estimate the area of the whole circle and find the percentage error in your estimate.

**Solution**

It seems sensible to have 5 strips each of width 1 unit.

$y = \sqrt{25 - x^2}$

| | |
|---|---|
| $x = 0$ | $y_0 = 5$ |
| $x = 1$ | $y_1 = \sqrt{24}$ |
| $x = 2$ | $y_2 = \sqrt{21}$ |
| $x = 3$ | $y_3 = 4$ |
| $x = 4$ | $y_4 = 3$ |
| $x = 5$ | $y_5 = 0$ |

So the area A of the quarter circle, using the trapezium rule is approximately (an underestimate here)

$h = 1$

$\frac{1}{2}[y_0 + 2(y_1 + y_2 + y_3 + y_4) + y_5](1)$

$= \frac{1}{2}[5 + 2(\sqrt{24} + \sqrt{21} + 4 + 3) + 0](1)$

$\approx 18.98.$

Hence the full circle is $4A \approx 75.92$

The actual area is $\pi r^2 = 78.54$ (2 d.p.) (exactly $25\pi$!)

$\therefore$ The percentage error is $\approx \dfrac{78.54 - 75.92}{78.54} \times 100 \approx 3.3\%$

## Example 2

(a) Use the trapezium rule with four strips to find $\int_{-2}^{2} (x^3 - 4x + 5)\,dx$.

(b) Sketch the graph of $y = x(x - 2)(x + 2)$ and explain the transformation needed to obtain $y = x^3 - 4x + 5$ from your graph.

(c) Explain, using the graph of $y = x^3 - 4x + 5$ why the trapezium rule gives the exact value of the integral.

**Solution**

(a) Let $y = x^3 - 4x + 5$

For four strips we need five $x$ values and we need to take h to be one unit

$x_0 = -2 \qquad y_0 = -8 + 8 + 5 = 5$

$x_1 = -1 \qquad y_1 = -1 + 4 + 5 = 8$

$x_2 = 0 \qquad y_2 = 5$

$x_3 = 1 \qquad y_3 = 1 - 4 + 5 = 2$

$x_4 = 2 \qquad y_4 = 8 - 8 + 5 = 5$

Using the trapezium rule

$$\int_{-2}^{2} (x^3 - 4x + 5)\,dx \approx \tfrac{1}{2}[y_0 + 2(y_1 + y_2 + y_3) + y_4](1)$$

$$= \tfrac{1}{2}[5 + 2(8 + 5 + 2) + 5](1)$$

$$= \tfrac{1}{2}[5 + 30 + 5]$$

$$= 20$$

(b) $y = x(x - 2)(x + 2)$

The zeros of the graph are at $x = 0$, $x = 2$, $x = -2$.

When $x = 0$, $y = 0$

['positive' $x^3$ shape – i.e. bottom left to top right]

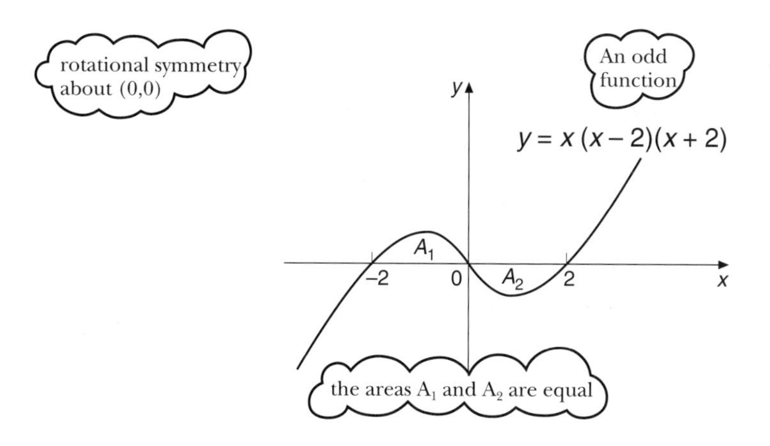


$y = x(x-2)(x+2) = x(x^2-4) = x^3 - 4x$

It is necessary to work out the brackets here so that you can compare your graph with that of $y = x^3 - 4x + 5$ given in the question. The transformation needed now seems clear (hopefully!) as the graph of

$y = x^3 - 4x$ needs to be translated $\begin{pmatrix} 0 \\ 5 \end{pmatrix}$ (moved 5 units 'upwards')

(c)

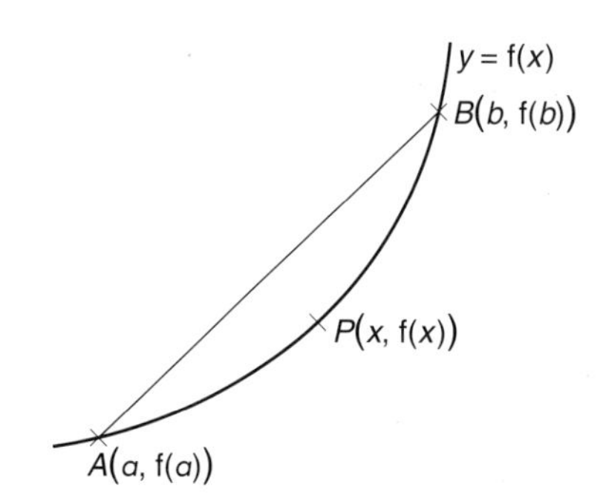


This graph has rotational symmetry about (0,5). Using the trapezium rule the 'under'-estimate of the area between $x = -2$ and $x = 0$ is the same numerical value as the 'over'-estimate of the area between $x = 0$ and $x = 2$ because of the symmetry of the curve. This means that the trapezium rule gives the exact value of the integral (i.e. of the area under the curve bteween $x = -2$ and $x = 2$).

## Exercise 12.4

**A1** (a) Use the trapezium rule with 4 strips to estimate the value of the integral

$$\int_1^5 \ln x \, dx.$$

(b) Differentiate $x(\ln x - 1)$ w.r.t. $x$, using the product rule and hence find the exact value of $\int_1^5 \ln x \, dx$.

(c) Find the percentage error in using the trapezium rule to estimate the value of $\int_1^5 \ln x \, dx$.

**A2**

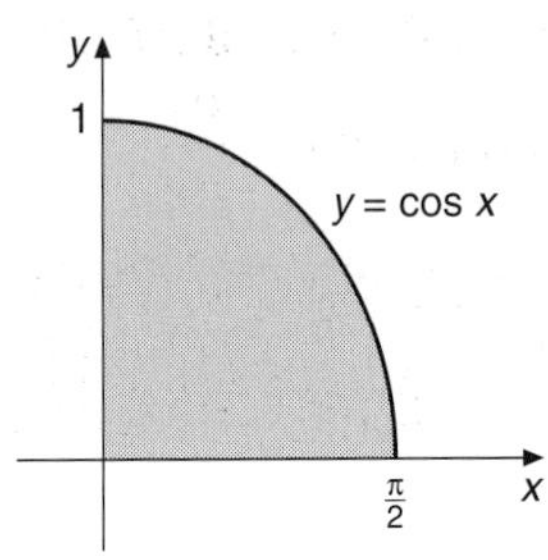


The diagram shows the graph of $y = \cos x$, $0 \leqslant x \leqslant \frac{\pi}{2}$.

(a) Use the trapezium rule and three strips to estimate the area shaded in the diagram.

(b) Use integration to find the exact value of the shaded area.

(c) Find the percentage error in using the trapezium rule to estimate this area.

**A3** Estimate the value of $\int_2^6 \frac{1}{\ln x} dx$ using the trapezium rule with four strips.

**A4** Find an estimate for the value of the integral $\int_0^2 e^x \sqrt{x} dx$ (where $x$ is positive) using the trapezium rule with 5 strips. Give your answer to 2 decimal places.

**A5**

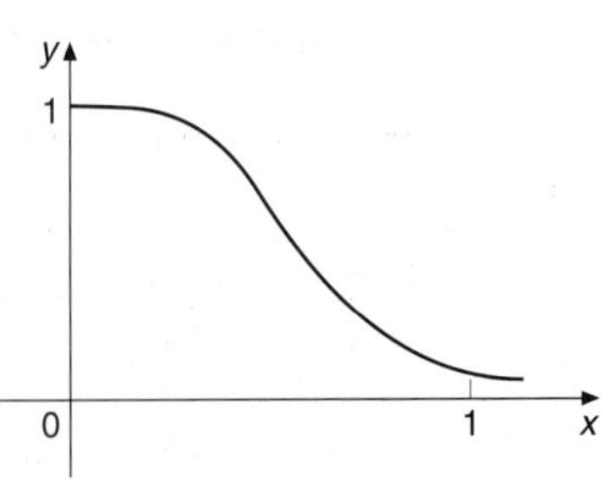


The graph of $y = e^{-x^2}$ is sketched here. Use the trapezium rule with four strips to estimate the area under the curve between $x = 0$ and $x = 1$. Give your answer to 3 decimal places.

**A6** (a) Estimate $\int_0^{\pi} 2\sin^2 x dx$ using the trapezium rule with four strips each of width $\frac{\pi}{4}$.

[N.B. Don't use your calculator here but use the exact values of $\sin\frac{\pi}{4}$ and $\sin\frac{3\pi}{4}$]

(b) Verify that the trapezium rule gives the exact value of the integral.

**A7** Given that the exact value of $\int_0^{0.5} \frac{6}{\sqrt{1 - x^2}} dx$ is $\pi$, find the percentage error in using the trapezium rule with 5 strips to estimate the value of the integral.

## 12.5 Using numerical methods to estimate the value of a derivative

### Key points

- A 2-sided approach.

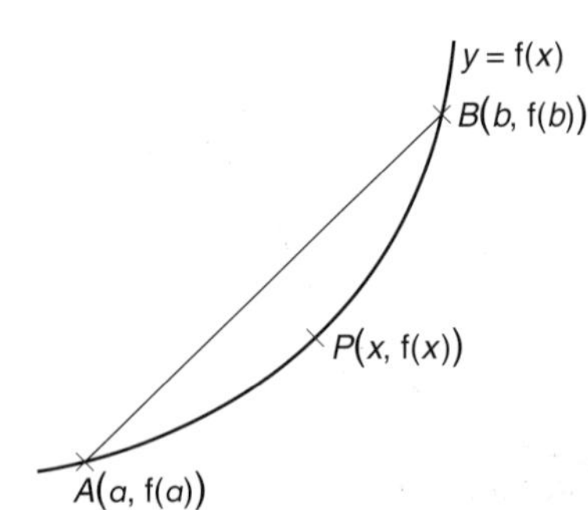

If $a$ and $b$ are very close to $x$ then the gradient of the chord $AB$ will be an approximation to the gradient of the tangent at $P$ i.e. $\frac{dy}{dx}$

$$\frac{dy}{dx} \approx \frac{f(b) - f(a)}{b - a}$$

- A 1-sided approach.

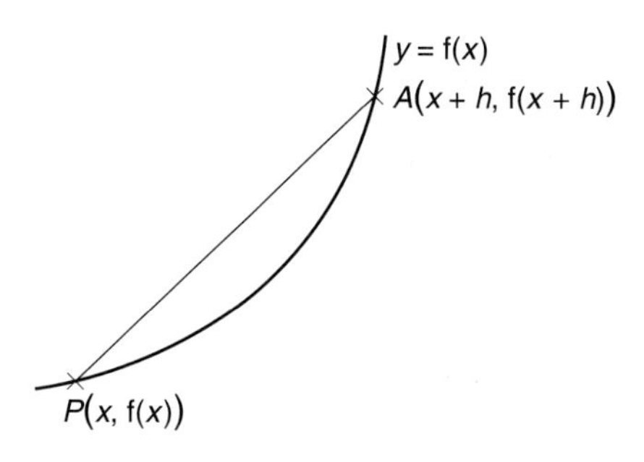


When $h$ is very small $A$ is close to $P$ and the gradient of the chord $AP$ is an approximation to the gradient of the tangent at $P$ i.e. $\frac{dy}{dx}$

$$\frac{dy}{dx} \approx \frac{f(x + h) - f(x)}{h}$$

## Example 1

If $y = 2^x$ estimate the value of $\frac{dy}{dx}$ at $x = 3$.

### Solution

(a) Using a 2-sided approach.

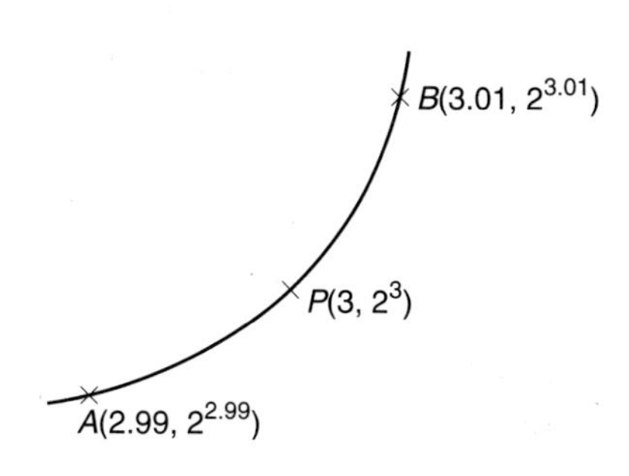

$$\text{Gradient of chord } AB = \frac{2^{3.01} - 2^{2.99}}{3.01 - 2.99} \approx 5.55$$

$$\therefore \text{At } x = 3, \ \frac{dy}{dx} \approx 5.55$$

(b) Using a 1-sided approach.

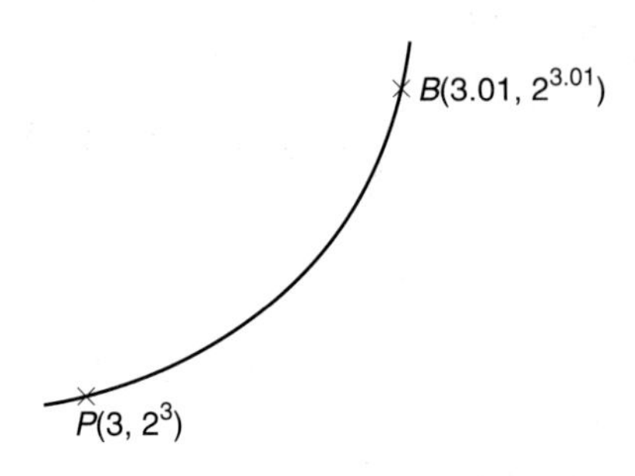


$$\text{Gradient of chord } BP = \frac{2^{3.01} - 2^{3}}{3.01 - 3} \approx 5.56$$

$$\therefore \text{At } x = 3, \ \frac{dy}{dx} \approx 5.56$$

## Example 2

If $P = 28(1.05)^t$ estimate $\frac{dP}{dt}$ when $t = 2$.

**Solution**

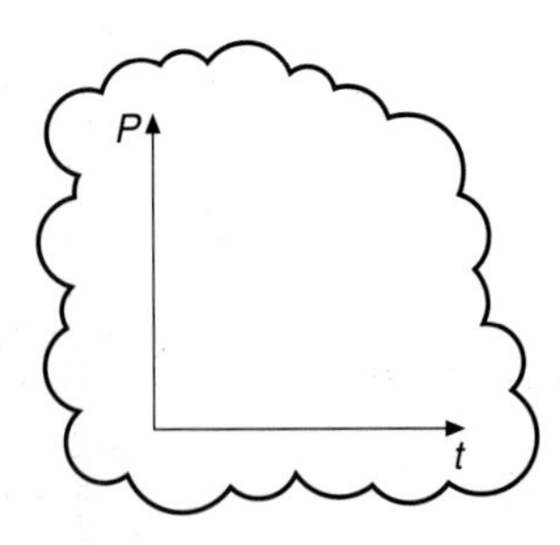


(a) Using a 2-sided approach for $P = 28(1.05)^t$

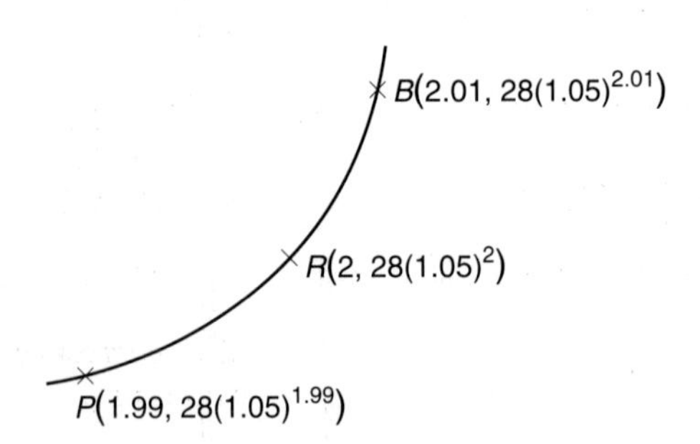

$$\text{Gradient of chord } AB = \frac{28(1.05)^{2.01} - 28(1.05)^{1.99}}{2.01 - 1.99}$$

$$\approx 1.51$$

Hence when $t = 2$ $\dfrac{dP}{dt} \approx 1.51$

(b) Using a 1-sided approach.

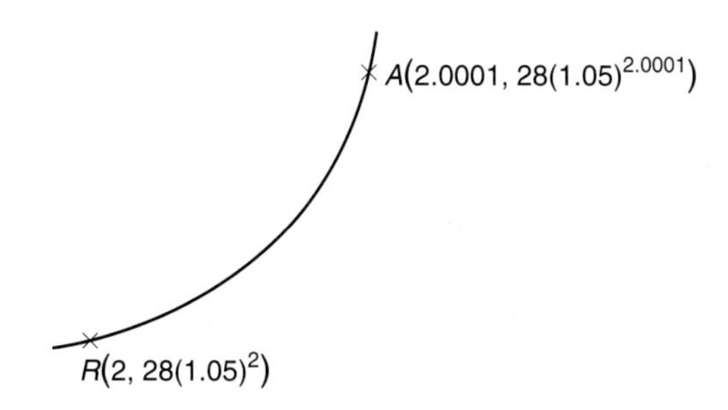


$$\text{Gradient of chord } AR = \frac{28(1.05)^{2.0001} - 28(1.05)^{2}}{2.0001 - 2}$$

$$\approx 1.51$$

Hence when $t = 2$, $\dfrac{dP}{dt} \approx 1.51$

## Exercise 12.5

**A1** (a) Use a numerical method to obtain an estimate of the gradient of the curve $y = 2^{-x}$ at the point where $x = 3$

(b) Write down an estimate of the gradient of the curve $y = 6 + 2^{-x}$ at the point where $x = 3$.

**A2** (a) Use a numerical method to estimate the derivative $\dfrac{dV}{dt}$ when $t = \frac{1}{2}$ given that $V = 8(3^t)$.

(b) Estimate the value of $\dfrac{dV}{dt}$ when $t = \frac{1}{2}$ if

(i) $V = -8(3^t)$ (ii) $V = 12 - 8(3^t)$.

**A3** Find an estimate for $f'(x)$ at the point where $x = 1.4$ on the graph of $f(x) = \sin(x^2)$ by using two appropriate values for $x$.

**A4** Given that $y = e^{x^2}$ estimate the value of $\dfrac{dy}{dx}$ when $x = 0.7$ by first finding the values of $y$ corresponding to two appropriate values of $x$.

**A5** The number of insects $N$ in a closed cage (assuming no escape route and no fatalities), $t$ days after the beginning of an experiment, can be modelled by the formula $N = 800 \times 1.5^t$. Estimate the value of $\dfrac{dN}{dt}$ when $t = 2$ by using two appropriate values of $t$.

**A6** At time $t$ hours the mass $M$ of a radioactive substance can be modelled by the formula $M = 20 \times 2.7^{-0.2t}$. Estimate the value of $\dfrac{dM}{dt}$ when $t = 5$ by first finding the values of $M$ corresponding to two appropriate values of $t$.

## Chapter 12: A level questions

**C1** Given the relationship $\frac{1}{v} = \frac{1}{f} - \frac{1}{u}$ and that $f = 9$ and $u = 16$ each correct to the nearest whole number, find

(a) the maximum possible value of $v$ giving your answer to 2 decimal places.

(b) Taking the true values of $f$ and $u$ as 9 and 16 respectively, calculate the percentage error in your value of $v$ found in part (a).

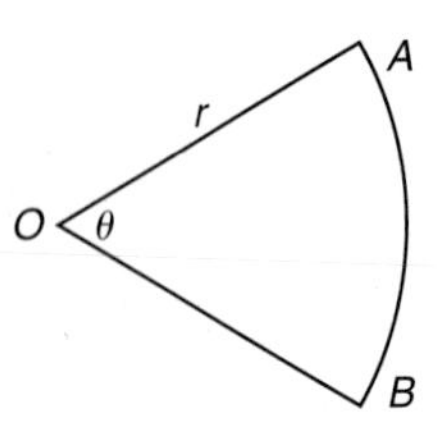


**C2** A piece of wire of length $p$ cm is bent into the shape of the sector $AOB$ shown in the diagram ($\theta$ in radians).

(a) Find $\theta$ in terms of $p$ and $r$

(b) Given that the length of the wire is 40 cm (to the nearest cm) and the radius of the sector is 11 cm (to the nearest cm) find the range of possible values of $\theta$. (You may be surprised how big it is!)

**C3** (a) Estimate $\int_0^{1.2} e^{\frac{x}{3}} dx$ using the trapezium rule and 4 strips.

(b) Calculate $\int_0^{1.2} e^{\frac{x}{3}} dx$

(c) Illustrate why the trapezium rule gives an overestimate of the area.

**C4** (a) Use the trapezium rule and 4 strips to estimate the area enclosed by the curve $y = 2^x$, the $x$ axis and the lines $x = -2$ and $x = 2$

(b) Using the fact that $\frac{d}{dx}(2^x) = 2^x\ln 2$ evaluate $\int_{-2}^{2} 2^x dx$ to 3 decimal places.

(c) Write down the error in using the trapezium rule for this area correct to 2 decimal places.

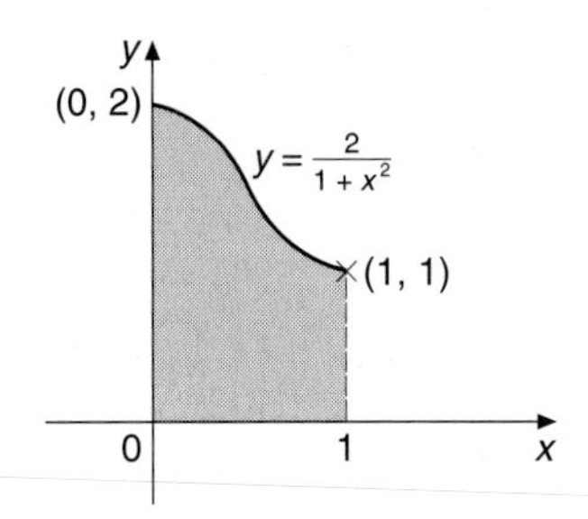


**C5** The diagram shows part of the curve $y = \frac{2}{1 + x^2}$, $0 \leqslant x \leqslant 1$

(a) Give reasons why 1.5 is a sensible guess for the area shaded in the diagram.

(b) Use the trapezium rule and strips of width 0.2 to estimate the value of $\int_0^1 \frac{2}{1 + x^2} dx$.
Give your answer to 2 decimal places.

(c) Given that $\int_0^1 \frac{1}{1 + x^2} dx = \frac{\pi}{4}$ estimate the percentage error in your answer calculated in part (b).

**C6** The value £$V$ of a car $t$ years after purchase can be modelled by the formula $V = 15\,000(0.8)^t$. Use a numerical method to estimate the rate of depreciation after 6 months and after 3 years. Comment on your answers.

**C7** (a) Show that $2 + x^2 - x^3 = 0$ has a root in the interval (1,2).

## Chapter 12: A level questions *continued*

(b) Starting with a first approximation of 1.5 and one application of the Newton Raphson formula obtain a better approximation to the root of $2 + x^2 - x^3 = 0$.

(c) Show that $x_{n+1} = \sqrt[3]{x_n^2 + 2}$ is a possible iterative formula for $2 + x^2 - x^3 = 0$ and use it with $x_1 = 1.7$ to find the values of $x_2$, $x_3$ and $x_4$ each to 3 decimal places. Use this evidence to estimate this root correct to 2 decimal places.

**C8** (a) If $f(x) \equiv x - 2\sin x$ show that $f(x) = 0$ has a root in the interval (1.5,2)

(b) Use the iteration $x_{n+1} = 2\sin x_n$ starting with $x_1 = 2$ to estimate the root to 1 decimal place, showing all the necessary working.

**C9** (a) Sketch the graph of $y = \tan 2x$ for $0 \leqslant x \leqslant \frac{\pi}{2}, \left(x \neq \frac{\pi}{4}\right)$.

(b) Show, by sketching another graph on the same axes that the equation $\tan 2x + 2x = 0$ has just one non zero root, $\alpha$, in the interval $0 \leqslant x \leqslant \frac{\pi}{2}$.

(c) Show that $\alpha$ lies in the interval (1,1.1) and determine $\alpha$ to 1 decimal place.

(d) If $y = x\sin 2x$, $0 \leqslant x \leqslant \frac{\pi}{2}$, has a stationary point at $P(a,b)$, then estimate the values of $a$ and $b$.

**C10**

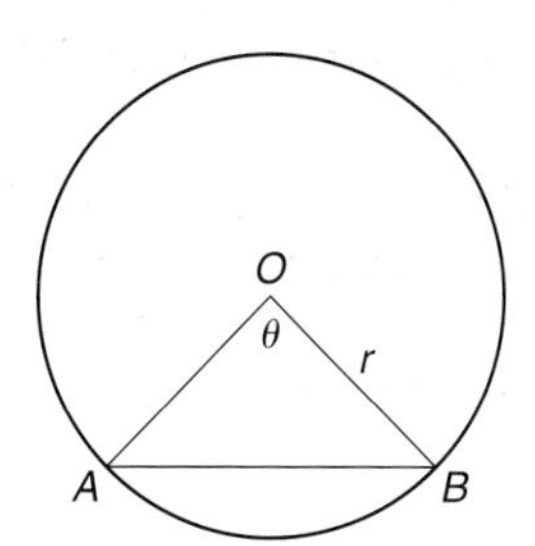


The diagram shows a circle, centre $O$ and radius $r$. Angle AOB = $\theta$ radians.

(a) Write down, in terms of $r$ and $\theta$, the area of triangle $AOB$ and the area of sector $AOB$.

(b) If the area of triangle $AOB$ is $\frac{2}{3}$ of the area of the sector $AOB$ show that $3\sin\theta - 2\theta = 0$.

(c) Given that $f(\theta) \equiv 3\sin\theta - 2\theta$ show that a root of the equation $f(\theta) = 0$ lies in the interval (1.4,1.5).

(d) Show that $\theta_{n+1} = \frac{3}{2}\sin\theta_n$ is a possible iterative formula for $f(\theta) = 0$ and starting with $\theta_1 = 1.5$ estimate the root of $f(\theta) = 0$ correct to 3 decimal places.

# ANSWERS

## Chapter 1

### Exercise 1.1

**A1** $2x^3 + x^2 - 2x + 8$
**A2** $2x^4 - 3x^3 - 4x^2 - 4x + 15$
**A3** $8x^3 - 36x^2 + 54x - 27$
**A4** $x^4 - 3x^3 - x^2 + 9x - 6$
**A5** $2x^3 - 5x^2 - x + 6$
**A6** $x^4 + 2x^3 - 3x^2 - 8x - 4$
**A7** $x + 3$
**A8** $x(x + 3)$
**A9** $\dfrac{x+3}{x-3}$
**A10** $\dfrac{x-3}{2-x}$

**B1** $-\dfrac{1}{12(x-2)}$
**B2** $\dfrac{4x-1}{2x(x-3)}$
**B3** $\dfrac{3x+8}{(x+2)^2}$
**B4** $\dfrac{3(1+x)}{(x+3)^2(3-x)}$
**B5** $\dfrac{5x+7}{(x-2)(x-1)(x+3)}$
**B6** $\dfrac{x(x+2)}{(x-1)(x-2)}$
**B7** $\dfrac{(x-2)(x+1)}{(1-x)x}$
**B8** $x^2 - 3x + 4 - \dfrac{3}{2x+5}$
**B9** $x^2 - 6 - \dfrac{27}{x-3}$
**B10** $2x^2 + x + 2 + \dfrac{11}{x-2}$

### Exercise 1.2

**A1** a) $4\sqrt{3}$ b) $9\sqrt{2}$ c) $20\sqrt{2}$ d) $2\sqrt{21}$
**A2** a) $\dfrac{\sqrt{3}}{3}$ b) $\sqrt{2}$ c) $\dfrac{5\sqrt{2}}{4}$ d) $\dfrac{\sqrt{5}}{5}$
**A3** a) $-11$ b) $47$
**A4** a) $7 + 4\sqrt{3}$ b) $86 - 60\sqrt{2}$
**A5** $148 - 53\sqrt{5}$

**B1** a) $-\dfrac{\sqrt{3}}{6}$ b) $\dfrac{\sqrt{5}}{4}$
**B2** a) $-\dfrac{16 + 7\sqrt{5}}{11}$ b) $\dfrac{2 - \sqrt{7}}{3}$
**B3** $-\frac{1}{60}$
**B4** $-7 - 5\sqrt{2}$
**B5** $p = -2$, $q = 2$

### Exercise 1.3

**A1** i) $x = \pm 2$ ii) $x = 5, 1$ iii) $x = 3, 7$
iv) $x = 2$ (repeated)
**A2** i) $x = 0, 4$ ii) $a = 0, b$
**A3** i) $x = 0, 3$ ii) $x = 0, -7$ iii) $x = 0, 4$
**A4** i) $x = 2a$ or $\dfrac{1}{2a}$ ii) $y = \dfrac{3}{a}$ or $\dfrac{7}{a}$
**A5** $x = \pm 2\sqrt{2}$ ii) $x = -1 \pm 2\sqrt{2}$
iii) $x = 3 \mp 2\sqrt{2}$
**A6** $x = 0, 3$
**A7** i) $x = 3, 1$ ii) $x = 2$ (repeated)
iii) $x^2 - 4x + 4 = -1$
i.e. $(x - 2)^2 < 0$ which isn't possible
**A8** a) $x = \pm 1, \pm 2$ b) $x = 9, 4$
**A9** i) $x = -2 \pm \sqrt{5}$ ii) $x = -2 \pm \sqrt{2}$
iii) $x = 28$ or $-32$
**A10** $x = \frac{7}{4}$

**B1** i) $x = 2$ or $-\frac{2}{3}$ ii) $x = \frac{3}{2} \pm \sqrt{2}$
**B2** $x = 3 \pm 3\sqrt{2}$
**B3** Dimensions are 28 by 20
**B4** i) $x = \frac{1}{2}$ or 1 ii) $x = -2, -\frac{1}{4}$
iii) $x = 3$ or 2
**B5** Length of AB $= 10\sqrt{2}$
**B6** i) $x = \dfrac{5 \pm \sqrt{33}}{2}$ ii) $x = 1 \pm \sqrt{\frac{5}{2}}$

**B7** i) $x = 5$ or $-1$ ii) $x = 2$ or $4$

**B8** a) $2^x = 3$ or $2^x = 1$ b) $x = 49$ or $1$

**B9** i) $x = \dfrac{3 \pm \sqrt{41}}{4}$ ii) $x = \dfrac{1 \pm \sqrt{2}}{2}$

**B10** i) $x = -\frac{2}{5}$ or $-12$ ii) $x = 0$ or $-\frac{22}{13}$
iii) $x = \frac{5}{2}$

## Exercise 1.4

**A1** $x = -3 \quad y = -13$
**A2** $x = \frac{1}{3} \quad y = 3$
**A3** $x = 8 \quad y = 2$
**A4** $x = 9 \quad y = 3$
**A5** $x = 6 \quad y = -2$
**A6** $x = -2 \quad y = -1$
**A7** $x = \frac{22}{23} \quad y = -\frac{16}{23}$
**A8** $x = -5 \quad y = -1$
**A9** $x = 3 \quad y = 4$
**A10** $x = 3 \quad y = 3$

**B1** $(8, -4)$ and $(2, 2)$
**B2** $(3, -4)$ and $(-2, -4)$
**B3** $(\sqrt{6}, 2)$ and $(-\sqrt{6}, 2)$
**B4** $x = 0 \quad y = 3$ A is $(0, 3)$ Area is $\frac{27}{4}$
**B5** $(-3, -1)$ and $(-1, 3)$
**B6** $x = \frac{1}{3}, 3$ Solutions are $(\frac{1}{3}, -\frac{13}{3})$ and $(3, 1)$
**B7** $y = -\frac{3}{5}, 1$ Solutions are $(2, 1)$ and $(-\frac{14}{5}, -\frac{3}{5})$
**B8** $x = 4, -3$ Solutions $(4, 5)$ and $(-3, 12)$
**B9** $x = \frac{7}{2}$ or $1$ Solutions $(\frac{7}{2}, -3)$ and $(1, 2)$
**B10** $x = \pm 3, \pm 4$ Solutions $(3, 4)(-3, -4)$, $(4, 3)$ and $(-4, -3)$

## Exercise 1.5

**A1** $\log_3 81 = 4$
$\log_2 32 = 5$
$\log_2 \sqrt{2} = \frac{1}{2}$
$\log_5 5 = 1$
$\log_4 4^{\frac{1}{3}} = \frac{1}{3}$

**A2** $\log_8 64 = 2$
$\log_{16} 4 = \frac{1}{2}$
$\log_7 1 = 0$
$\log_3 \frac{1}{81} = -4$

**A3** a) $\log \frac{9}{4}$ b) $\log 72$

**A4** $64^{-\frac{1}{2}} = \frac{1}{8} \quad 32^{\frac{3}{5}} = 8 \quad 27^{-\frac{2}{3}} = \frac{1}{9} \quad (\frac{16}{81})^{\frac{3}{4}} = \frac{8}{27}$
$\left(\dfrac{3^3}{2^6}\right)^{-\frac{1}{3}} = \frac{4}{3}$

**A5** $\log_2 8 = 3$
$\log_5 25 = 2$
$\log_3(\frac{1}{9}) = -2$
$\log_{10}(0.00001) = -5$
$\log_4 8 = \frac{3}{2}$

**A6** a) $\log_a(a^2) = 2$ b) $\log_b(\sqrt{b}) = \frac{1}{2}$
c) $\log_{10} 10000 = 4$ d) $\log_a 1 = 0$

**A7** $4 + \log_3 2$

**A8** a) $x = \ln 2 \approx 0.69$ b) $x = 3$
c) $x = \frac{1}{2} \ln 5 \approx 0.80$
d) $x = \log_{10} 1240 \approx 3.09$

**A9** $x = \dfrac{\log 9}{\log 2} \approx 3.17$

**A10** $x = \dfrac{\log 16}{\log 3} \approx 2.52$

**B1** $a = \pm 2$
**B2** $a = 10^2 = 100$
**B3** 3.672 (3 sfs)
**B4** $x - 1$
**B5** $x = -\frac{1}{2}$
**B6** $\log\left(\dfrac{x-2}{x+2}\right)$
**B7** $x = \dfrac{\log 2}{\log 5} \approx 0.431$ or $x = 1$
**B8** $x = 0$
**B9** $x = 3$ or $2$
**B10** $x = 3^9$ or $3$

## Exercise 1.6

**A1** i) $A = 3 \quad B = -7 \quad C = -2$
ii) $A = 6 \quad B = 0 \quad C = 9$
iii) $A = 0 \quad B = 3 \quad C = 0$
iv) $A = -1 \quad B = -2 \quad C = 6$
v) $A = 2 \quad B = 11 \quad C = 0$

**A2** i) $A = 4 \quad B = 3$
ii) $A = 10 \quad B = -12$

**A3** i) $A = 1 \quad B = 5$
ii) $A = 5 \quad B = 16$

**A4** $A = 1 \quad B = 20$

**A5** $A = 1 \quad B = 3 \quad C = -7$

**A6** $\dfrac{3}{x-1} - \dfrac{2}{x+2}$

**A7** $\dfrac{2}{4x-1} - \dfrac{1}{2x+3}$

**A8** $\dfrac{3}{5-2x} + \dfrac{2}{3+x}$

**A9** $\dfrac{3}{x+1} + \dfrac{2}{x-1}$

**A10** $\dfrac{2}{x} + \dfrac{4}{x+2} + \dfrac{3}{x-2}$

**B1** i) $A = 3 \quad B = 1 \quad C = 5$

ii) $A = \frac{10}{3}$ $B = -2$ $C = +\frac{5}{3}$

**B2** $A = 8$ $B = 18$ $C = 13$

**B3** $p = a,\ q = \dfrac{a-b}{2},\ r = \dfrac{c}{a}$

**B4** $A = \frac{1}{12}$ $C = -\frac{75}{2}$ $B = 5\frac{11}{12}$

**B5** $A = -\frac{2}{7}$ $C = -\frac{4}{7}$ $B = \frac{15}{7}$

**B6** $\dfrac{x+2}{x^2+1} + \dfrac{1}{2-x}$

**B7** $\dfrac{3x-2}{x^2+2x-1} + \dfrac{1}{x-2}$

**B8** $\dfrac{3}{x-2} - \dfrac{1}{x+1} - \dfrac{1}{(x+1)^2}$

**B9** $\dfrac{3}{(3-x)^2} - \dfrac{1}{3-x} + \dfrac{2}{1-2x}$

**B10** $3 + \dfrac{1}{x+1} + \dfrac{1}{x-1}$

**A level questions**

**C1** a) $x = 4$ b) $x = -1$ or 2

**C2** a) $x = 25$ or 2
If $x = 25$ $y = 4$ If $x = 2$ $y = 50$
b) $y^3 = 8$ or $y = 2$

**C3** a) $x = 2$ b) $x = \dfrac{\ln 4}{\ln 5} \approx 0.86$

**C4** i) $\log_a 1 = 0$ ii) $\log_a a = 1$
iii) $\log_a a^2 = 2$ iv) $\log_a\left(\dfrac{1}{a}\right) = -1$
i) $x = 2$ ii) $x = 3$ iii) $x = -13$ or 7

**C5** $P(x) \equiv x(x+2)^2$ $Q(x) \equiv x^2(x+2)(x-2)$
i) $A = 1$, $B = -4$ $C = 8$
ii) $R(x) \equiv 2x^2(x+2)(x+4)$ $x = 0, -2, -4$

**C6** $P(x) \equiv (x+1)(x-1)(x-2)(x-3)$
$x = \pm 1, 2$ or 3

**C7** $A = 10, B = 7, C = -1$ and $D = -10$

**C8** Sides are 20, 21 and 29 cm
Area $= \frac{1}{2} \times 20 \times 21 = 210\ \text{cm}^2$

**C9** a) $h_{max} = 20$ metres
b) $1 \leqslant t \leqslant 3$ 2 seconds
c) $t = 4$ Back after 4 secs

**C10** i) $x_1 + x_2 = 4$ ii) $x_1x_2 = -1$
iii) $\dfrac{1}{x_1} + \dfrac{1}{x_2} = -4$ iv) $x_1^2 + x_2^2 = 18$

# Chapter 2

**Exercise 2.1**

**A1** a) grad 3 thro' $(0, -2)$

**A3** min $(0, -9)$ thro' $(\pm 3, 0)$

**A5** a) touches $x$ axis at $(-1, 0)$ and thro' $(0, 1)$

**A7** b) thro' $(\pm 3, 0)$ and $(0, 0)$

**A10** a) $2y + 3x + 6 = 0$
b) Could be i) $y = -(x - 1\frac{1}{2})^2$
ii) $y = -(2x-3)^2$
iii) $y = k(2x-3)^2$ with $k < 0$
c) Probably $y = (x-1)(x-3)(x-6)$
d) Probably $y = -x^2(x-4)$ or $y = x^2(4-x)$

**Exercise 2.2**

**A1** a) $x < \frac{5}{2}$ b) $x < 2$ c) $x < \frac{1}{3}$

**A2** a) $x > -2$ b) $x < -2$ c) $x < 2$

**A3** a) $x < \frac{5}{3}$ b) $x < -3$ c) $x > -\frac{1}{4}$

**A4** $-4 < x < 1$

**A5** a) $x < -\frac{1}{2}$ or $x > 4$ b) $-1 < x < -\frac{1}{3}$
c) $x < -3$ or $x > 0$ d) $-8 < x < 8$
e) $-7 \leqslant x \leqslant 13$
f) $3 - 3\sqrt{2} \leqslant x \leqslant 3 + 3\sqrt{2}$

**A6** $x < 2$

**A7** $x \leqslant \frac{11}{2}$

**A8** a) $-3 < x < 3$ b) $x \leqslant 0$ or $x \geqslant 9$

**A9** $x \leqslant -\frac{2}{3}$ or $x \geqslant \frac{3}{2}$

**A10** $-1 < x < \frac{1}{2}$ or $x > 3$

**B1** a) $-9 < x < 1$ b) $-1 < x < 2$
c) $\frac{1}{3} < x < 1$

**B2** a) $-\frac{3}{2} < x < 12$ b) $-1 \leqslant x \leqslant 4$
c) $5 \leqslant x < 9$

**B3** $x < -4$ or $x > \frac{2}{3}$

**B4** $x < -\frac{3}{4}$ or $x > \frac{5}{3}$

**B5** $x \geqslant 3$ and also $x = \frac{1}{2}$

**B6** $-2 \leqslant x \leqslant 0$ or $x \geqslant 2$

**B7** $x < -\frac{1}{3}$ or $0 < x < \frac{5}{2}$

**B8** $x \geqslant \frac{25}{2}$ i.e. width must be at least $12\frac{1}{2}$ metres

**B9** a) The shorter side must not exceed 10 cm
b) Perimeter must not exceed
$(2 + \sqrt{2})10$ cm

**B10** a) $x = 4 \pm 2\sqrt{5}$, $4 - 2\sqrt{5} < x < 4 + 2\sqrt{5}$
b) If $(x^2 - 8x - 4)(x + 10) \leqslant 0$
$x \leqslant -10$ or $4 - 2\sqrt{5} \leqslant x \leqslant 4 + 2\sqrt{5}$

**Exercise 2.3**

**A1** a) $y = |x - 3|$ b) $y = x^2 + 2$
c) $y = (x+3)^2$ d) $y = -|x| - 1$ or $-(1 + |x|)$

**A2** $y = |x + 2| + 3$

**A3** $y = (x-3)^2 - 4$

**A4** $y = -(x-2)^2 + 4$ or $y = 4 - (x-2)^2$

**A5** $y = -|x - 5| - 2$

**B5** Possibly use $y = x(6 - x)$

**B6** $y = x^2$ trans $\begin{pmatrix} -2 \\ 4 \end{pmatrix}$

**B7** $y = x^2$ trans $\begin{pmatrix} 1 \\ -8 \end{pmatrix}$

**B8** $y = x^2$ reflected in $x$ axis to give $y = -x^2$ and then translated $\begin{pmatrix} -\frac{3}{2} \\ 8\frac{1}{4} \end{pmatrix}$

**B9** $y = x^2$ reflected in $x$ axis and translated $\begin{pmatrix} 3 \\ 17 \end{pmatrix}$

**B10** $y = (x - 3)(x - 1)$ translated $\begin{pmatrix} 0 \\ 2 \end{pmatrix}$

**Exercise 2.4**

**A1** a) $a = 1, b = -3, c = -11$
b) $a = 2, b = -2, c = -9$
c) $a = 3, b = -1, c = 2$

**A2** a) Min $y = -11$ at $x = -3$
b) Min $y = -9$ at $x = -2$
c) Min $y = 2$ at $x = -1$

**A3** a) Translate $\begin{pmatrix} -1 \\ 0 \end{pmatrix} \rightarrow$ stretch SF 2 $\parallel$ $y$ axis $\rightarrow$ trans $\begin{pmatrix} 0 \\ -5 \end{pmatrix}$
b) Trans $\begin{pmatrix} -1 \\ 0 \end{pmatrix} \rightarrow$ stretch SF $\frac{1}{2}$ $\parallel$ $y$ axis $\rightarrow$ trans $\begin{pmatrix} 0 \\ -5 \end{pmatrix}$
c) Trans $\begin{pmatrix} -1 \\ 0 \end{pmatrix} \rightarrow$ reflect in $x$ axis $\rightarrow$ stretch SF 2 $\parallel$ $y$ axis $\rightarrow$ trans $\begin{pmatrix} 0 \\ -5 \end{pmatrix}$

**A4** a) $y = (x - 3)^2 + 8$ has minimum 8 at $x = 3$
b) $y = 2(x - 3)^2 + 8$ has minimum 8 at $x = 3$
c) $y = 5 - 3(x - 4)^2$ has maximum 5 at $x = 4$

**A5** Minimum $-28$

**B1** $y = 2(x - 3)^2 - 7$, minimum $(3, -7)$

**B2** $y = \frac{1}{3}(x - 1)^2$, minimum $(1, 0)$

**B3** Both through $(-2, 0)$ and $(2, 0)$. Maxima $(0, 4)$ $(0, 8)$

**B4** Both through $(-3, 0)$, $(2, 0)$. Maxima at $(-\frac{1}{2}, 25)$ and $(-\frac{1}{2}, \frac{25}{4})$ $y = (2 - x)(x + 3)$ stretched SF 4

**B5** $y = x(4 - x)$ stretch SF $\frac{1}{2}$ $\parallel$ $y$ axis and translated $\begin{pmatrix} 0 \\ 3 \end{pmatrix}$ i.e. max $(2, 5)$

**A level questions**

**C1** $-4 < x < \frac{2}{3}$

**C2** $x(3 - x)(1 + x)$, $-1 \leqslant x \leqslant 0$ or $x \geqslant 3$

**C3** i) $(x - 3)^2 - 7$ ii) $x = 3 \pm \sqrt{7}$
iii) Zeros at $-2, 3 \pm \sqrt{7}$
iv) $(x + 2)(x^2 - 6x + 2) < 0$ when $x < -2$ or $3 - \sqrt{7} < x < 3 + \sqrt{7}$

**C4** Intersect at $(1\frac{1}{2}, 3\frac{1}{2})$, $x \leqslant 1\frac{1}{2}$

**C5** $a = 2, b = 1, c = -3$ Translate $\begin{pmatrix} -1 \\ 0 \end{pmatrix}$, stretch S.F.2 parallel to $y$ axis and then translate $\begin{pmatrix} 0 \\ -3 \end{pmatrix}$ Turning point $(-1, -3)$ (a minimum) Line of symmetry $x = -1$ (zeros at $x = -1 \pm \sqrt{\frac{3}{2}}$)

**C6** Dimensions of pen are 25 by 50 metres (max area is 1250 m$^2$)

**C7** $k = 5$. Smallest value of OP is $\sqrt{5}$ $z_{min} = 1$ (when P is (2, 1))

**C8** Graphs meet at (0, 0), (5, 5). A is (3, 9) B is (2, −4) Area is 65

**C9** Pts (4, 5), $(\frac{2}{3}, 1\frac{2}{3})$ $|2x + 3| < x + 1$ gives $\frac{2}{3} < x < 4$

**C10** Area is $\frac{a^2}{4}$ P is $\left(\frac{a}{4}, \frac{a}{4}\right)$ Q is $\left(\frac{a}{2}, \frac{a}{2}\right)$ R is $(a/3, 0)$

# Chapter 3

**Exercise 3.1**

**A1** 1, 4, 9, 16, ...

**A2** −3, −1, 1, 3, ...

**A3** 1, 8, 27, 64, ...

**A4** $\frac{1}{2}, \frac{1}{3}, \frac{1}{4}, \frac{1}{5}, \ldots$

**A5** $-1, \frac{1}{4}, -\frac{1}{9}, \frac{1}{16}, \ldots$

**A6** A1 divergent
A2 divergent
A3 divergent
A4 convergent
A5 oscillating

**A7** $t_r = 10 - 2r$ $t_4 = 2$ $t_9 = -8$ $t_{10} = -10$

**A8** $t_r = (2r + 1)(r + 2)$ $t_4 = 54$ $t_9 = 209$ $t_{10} = 252$

**A9** $t_r = r + \dfrac{2}{r}$ $t_4 = 4\frac{1}{2}$ $t_9 = 9\frac{2}{9}$ $t_{10} = 10\frac{1}{5}$

**A10** i) $t_r = (-1)^r$ $t_4 = 1$ $t_9 = -1$ $t_{10} = 1$
ii) $t_r = (-1)^{r+1}$ $t_4 = -1$ $t_9 = 1$ $t_{10} = -1$

**B1** $4, 2, 1, \frac{1}{2}, \ldots$ convergent
**B2** $2, 3, 8, 63, \ldots$ divergent
**B3** $0, 4, -12, -140, \ldots$ divergent
**B4** $-\frac{1}{2}, +\frac{1}{4}, -\frac{1}{8}, +\frac{1}{16}, \ldots$ convergent
**B5** $0, 3, 6, 3, (-12, -33, \ldots)$ divergent
**B6** $0, 2, 0, 2, \ldots$ periodic
**B7** $1, 8, 19, 32, \ldots$ divergent
**B8** $2, 1, 0, 1, \ldots$ divergent
**B9** $-2, 0, 2, 4, \ldots$ divergent
**B10** $0, 8, 0, 32, \ldots$ divergent

## Exercise 3.2

**A1** i) 30 ii) 45
**A2** i) $\sum_{r=1}^{6} r^2$ ii) $\sum_{r=5}^{8} r^2$ iii) $\sum_{r=10}^{12} r^2$
**A3** i) $10a + 4$ ii) $21a^2 + 21$ iii) $70a$
**A4** i) $\sum_{r=8}^{12} r$ ii) $\sum_{r=8}^{50} r$ iii) $\sum_{r=1}^{25} 2r$
**A5** i) $-119$ ii) $-170$

**B1** i) $\frac{9}{6} + \frac{11}{7} + \frac{13}{8} + \frac{15}{9} + \ldots + \frac{97}{50}$
ii) $\frac{1}{1} + \frac{1}{4} + \frac{1}{9} + \frac{1}{16} + \ldots + \frac{1}{49}$
**B2** i) $1 + \frac{1}{2} + \frac{1}{4} + \frac{1}{8} + \ldots + \dfrac{1}{2^{17}}$
ii) $0.1 + 0.01 + 0.001 + 0.0001 + \ldots + 0.000001$
**B3** $-16 - 2 + 0 + 2 + \ldots + 2000$
**B4** $0 - 1 + 2 - 3 + \ldots + 10$
**B5** $2 - 5 + 10 - 17 + \ldots - 401$

## Exercise 3.3

**A1** a) $2, 5, 8, \ldots, 41, \ldots$
b) $7, 5, 3, \ldots, -19, \ldots$
c) $6, 13, 20, \ldots, 97, \ldots$
d) $-5, -9, -13, \ldots, -57, \ldots$
**A2** a) 301 b) $-84$ c) 721 d) $-434$
**A3** a) $n = 11$ b) $n = 21$
**A4** 3600
**A5** 3660
**A6** a) 1010 b) $-272$
**A7** a) 360 b) 473
**A8** a) 110 b) 470
**A9** a) 145 b) 75
**A10** 3050

**B1** $a = 7$, $d = 3$, $t_{50} = -140$, $S_{50} = -3325$
**B2** $d = -6$, $n = 11$
**B3** 500500
**B4** $n = 24$
**B5** i) 99 ii) $d = \frac{1}{2}$ iii) $22\frac{1}{2}$
**B6** 867
**B7** $n = 20$
**B8** $7 + 11 + 15 + 19 + \ldots$
**B9** The numbers are 3, 10 and 17

## Exercise 3.4

**A1** a) $2^{-18}$ b) $2^{39}$ c) $-3 \times 2^{19}$ d) $-3^{-18}$
**A2** a) $4\left(1 - \dfrac{1}{2^{20}}\right)$ b) $\frac{5}{3}(4^{20} - 1)$
c) $-3(2^{20} - 1)$ d) $4\left(1 - \dfrac{1}{3^{20}}\right)$
**A3** a) $\frac{511}{2}$ b) $5000\left(1 - \dfrac{1}{5^7}\right)$
**A4** a) $2(2^{10} - 1)$ b) $\frac{1}{3}(1 + 2^9)$
**A5** a) $\frac{9}{4}\left(1 - \dfrac{1}{3^8}\right)$ b) $\frac{32}{3}\left(1 - \dfrac{1}{4^7}\right)$
**A6** a) $\frac{1}{24}(4^5 - 1)$ b) $\frac{243}{4}\left(1 + \dfrac{1}{3^{10}}\right)$
**A7** a) $16\left(1 - \dfrac{1}{2^{10}}\right)$ b) $\frac{27}{5}[1 - (\frac{2}{3})^8]$
**A8** $6(2^8 - 1)$
**A9** $r = -3$ or 2. Only $r = 2$ possible as terms are positive
**A10** $t_{12} = -\dfrac{4}{3^9}$, $27\left(1 - \dfrac{1}{3^{10}}\right)$

**B1** 1
**B2** $S_1 = -6$, $S_2 = 12$, $S_3 = -42$, $S_4 = 120$ $S_n = \frac{3}{2}[(-3)^n - 1]$
**B3** $n = 9$
**B4** £2000 $\dfrac{(1.07)^8 - 1}{0.07} \approx$ £20 519.61
**B5** height $\frac{64}{729}d$, distance $= 5d[1 - (\frac{2}{3})^6]$
**B6** $-63$
**B7** $r = \frac{1}{2}$
**B8** Numbers are 25, 35 and 49. Ratio is $\frac{7}{5}$
**B9** Series could be $54 + 18 + 6 + 2 + \ldots$ or $108 - 36 + 12 - 4 + \ldots$
*Not* unique
**B10** $n = 8$

### Exercise 3.5

**A1** a) $1 - 4x + 6x^2 - 4x^3 + x^4$
b) $1 + 6x + 15x^2 + 20x^3 + 15x^4 + 6x^5 + x^6$
**A2** a) $1 - 15x + 90x^2 - 270x^3 + 405x^4 - 243x^5$
b) $16 - 32x + 24x^2 - 8x^3 + x^4$
**A3** a) $1 + 16x + 112x^2 + 448x^3 + \ldots$
b) $1 - 30x + 405x^2 - 3240x^3 + \ldots$
c) $2^9 + 3^3 \cdot 2^8x + 3^4 \cdot 2^9x^2 + 7.3^4 \cdot 2^8x^3 + \ldots$
**A4** a) $1 + 100x + 190 \times 25x^2 + 1140 \times 125x^3 + \ldots + 5^{20}x^{20}$
b) $1 - 100x + 190 \times 25x^2 - 1140 \times 125x^3 + \ldots + 5^{20}x^{20}$
c) $2^{10} + 10.2^9x + 45.2^8x^2 + 120.2^7x^3 + \ldots + x^{10}$
**A5** a) $1 - 2x + \frac{3x^2}{2} - \frac{x^3}{2} + \frac{x^4}{16}$
b) $1 - 4px + 6p^2x^2 - 4p^3x^3 + p^4x^4$
**A6** $p^5 + 5p^4qx + 10p^3q^2x^2 + 10p^2q^3x^3 + 5pq^4x^4 + q^5x^5$
**A7** $3 - 32x + 132x^2 + \ldots$
**A8** $64 + 704x + 2800x^2 + \ldots$
**A9** $1 - 18x + 128x^2 + \ldots$
**A10** 256.1024179218 correct to 10 dp

**B1** a) $1120x^4$ b) 252 c) 540
**B2** $-5376$
**B3** i) $17 + 12\sqrt{2}$ ii) $25 - 22\sqrt{2}$
iii) $198\sqrt{2} - 280$
**B4** i) $-2x(5 + 10x^2 + x^4)$
ii) $1 - 5x^2 + 10x^4 - 10x^6 + 5x^8 - x^{10}$
**B5** $1024 + 1280x + 640x^2 + 160x^3 + 20x^4 + x^5$ 1011.2638401999
**B6** $3^8x^6$
**B7** $-2^5 \times 3^3 \times 7 \times 29x^5$
**B8** i) $2^6 \times 3^2 \times 5^4 \times 7$ ii) $2^6 \times 3^6 \times 7$
**B9** $\frac{14}{25}$
**B10** $2(16x + 448x^3 + 1792x^5 + 1024x^7)$

### A level questions

**C1** $t_{12} = 47$
$S_{12} = 300$
$a + 11d = 47$
$6(2a + 11d) = 300$
$\left.\begin{array}{l} a + 11d = 47 \\ 2a + 11d = 50 \end{array}\right\} a = 3$
$\therefore 11d = 44$
$d = 4$
$t_7 = a + 6d = 3 + 24 = 27$
$= 3^3$
$= a^3$
Hence shown.
**C2** $3 + 6 + 9 + 12 + 15 + \ldots$ We require 45 terms
**C3** $t_n = x^{2n-1}$, $S_n = \dfrac{x(1 - x^{2n})}{1 - x^2}$
**C4** It took just over 23 months to double length
i) Fathers underestimate is about 5.4 months
ii) Mothers overestimate is about 6.6 months
**C5** Required angle is 18°.
**C6** $a : b = 8 : 7$
**C7** a) $n = 20$ b) $n = 9$
**C8** i) $t_5 = \frac{1}{2}$ $t_6 = -\frac{1}{4}$
ii) $t_{r+2} : t_r = 1 : 4$ iii) $\frac{16}{3}$
**C9** Plan is worth £8870.16
**C10** 1.005010010005001
**C11** $r = \frac{1}{10}$ $S_5 = 9.9999$ Ratio 9 : 1

## Chapter 4

### Exercise 4.1

**A1** $\sqrt{8^2 + 5^2} \approx 9.43$ km, 302.0°
**A2** $\sqrt{5^2 + 4^2} \approx 6.40$ km, 308.7°
**A3** Dist ≈ 15.93 km, 081.7°
**A4** Bearing ≈ 115.0° Dist ≈ 15.85 km
**A5** Area ≈ 93.97 cm²
**A6** Area = 120 mm²
**A7** Area ≈ 28.44 cm² b ≈ 6.73
**A8** Area ≈ 6.10 cm² a ≈ 3.60
**A9** Area ≈ 18.97 cm² A = 115.4°
**A10** Area ≈ 11.68 cm² A = 90°

**B1** Area ≈ 21.06 cm²
**B2** Area ≈ 4 × 9.165 = 36.66 cm² Perimeter 26.33 cm
**B3** C = 30° or 150°
**B4** Side = 4.30 cm (2 dp)
**B5** Difference ≈ 8.94 cm
**B6** Dist ≈ 8.62 km Bearing ≈ 025.8°
**B7** Dist ≈ $\sqrt{12^2 + 2.660^2} \approx 12.29$ km Bearing 102.5°
**B8** X = 46.6° Y = 29.0°
Z = 104.5° each to 1 dp
**B9** C = 22.6° (1 dp) $b$ = 19.22 cm (1 dp)
Area = 40.61 cm² (2 dp)
**B10** Possible lengths are $5\sqrt{3} \pm 2\sqrt{6} \approx 13.56$ and 3.76

### Exercise 4.2

**A1** It takes about 66 secs and average speed is 0.94 ms$^{-1}$ (2 dp)

**A2** i) $\tan^{-1}\frac{3}{4} \approx 36.9°$

ii) $\tan^{-1}\left(\frac{3}{\sqrt{32}}\right) \approx 27.9°$

iii) $\tan^{-1}\left(\frac{3}{2\sqrt{2}}\right) \approx 46.7°$

**A3** CD is 17.94 cm (2 dp)

**A4** i) $\tan^{-1}\left(\frac{10}{\sqrt{32}}\right) \approx 60.5°$

ii) $\tan^{-1}(\frac{10}{4}) \approx 68.2°$

**A5** i) 64.6° ii) 31.0° iii) 73.4°

**B1** $\sin^{-1}\left(\frac{1}{\sqrt{3}}\right) \approx 35.26°$

**B2** 9.03° (2 d.p.)

**B3** a) $\tan^{-1}\left(\frac{\text{VO}}{\text{OB}}\right) = \tan^{-1}\left(\frac{h}{\sqrt{a^2+b^2}}\right)$

b) $\tan^{-1}\left(\frac{h}{b}\right)$

c) $\tan^{-1}\frac{\text{VO}}{\text{ON}} = \tan^{-1}\left(\frac{h}{a}\right)$

**B4** Required angle is approx 20.2°

**B5** Angle between planes is 46.7° (1 dp)

**Exercise 4.3**

**A1** $\frac{\pi}{6}, 4\pi, \frac{5\pi}{6}, \frac{\pi}{4}, \frac{\pi}{10}$

**A2** a) Arc = 2.4 cm Area = 14.4 cm$^2$

b) Arc = 5.13 cm Area ≈ 14.62 cm$^2$

c) Arc = $\frac{10\pi}{3}$ Area = $\frac{50\pi}{3}$

**A3** a) $\frac{8^c}{25}$ Arc = $25 \times \frac{8}{25} = 8$ cm, Add $\frac{8^c}{25}$ first then 8 cm part

b) Angle $2^c$ Arc = $10 \times 2 = 20$ cm

**A4** 4.02 cm$^2$

**A5** Area 0.008 m$^2$ Perimeter 0.48 m

**A6** i) $\frac{24\pi}{5}$ cm ii) $\frac{56\pi}{5}$ cm iii) 28.02 cm

**A7** i) 24 cm ii) 38.83 cm iii) 42.64 cm

**A8** i) 43.01 cm$^2$ ii) 148.13 cm$^2$ iii) 12.96 cm$^2$

**A9** i) 11.37 cm$^2$ ii) 46.72 cm$^2$ iii) 55.4 cm$^2$ (1 dp)

**B1** Area ≈ 0.50 cm$^2$

**B2** Radius 40 cm $\theta = \frac{3}{4}^c$

**B3** Radius 12 cm angle $\frac{\pi}{6}^c$

**B4** Vol ≈ 101567 cm$^3$ = 0.1016 m$^3$

**B6** i) Segment ≈ $(0.251)r^2$

ii) Segment ≈ $(0.352)r^2$

**B7** i) Perim ≈ 47.13 cm

ii) Area ≈ 165.0 cm$^2$

**B8** Required area is 8.18 cm$^2$ (2 dp)

Boundary = 12.9 cm (1 dp)

**B9** Area ≈ 2.54 cm$^2$ Perim ≈ 12.55 cm

**B10** Shaded area ≈ $(0.161)r^2$

Exact area = $\frac{1}{2}r^2(2\sqrt{3}-\pi)$

**Exercise 4.4**

**A1** i) 48.6, 131.4 ii) ±131.8

iii) 63.4, −116.6

iv) no solutions as $|\cos\theta| \leqslant 1$

**A2** i) −360, −180, 0, 180, 360

ii) ±90, ±270 iii) 0, ±180, ±360

**A3** $\sin\theta = 1$ or $\sin\theta = \frac{1}{2}$

↓ ↓

90, −270 30, 150, −330, −210

**A4** i) $\frac{\pi}{2}, -\frac{3\pi}{2}$ ii) $\pm\pi$

iii) $\frac{\pi}{4}, \frac{5\pi}{4}, -\frac{3\pi}{4}, -\frac{7\pi}{4}$

**A5** $\sin^2\theta = \frac{1}{16} \Rightarrow \sin\theta = \pm\frac{1}{4}$

$\sin\theta = \frac{1}{4}$ gives $\theta \approx 14.5, 165.5$

$\sin\theta = -\frac{1}{4}$ gives $\theta \approx 194.5, 345.5$

**A6** i) −60, −120, 300, 240

ii) ±45, ±315 iii) −30, −210, 150, 330

**A7** $\sin\theta = 0$ or $\cos\theta = 1$

↓ ↓

$\theta = 0, \pm180, 360$ 0, 360

$\cos\theta = 1$ solutions are amongst those of $\sin\theta = 0$ and give no extra values

**A8** i) $\frac{\pi}{3}, \frac{4\pi}{3}, -\frac{2\pi}{3}, -\frac{5\pi}{3}$

ii) $\frac{2\pi}{5}, \frac{3\pi}{5}, -\frac{8\pi}{5}, -\frac{7\pi}{5}$

**A9** Only solution is $\theta = 180$

**A10** i) $\sin A = \frac{5}{13}$ $\tan A = \frac{5}{12}$

ii) $\cos B = -\frac{15}{17}$ $\tan B = -\frac{8}{15}$

**B1** i) $X = \frac{\pi}{6}, \frac{5\pi}{6}$ ii) $x - \frac{\pi}{2} = \frac{\pi}{6}, \frac{5\pi}{6}$

so $x = \frac{2\pi}{3}$ or $\frac{4\pi}{3}$

**B2** i) $\theta = 30, 150, -90$ ii) $\theta = \pm 45, \pm 135$

iii) $\frac{\theta}{2} = -45$ i.e. $\theta = -90$

**B3** i) $X = \pi$

ii) $x + \frac{\pi}{3} = \pi$ so $x = \frac{2\pi}{3}$

**B4** i) $x = -\frac{\pi}{6}, -\frac{\pi}{3}, \frac{5\pi}{6}, \frac{2\pi}{3}$

ii) $x = \pm\frac{4\pi}{9}, \pm\frac{8\pi}{9}$

iii) $x = -\frac{\pi}{4}, -\pi, \frac{\pi}{2}$

**B5** a) $X = 45, 225$ b) $x = 65, 245$

**B6** i) $x = \frac{\pi}{6}, \frac{5\pi}{6}, \frac{7\pi}{6}, \frac{11\pi}{6}$

ii) $x = \frac{\pi}{12}, \frac{11\pi}{12}, \frac{13\pi}{12}, \frac{23\pi}{12},$

$\frac{5\pi}{12}, \frac{7\pi}{12}, \frac{17\pi}{12}, \frac{19\pi}{12}$

iii) $x = \frac{\pi}{2}, \frac{3\pi}{2}$

**B7** i) $\theta = 20, 140$ ii) $\theta = 30, 90, -90, -150$

**B8** i) $\theta = 179.7, 113.3$ (1 dp)

ii) $\theta = -5.2, -32.8, 87.2, -125.2, 114.8, -152.8$ (1 dp)

**B9** $x = 1.07, 2.35$ (2 dp)

**B10** $x = 0, -\frac{\pi}{3}$

**A level questions**

**C1** Distance $25\sqrt{2}$ km $\approx 35.36$ km

Bearing is 095°

**C2** i) Dist is $= 19\frac{1}{2}$ cm

ii) Dist is $\approx 13.1$ cm

iii) Time will be about 08.10 + 3.11 i.e. 11.21

**C3** $\frac{\pi}{3} \leqslant x \leqslant \frac{2\pi}{3}$ or $\frac{4\pi}{3} \leqslant x \leqslant \frac{5\pi}{3}$

**C4** $\sin C = \frac{\sqrt{7}}{4}$,

Area $= 375\sqrt{7}$ m$^2$

**C5** Area $= 4(6 + \sqrt{17})$ or $4(6 - \sqrt{17})$

**C6** i) $\Delta AOB = \frac{1}{2}r^2$

iii) Sector AOB $= \frac{1}{4}\pi r^2$ sector BOD $= \frac{1}{2}r^2\theta$

iv) When $\theta = \frac{\pi}{12}$ this is $\frac{1}{2}r^2\left(1 + \frac{\pi}{6} - \frac{\sqrt{3}}{2}\right)$

**C7** $\phi = 30°$

**C8** i) $\angle AOC = \pi - \theta$

$$\begin{aligned} AC^2 &= r^2 + r^2 - 2rr\cos(\pi - \theta) \\ &= 2r^2 - 2r^2(-\cos\theta) \text{ because } \cos(\pi - \theta) = -\cos\theta \\ &= 2r^2 + 2r^2\cos\theta \\ AC &= \sqrt{2r^2(1 + \cos\theta)} \\ &= r\sqrt{2}(1 + \cos\theta)^{\frac{1}{2}} \end{aligned}$$

ii) $\Delta BOC = \frac{1}{2}r^2 \sin\theta$

$\Delta AOC = \frac{1}{2}r^2 \sin(\pi - \theta)$

But $\sin(\pi - \theta) = \theta$ hence result

iii) $\theta = \frac{\pi}{3}$

**C9** i) $h = 6 - 5\cos\theta$

ii) $h = 3.5, \theta = 60°$ $h = 6, \theta = 90°$

$h = 11, \theta = 180°$

iii) Dist $= \frac{25\pi}{9}$ m ($\approx 8.73$)

Dist $= \frac{25\pi}{2}$ m ($\approx 39.3$)

**C10** i) 0300 hrs ii) 0600 hrs and 1200 hrs

iii) 0900 hrs iv) 0100 and 0500 hrs

# Chapter 5

## Exercise 5.1

**A1** i) $\theta = 60, 300$ ii) $\theta \approx 199.5, 340.5$

iii) $\theta \approx 63.4, 243.4$

**A2** i) $x = -\frac{\pi}{3}, \pi, -\pi$

ii) $x \approx 1.03, 2.34, -0.80, -2.12$

iii) $x = \frac{1}{2} + \frac{\pi}{8}, \frac{1}{2} + \frac{5\pi}{8}, \ldots,$

$\frac{1}{2} - \frac{3\pi}{8}, \frac{1}{2} - \frac{7\pi}{8}, \ldots$

**A3** $\theta = \pm 45, \pm 135$

**A4** i) $\theta \approx 51.3, -128.7$ ii) $\theta = -45, 135$

**A5** i) $\theta = 45, 135, -45, -135$

ii) $\theta = \pm 60, \pm 120$

**A6** a) $\theta = 90, 270, \theta = 30, 150$

b) $\theta = 0, 180, 360$ or $\theta \approx 70.5, 289.5$

**A7** $x = \pm\frac{\pi}{3}, \pm\frac{5\pi}{3}, \pm\pi$

**A8** $\sin\theta° = 1$ gives $\theta = 90$
$\sin\theta° = -\frac{2}{3}$ gives $\theta \approx -41.8, -138.2$

**A9** $\tan\theta° = 3$ gives $\theta \approx 71.6, 251.6$
$\tan\theta° = -2$ gives $\theta \approx 116.6, 296.6$

**Exercise 5.2**

**A1** a) $\tan\theta = \pm\frac{12}{5}$ b) $\sec\theta = \pm\frac{17}{8}$

**A2** a) $\theta = 30, 150$ b) $\theta = 0, 360$

**A3** a) $\theta \approx 199.5, 340.5$ or $\theta = 30, 150$
b) $\theta = 60, 300$

**A4** a) $\theta \approx 116.6, 296.6$ or $\theta = 135, 315$
b) $\theta \approx 48.2, 311.8$ or $\theta = 60, 300$

**A5** a) $\theta = 45, 225$ b) $\theta = 199.5, 340.5, 30, 150$

**A6** $\theta = 120, 300, 135, 315$

**A7** a) $\theta \approx 109.5, 250.5$ b) $\theta \approx 14.5, 166.5$

**A8** a) $x^2 + y^2 = 1$ b) $x^2 + 4y^2 = 4$

**A9** a) $\sin^2\theta$ b) 2 c) $\cot^2\theta$

**A10** a) $9x^2 - 4y^2 = 36$ b) $4x^2 - 9y^2 = 36$

**B1** $\text{LHS} \equiv \sin^2\theta + 4\cos^2\theta$
$\equiv \sin^2\theta + 4(1 - \sin^2\theta)$
$\equiv \sin^2\theta + 4 - 4\sin^2\theta$
$\equiv 4 - 3\sin^2\theta$
$\equiv \text{RHS}$

**B2** $\text{LHS} \equiv (\sin\theta + \operatorname{cosec}\theta)^2$
$\equiv \sin^2\theta + \operatorname{cosec}^2\theta + 2\sin\theta\operatorname{cosec}\theta$
$\equiv \sin^2\theta + 1 + \cot^2\theta + 2$
$\equiv \sin^2\theta + \cot^2\theta + 3$
$\equiv \text{RHS}$

**B3** $\text{LHS} \equiv \cos\theta - \sec\theta$
$\equiv \cos\theta - \frac{1}{\cos\theta}$
$\equiv \frac{\cos^2\theta - 1}{\cos\theta} \equiv -\frac{1 - \cos^2\theta}{\cos\theta}$
$\equiv -\frac{\sin^2\theta}{\cos\theta} \equiv -\frac{\sin\theta}{\cos\theta}\cdot\sin\theta$
$\equiv -\sin\theta\tan\theta$
$\equiv \text{RHS}$

**B4** $\text{LHS} \equiv \operatorname{cosec}^2\theta(\tan^2\theta - \sin^2\theta)$
$\equiv \frac{1}{\sin^2\theta}\left(\frac{\sin^2\theta}{\cos^2\theta} - \sin^2\theta\right)$
$\equiv \frac{1}{\cos^2\theta} - 1$
$\equiv \sec^2\theta - 1$
$\equiv \tan^2\theta$
$\equiv \text{RHS}$

**B5** $\text{LHS} \equiv (\cos\theta + \sin\theta)^2 + (\cos\theta - \sin\theta)^2$
$\equiv \cos^2\theta + 2\cos\theta\sin\theta + \sin^2\theta + \cos^2\theta - 2\cos\theta\sin\theta + \sin^2\theta$
$\equiv 2\cos^2\theta + 2\sin^2\theta$
$\equiv 2(\cos^2\theta + \sin^2\theta) \equiv 2$
$\equiv \text{RHS}$

**B6** $\tan\theta + \cot\theta$
$\equiv \tan\theta + \frac{1}{\tan\theta}$
$\equiv \frac{\tan^2\theta + 1}{\tan\theta}$
$\equiv \frac{\sec^2\theta}{\tan\theta}$
$\equiv \sec\theta\cdot\frac{\sec\theta}{\tan\theta} \equiv \sec\theta\cdot\frac{\sec\theta\cos\theta}{\sin\theta}$
$\equiv \frac{\sec\theta}{\sin\theta} \equiv \sec\theta\operatorname{cosec}\theta$

**B7** $\frac{1 - \tan^2\theta}{1 + \tan^2\theta} \equiv \frac{1 - \tan^2\theta}{\sec^2\theta}$
$\equiv (1 - \tan^2\theta)\cos^2\theta$
$\equiv \cos^2\theta - \frac{\sin^2\theta}{\cos^2\theta}\cos^2\theta$
$\equiv (1 - \sin^2\theta) - \sin^2\theta$
$\equiv 1 - 2\sin^2\theta = \text{RHS}$

**B8** $\operatorname{cosec} x - \sin x$
$\equiv \frac{1}{\sin x} - \sin x \equiv \frac{1 - \sin^2 x}{\sin x} \equiv \frac{\cos^2 x}{\sin x}$
$\equiv \cos x\cdot\frac{\cos x}{\sin x} \equiv \cos x\cdot\cot x$

$\sec x - \cos x$
$\equiv \frac{1}{\cos x} - \cos x \equiv \frac{1 - \cos^2 x}{\cos x}$
$\equiv \frac{\sin^2 x}{\cos x} \equiv \sin x\cdot\tan x$

$\therefore (\operatorname{cosec} x - \sin x)(\sec x - \cos x)$
$\equiv \cos x\cot x\sin x\tan x$
$\equiv \sin x\cos x\cdot\tan x\cot x$
$\equiv \sin x\cos x$ (as $\tan x\cot x \equiv 1$)

**B9** a) $(y - 3)^2 = 4 + (x + 1)^2$
b) $4(2 - y)^2 + 9(3 - x)^2 = 36$
c) $x^2 + y^2 = 2$

**B10** $z = \frac{2}{\tan^2\theta}$, $\theta = 150$ or $\frac{5\pi}{6}$

**Exercise 5.3**

**A1** a) $\frac{120}{169}$ b) $\frac{119}{169}$ c) $\frac{120}{119}$

**A2** a) $-\frac{24}{25}$ b) $\frac{25}{7}$ c) $-\frac{24}{7}$

**A3** a) $-\frac{15}{17}$ b) $\frac{8}{17}$ c) $-\frac{240}{289}$

**A4** a) $\dfrac{1}{\sqrt{3}}$ b) $\sqrt{\dfrac{2}{3}}$

**A6** a) $\theta = 0, 180, 360$ or $\theta \approx 80.4, 279.6$
b) $\theta = 90, 270$ or $\theta \approx 7.18, 172.82$

**A7** $\theta = \pm 120$

**A9** $\tan\dfrac{\theta}{2} = \frac{1}{4}$ or $-4$ b) $\tan\dfrac{\theta}{2} = -\frac{1}{5}$ or $+5$

**A10** a) $\text{LHS} \equiv \dfrac{\sin 2\theta}{1 - \cos 2\theta}$

$$\equiv \frac{2\sin\theta\cos\theta}{1 - (1 - 2\sin^2\theta)} \equiv \frac{2sc}{2s^2}$$

$$\equiv \frac{\cos\theta}{\sin\theta} \equiv \cot\theta$$

$\equiv \text{RHS}$

b) $\text{LHS} \equiv \dfrac{1 + \cos 2\theta}{\sin 2\theta} \equiv \dfrac{2c^2}{2sc} \equiv \dfrac{c}{s}$

$\equiv \cot\theta$
$\equiv \text{RHS}$

**B1** i) $-\frac{117}{44}$ ii) $\frac{117}{125}$ iii) $-\frac{44}{125}$

**B2** i) $-\frac{24}{7}$ ii) $\frac{7}{25}$ iii) $-\frac{24}{25}$ iv) $-\frac{336}{625}$ v) $\frac{336}{527}$

**B3** i) $x = 0, \pm\dfrac{\pi}{4}, \pm\dfrac{3\pi}{4} \pm \pi$ ii) $x = \pm\dfrac{2\pi}{3}, 0$

iii) $x = 0, \pm\pi$ or $x = \dfrac{\pi}{4}, -\dfrac{3\pi}{4}$

**B4** $\frac{24}{25}$ $\tan\dfrac{\theta}{2} = \frac{1}{3}$ or $-3$

**B5** Given $\cos 2\theta = \dfrac{1 - t^2}{1 + t^2}$ $(t = \tan\theta)$ and

knowing that $\tan 2\theta = \dfrac{2t}{1 - t^2}$

then $\sec 2\theta + \tan 2\theta$

$$= \frac{1 + t^2}{1 - t^2} + \frac{2t}{1 - t^2} = \frac{1 + 2t + t^2}{1 - t^2}$$

$$= \frac{(1 + t)^2}{(1 - t)(1 + t)} = \frac{1 + t}{1 - t} = \frac{1 + \tan\theta}{1 - \tan\theta}$$

$$= \frac{1 + \dfrac{1}{\cot\theta}}{1 - \dfrac{1}{\cot\theta}} = \frac{\cot\theta + 1}{\cot\theta - 1}$$

**B6** $\cos 15° = \dfrac{\sqrt{3} + 1}{2\sqrt{2}}$, $\tan 15° = 2 - \sqrt{3}$,

a = 2, b = −1

**B7** i) $\theta = 27, 207, \ldots$ ii) $\theta = 117$ Max $y = 2$
iii) $\theta = 297$ Min $y = -2$

**B8** $\tan x = \sqrt{3}$, $x = \dfrac{\pi}{3}, \dfrac{4\pi}{3}, -\dfrac{2\pi}{3}, -\dfrac{5\pi}{3}$

**B9** $\tan\theta = \frac{1}{3}$ or $-3$
$\tan(45° + \theta) \times \tan(45° - \theta)$

$$= \frac{1 + t}{1 - t} \times \frac{1 - t}{1 + t} = 1$$

**B10** $x = \dfrac{\pi}{2}, \dfrac{3\pi}{2}$ $(\cos x = 0)$

$x = 0, 2\pi$ $(\cos x = 1)$
$x \approx 2.42, 3.86$ $(\cos x = -\frac{3}{4})$

**Exercise 5.4**

**A1** i) Translation $\begin{pmatrix} 25 \\ 0 \end{pmatrix}$

ii) Translation $\begin{pmatrix} -57 \\ 0 \end{pmatrix}$ with stretch SF 3 $\parallel$ $y$ axis

iii) Translation $\begin{pmatrix} \alpha \\ k \end{pmatrix}$

**A2** i) Trans $\begin{pmatrix} \pi/3 \\ 0 \end{pmatrix}$ with stretch SF 2 $\parallel$ $y$ axis

ii) Trans $\begin{pmatrix} -\pi/6 \\ 0 \end{pmatrix}$ with stretch SF $\frac{1}{2}$ $\parallel$ $y$ axis

iii) Trans $\begin{pmatrix} -\beta \\ 0 \end{pmatrix}$ stretch SF $a$ then trans $\begin{pmatrix} 0 \\ b \end{pmatrix}$

**A3** i) Trans $\begin{pmatrix} 17 \\ 0 \end{pmatrix}$ with stretch SF 3 $\parallel$ $y$ axis

ii) Reflection in $\theta$ axis with stretch SF 2 $\parallel$ $y$ axis

iii) Trans $\begin{pmatrix} -42 \\ 0 \end{pmatrix}$ with stretch SF $\frac{1}{3}$ $\parallel$ $y$ axis

### A level questions

**C1** i) $\theta = 30$ iii) $\dfrac{9\sqrt{3}}{2}$ cm$^2$

**C2** a) LHS

$\equiv \dfrac{1}{\sec\theta + \tan\theta} + \dfrac{1}{\sec\theta - \tan\theta}$

$\equiv \dfrac{s - t + s + t}{(s+t)(s-t)} \equiv \dfrac{2s}{s^2 - t^2}$

$\equiv \dfrac{2\sec\theta}{1} \equiv \dfrac{2}{\cos\theta}$

$\equiv$ RHS

b) $\dfrac{1}{\sec\theta - \tan\theta} - \dfrac{1}{\sec\theta + \tan\theta}$

$\equiv \dfrac{s + t - (s - t)}{s^2 - t^2} \equiv \dfrac{2t}{1} \equiv 2\tan\theta$

**C3** a) $\theta \approx 108.4, 288.4$ or $\theta \approx 63.4, 243.4$
b) $\tan\theta = -3$ or $\tan\theta = 2$
c) $\theta = 60, 300$

**C4** i) $\cos 2x \equiv 1 - 2\sin^2 x$
ii) $x = \pi, \dfrac{7\pi}{6}, \dfrac{11\pi}{6}$
iii) $x = 0, 2\pi, 4\pi, \dfrac{7\pi}{3}, \dfrac{11\pi}{3}$

**C5** $S = \dfrac{1}{1 - \sin^2\theta} = \dfrac{1}{\cos^2\theta}$

$T = \dfrac{1}{1 + \tan^2\theta} = \dfrac{1}{\sec^2\theta} = \cos^2\theta$

$S \times T = \dfrac{1}{\cos^2\theta} \times \cos^2\theta = 1$

**C6** ii) $h = 8\sin\theta + 8\sin 2\theta$ iii) $h = 5\sqrt{7}$

**C7** i) $PM = AB - AQ$
$= 3a - a\cos\theta$
$= a(3 - \cos\theta)$
ii) $PN = a(1 - \sin\theta)$
iii) $PM^2 + PN^2$
$= a^2(3 - \cos\theta)^2 + a^2(1 - \sin\theta)^2$
$= a^2[9 - 6\cos\theta + \cos^2\theta + 1 - 2\sin\theta + \sin^2\theta]$
$= a^2[9 + 1 + 1 - 6\cos\theta - 2\sin\theta]$
because $\cos^2\theta + \sin^2\theta = 1$
$= a^2(11 - 6\cos\theta - 2\sin\theta)$
$\therefore PC = a\sqrt{11 - 6\cos\theta - 2\sin\theta}$

**C8** a) $x = \dfrac{\pi}{6}, \dfrac{5\pi}{6}, -\dfrac{\pi}{2}$
b) $x = -\dfrac{\pi}{6}, \dfrac{5\pi}{6}$ or $x = \dfrac{\pi}{4}, -\dfrac{3\pi}{4}$
c) $x = 0$ or $x = \pm\dfrac{\pi}{3}$

**C9** i) $y_1 = \frac{3}{2}$ $y_2 = \dfrac{3\sqrt{3}}{2}$ $y_3 = 0$
ii) For $-\pi \leqslant x \leqslant \pi$
$2x - \dfrac{\pi}{6} = \pm\dfrac{\pi}{6}, \pm\dfrac{11\pi}{6}$,
$x = 0, \dfrac{\pi}{6}, -\dfrac{5\pi}{6}, \pi$

**C10** a) $\sin\alpha = \frac{4}{5}$, $\cos\alpha = \frac{3}{5}$
d) $y_{\max} = 10$ when $\theta = 90 + \alpha \approx 143.1$
$y_{\max} = -10$ when $\theta = 270 + \alpha \approx 323.1$

## Chapter 6

### Exercise 6.1

**A1** a) $4\sqrt{2}$ b) $2\sqrt{26}$ c) 3
**A2** a) 1 b) $-\frac{1}{5}$ c) zero
**A3** a) Grad 7 intercept $(0, -2)$
b) Grad $-3$ intercept $(0, 5)$
c) Grad $-1$ intercept $(0, 5)$
d) Grad 0 intercept $(0, 7)$
**A5** a) $y = 6x - 11$ b) $6y + x + 29 = 0$
c) $y + 4x = 4$ d) $4y = x - 1$
**A6** a) Grad $\frac{3}{2}$, $3x - 2y - 14 = 0$
b) $-\frac{1}{9}$, $x + 9y + 3 = 0$
c) $\frac{1}{2}$, $x - 2y - 6 = 0$ d) 0, $y = 1$
**A7** $x = 7$ b) $y = 9$ c) $y = 6x$
d) $2y - x + 1 = 0$
**A8** a) A is $(\frac{5}{2}, 0)$ and B is $(0, 5)$ b) $\frac{25}{4}$

**B2** a) Grad $-\frac{4}{3}$ b) Grad $-\frac{3}{2}$ c) Grad $\frac{5}{2}$
d) Grad $-\dfrac{a}{b}$
**B3** a) $3x + 4y - 20 = 0$ b) $4x - 5y + 10 = 0$
**B4** a) $3x - y + 5 = 0$ b) $2x + 7y - 10 = 0$
c) $7x - 5y + 19 = 0$
**B5** a) $4x + 3y - 23 = 0$ b) $x + 4 = 0$
c) $4x - 3y + 12 = 0$ d) $x + y - 2 = 0$
e) $y + 2 = 0$
**B6** A(1, 2) B(5, 5) C(−2, 6)
$AB = \sqrt{(5-2)^2 + (5-1)^2}$
$= \sqrt{3^2 + 4^2} = 5$

$BC = \sqrt{(5 - -2)^2 + (5 - 6)^2}$
$= \sqrt{7^2 + 1^2}$
$CA = \sqrt{(1 - -2)^2 + (2 - 6)^2}$
$= \sqrt{3^2 + (-4)^2} = 5$
AB = CA hence $\Delta$ is isosceles

**B7** Area = 6
**B8** $h = 2, k = 5$
**B9** Area is $\frac{117}{8}$
**B10** Area = $21\frac{1}{2}$

**Exercise 6.2**

**A1** a) (5, 5) b) $(4, \frac{1}{2})$ c) $(-1, -1)$
**A2** a) $y = 3x - 8$ b) $3y + x = 26$
**A3** a) $y = -\frac{2}{3}x$ b) $y = \frac{3}{2}x$
**A4** a) Grad $= -\frac{1}{5}$ b) M is (3, 5)
c) Perp to AB has grad 5
perp bisector is $y = 5x - 10$
**A5** a) $y = x - 2$ b) $x = 10$
**A6** $4x - 3y + 29 = 0$
**A7** Grad AB is $\frac{9-5}{3-2} = 4$

grad BC is $\frac{13-9}{4-3} = 4$

point B is common $\therefore$ ABC is a straight line
**A8** Centre (9, 3) radius 3

**B1** $2x + 5y - 14 = 0$
**B2** a) C is (2, 3) b) D is $(\frac{9}{2}, 7)$
c) E is $(-13, -21)$
**B3** a) i) $y + 2x = 10$ ii) $2y - x = 10$
b) i) $y + 2x + 7 = 0$ ii) $2y - x = 1$
**B4** D is (1, 4)
**B5** Grad of AD is $\frac{7-3}{0--2} = \frac{4}{2} = 2$

Grad of BC is $\frac{4-0}{6-4} = 2$

So AD parallel to BC
Grad of AB = grad of DC $= -\frac{3}{6} = -\frac{1}{2}$
So AB parallel to DC
Hence parallelogram.
But grad AD $\times$ grad AB $= 2 \times -\frac{1}{2} = -1$
$\therefore$ AD perp to AB
$\therefore$ parallelogram with rt $\angle$ i.e. rectangle
**B6** a) $(\frac{3}{2}, \frac{1}{2})$ b) $\sqrt{58}$ c) $7y = 3x - 1$
**B7** Line is $2y + 3x + 17 = 0$
Foot of perpendicular is $(-3, -4)$
Distance from A to $l$ is $\sqrt{13}$
**B8** Area of $\Delta = 25$
**B9** D is (2, 6) E is (1, 2) F is (3, 4)
BE is $y = 2x$ CF is $y = 4$ G is (2, 4)
**B10** D is (1, 0)

$\therefore$ perp from B to AC has length $3\sqrt{5}$

**Exercise 6.3**

**A1** a) $(x + 1)^2 + y^2 = 9$ b) $x^2 + (y + 4)^2 = 4$
c) $(x + 2)^2 + (y - 3)^2 = 1$
d) $(x - 4)^2 + (y + 3)^2 = 25$
**A2** a) (2, 0), (−4, 0) $(0, \pm 2\sqrt{2})$
b) Meets $y$ axis at (0, −2) (0, −6). (0, −2) is nearest $x$ axis
c) (−1, 3) nearest $y$ axis. (−2, 2) nearest $x$ axis
d) At (0, 0) and (0, −6) and (8, 0)
**A3** a) Area is $40\pi$ Centre (−3, 5) and radius $2\sqrt{10}$
b) i) Centre (1, 2) rad 4
ii) Equation is satisfied only by $x = -2$ and $y = 3$
It represents the point (−2, 3)
iii) Centre (3, 1) rad 2
iv) Equation represents the point (4, 0)
v) Centre (2, 2) rad 2
**A4** Centre (2, 1) and radius 2 for given circle
i) $(x - 2)^2 + (y - 1)^2 = 1$
ii) $(x - 2)^2 + (y - 1)^2 = 36$

**B1** Gradient of OA $= -\frac{4}{3}$ $3x - 4y = 25$
$3x - 4y = -25$
**B2** a) $(x + 3)^2 + (y - 2)^2 = 58$
b) Equation is $(x - 2)^2 + (y - 3)^2 = 45$
**B3** $(x - 2)^2 + y^2 = 25$
**B4** Centre (2, 4) radius 5 $3x + 4y = 47$
$4y + 3x = -3$
**B5** E (4, 5), F (0, 1)
Circle is $(x - 3)^2 + (y - 1)^2 = 34$

**Exercise 6.4**

**A1** a) $Y = \frac{2}{3}X + 2$ b) $Y = -\frac{3}{2}(X - 5)$
c) $Y = 2X - 3$
**A2** a) $y^2 = \frac{3}{4}(x - 1)$ b) $\frac{1}{y} + \frac{1}{x} = 4$
**A3** a) $y = 3x^2 - 8$ b) $y = -\frac{1}{3}x(x - 7)$
**A4** $y = 100x^3$ so $a = 100$
**A5** $a = e^2, b = e^{-\frac{1}{2}}$

**B1** $a \approx 12.2, b \approx 0.7$
**B2** Period is about 2.1 seconds $a \approx 2.01$, $b \approx 0.5$
**B3** $a \approx 2.86$ and $b \approx 1.32$
**B4** $f \approx 8.5$

**A level questions**

**C1** Gradient of $L_1$ is $\frac{2}{3}$
Equation is $y - 1 = \frac{2}{3}(x - 2)$
$3(y - 1) = 2(x + 2)$

$$3y = 2x + 7$$
Gradient of $L_2$ is $-\frac{3}{2}$
Equation is $y + 4 = -\frac{3}{2}(x - 10)$
$$2y + 8 = -3x + 30$$
$$2y + 3x = 22$$
At C $\begin{cases} 2y + 3x = 22 \\ 3y - 2x = 7 \end{cases}$
Hence $4y + 6x = 44$
$$9y - 6x = 21$$
$$13y = 65$$
$$y = 5$$
$2x = 3y - 7 = 8$ so $x = 4$
C is (4, 5)

**C2** i) AB $y = 3x - 1$ ii) BC $2y = -x + 12$
Line thro' F ∥ AC is $3y = 2x + 4$
D is (4, 4)

**C3** b) B is $(\frac{11}{5}, -\frac{18}{5})$

**C4** b) $BE = 6\sqrt{5}$, $ED = \sqrt{5}$, $AE = 2\sqrt{5}$, $EC = 3\sqrt{5}$

**C5** a) $AC = \sqrt{130}$ $BC = \sqrt{130}$
i.e. C is equidistant from A and B
b) $(x - 7)^2 + (y + 11)^2 = 130$
c) D is (16, −18) Grad of DB $= -\frac{3}{2}$
grad of BA $= \frac{2}{3} \to$ product is $-1$ ∴ perp.
i.e. angle DBA is 90°

**C6** b) C′ is (6, −5)

**C7** a) $2y + x = 10$ b) B is (14, −2)
c) C is (−4, −2)
D is (4, −2)
d) BC = 18, BD = 10

**C8** a) $\frac{q}{p}$ b) $-\frac{p}{q}$ c) $px + qy = p^2 + q^2$
d) T is $\left(\frac{p^2 + q^2}{p}, 0\right)$
e) Area $= \frac{q(p^2 + q^2)}{2p}$

**C9** From graph points are nearly collinear ∴ belief is justified. $b \approx -5$ and $a \approx 16$

**C10** $l \approx (0.114)m + 10.97$ Unstretched length, when $m = 0$ is $\approx 11$ cm

## Chapter 7

### Exercise 7.1

**A1** i) $f(4) = 64 - 12 + 1 = 53$
ii) $f(-2) = -8 + 6 + 1 = -1$
iii) $f(-x) \equiv (-x)^3 - 3(-x) + 1$
$\equiv -x^3 + 3x + 1$
iv) $f(x) + f(-x) \equiv 2$

**A2** i) $g(2) = \frac{3}{-3} = -1$ ii) $g(-1) = 0$
iii) $g(x + 6) \equiv \frac{x + 7}{x + 1}$ $(x \neq -1)$

**A3** $h(x) = \frac{x + 1}{x - 1}$ $(x \neq 1)$
a) i) $h(2) = 3$
ii) $h(-2) = \frac{-1}{-3} = \frac{1}{3}$
iii) $h\left(\frac{1}{x}\right) \equiv \frac{\frac{1}{x} + 1}{\frac{1}{x} - 1} \equiv \frac{1 + x}{1 - x}$
iv) $h(x) + h\left(\frac{1}{x}\right) \equiv \frac{x + 1}{x - 1} + \frac{1 + x}{1 - x}$
$\equiv \frac{x + 1}{x - 1} - \frac{1 + x}{x - 1} \equiv 0$
b) $h(-x) \equiv \frac{-x + 1}{-x - 1} \equiv \frac{1 - x}{-(x + 1)} \equiv$
$-\frac{1 - x}{x + 1} \equiv \frac{x - 1}{x + 1} \equiv \frac{1}{h(x)}$

**A4** i) $g(3) = 10$
ii) $fg(3) = f[g(3)] = f(10) = 100$
iii) $fg(x) \equiv 9x^2 + 6x + 1$
$x = -\frac{1}{5}, -1$

**A5** $gf(x) \equiv \frac{2}{9x - 4}$
If $f = gf$ $x = \frac{1}{9}$ or $\frac{2}{3}$

**B1** i) $f(x - 3) = (x - 2)(2x - 7)(x - 6)$ $f(x) = 0$ $x = -1, \frac{1}{2}, 3$
ii) $f(x - 3) = 0$ $x - 3 = -1, \frac{1}{2}, 3$
or $x = 2, \frac{7}{2}$ or 6

**B2** If $ff(x) = 13$ $x = \pm 2, \pm 1$

**B3** a) $a = 2$ $g(a) = g(2) = \frac{2}{5}$
b) $g(-a) = g(-2) = \frac{-2}{-3} = \frac{2}{3}$
c) $g\left(\frac{1}{a}\right) = g\left(\frac{1}{2}\right) = \frac{\frac{1}{2}}{1 + 1} = \frac{1}{4}$ or
$\frac{1}{2 + 2} = \frac{1}{4}$ from $g\left(\frac{1}{x}\right)$

**B4** $h(x-2) = (2x-3)(x+3)(3x-8)$
$h(x-2) = 0$ when $x = \frac{3}{2}, -3, \frac{8}{3}$
Sols are $-\frac{1}{2}+p, -5+p$ and $\frac{2}{3}+p$

**B5** i) $x = \pm 5, \pm\sqrt{15}$ ii) $x = \pm 5$
iii) For only 2 sols $a - b < 0$
iv) $gf(x) = |x^2 - a|$

**B6** a) i) $f(1) = 0$ ii) $f(e) = 1$
iii) $f(e^3) = 3$ iv) $f(e^{-1}) = -1$
b) i) $g(0) = 1$ ii) $g(\ln x) \equiv x$
iii) $g(\ln e) = e$ iv) $g(2\ln x) \equiv x^2$
c) $x = \ln 3$ or $x = 0$

## Exercise 7.2

**A1** i) $f(x) \equiv 3x - 1$ $f^{-1}(x) \equiv \frac{x+1}{3}$
$f^{-1} \in R$ e.g. $f(7) = 20$ $f^{-1}(20) = \frac{21}{3} = 7$
ii) $g(x) \equiv \frac{x+4}{2}$ $g^{-1}(x) \equiv 2x - 4$
$g^{-1} \in R$ e.g. $g(6) = 5$ $g^{-1}(5) = 10 - 4 = 6$

**A2** i) $h(x) \equiv e^x$ $h^{-1}(x) \equiv \ln x$ range $h^{-1} \in R$
ii) $g(x) = 1 - e^{2x}$
i.e. $y = 1 - e^{2x} \sim x = 1 - e^{2y}$ $e^{2y} = 1 - x$
$2y = \ln(1-x)$ $y = \frac{1}{2}\ln(1-x)$
$g^{-1}(x) \equiv \frac{1}{2}\ln(1-x)$ $g^{-1} \in R$
iii) $f(x) = e^{2x-3}$ i.e. $y = e^{2x-3} \sim x = e^{2y-3}$
$2y - 3 = \ln x$ $y = \frac{1}{2}(3 + \ln x)$
$f^{-1}(x) \equiv \frac{1}{2}(3 + \ln x)$ $f^{-1} \in R$

**A3** $f^{-1}: x \to \frac{2x+1}{x-1}$ $(x \neq 1)$ $f^{-1} \in R$ except 2

**A4** i) $f^{-1}: x \to 3x - 5$ ii) $g^{-1}: x \to 7 - 2x$
iii) $h^{-1}: x \to 3(x-5)$

**A5** $g^{-1}$ given by $x = \frac{2-y}{2y-1}$ $g^{-1}: x \to \frac{x+2}{2x+1}$
$x \neq -\frac{1}{2}$

**A6** a) $f^{-1}(x) \equiv \frac{1}{2}(e^x - 1)$ $f^{-1} > -\frac{1}{2}$
b) $g^{-1}(x) \equiv \frac{1}{3}(e^{x-2})$ $g^{-1} > 0$

**A7** $f^{-1}$ given by $x = 2y - 3$ $y = \frac{x+3}{2}$
$(0 \leqslant y \leqslant 2)$
Range $[0, 2]$ domain $[-3, 1]$

**B1** a) $h \geqslant -1$ b) $h^{-1}: x \to -2 + \sqrt{x+1}$
$x \geqslant -1$ $h^{-1} \geqslant -2$

**B2** $f^{-1} = f$ $g^{-1} = g$

**B3** a) $f^{-1}: x \to \frac{5}{9}(x - 32)$
b) Graphs meet when $x = -40$
c) $t = -40$

**B4** If $f(x) \equiv -2x$ then $f^{-1}(x) = -\frac{x}{2}$

$$f[f^{-1}(x)] \equiv f\left(-\frac{x}{2}\right) \equiv -2\left(-\frac{x}{2}\right) \equiv x$$

$$f^{-1}[f(x)] \equiv f^{-1}(-2x) \equiv -\frac{-2x}{2} \equiv x \text{ Result}$$

If $g(x) \equiv 3 - 2x$ then $g^{-1}(x) \equiv \frac{1}{2}(3 - x)$
$g[g^{-1}(a^2)] = g[\frac{1}{2}(3 - a^2)]$
$= 3 - 2 \times \frac{1}{2}(3 - a^2) = a^2$
$g^{-1}[g(a^2)] = g^{-1}(3 - 2a^2)$
$= \frac{1}{2}[3 - (3 - 2a^2)]$
$= \frac{1}{2}2a = a^2$ Result

**B5** a) $f^{-1}(x) = \begin{cases} \frac{1}{2}x & 0 \leqslant x \leqslant 2 \\ 2x - 3 & 2 \leqslant x \leqslant 3 \end{cases}$

**B6** a) i) No (1 to many)
ii) Yes (1 to 1)
iii) Yes (many to 1)
iv) No ($x = 1$ gives 2 values, $\pm 1$)
b) i) and iv) Not functions
ii) $y = \tan x$ $\left(-\frac{\pi}{4} \leqslant x \leqslant \frac{\pi}{4}\right)$
iii) $y = \cos x$ $\left(-\frac{\pi}{2} \leqslant x \leqslant \frac{\pi}{2}\right)$
c) ii) Is $1 \to 1$ $\therefore$ inverse function exists

## Exercise 7.3

**A1** i) EVEN ii) NEITHER iii) EVEN

**A2**
$f(x) \equiv x\cos x$
$f(-x) \equiv -x\cos(-x)$
$\equiv -x\cos x$
$\equiv -f(x)$
$\therefore$ ODD

$g(x) \equiv x\sin x$
$g(-x) \equiv -x\sin(-x)$
$\equiv -x(-\sin x)$
$\equiv x\sin x$
$\equiv g(x)$
$\therefore$ EVEN

**A3**
$f(x) \equiv 4 - x^2 + 3x^4$
$f(-x) \equiv 4 - (-x)^2 + 3(-x)^4$
$\equiv 4 - x^2 + 3x^4$
$\equiv f(x)$
$\therefore$ EVEN

$g(x) \equiv 6x^5 - 2x^3 + 4x$
$g(-x) \equiv 6(-x)^5 - 2(-x)^3 + 4(-x)$
$\equiv -6x^5 - 2(-x^3) - 4x$
$\equiv -6x^5 + 2x^3 - 4x$
$\equiv -(6x^5 - 2x^2 + 4x)$
$\equiv -g(x)$
$\therefore$ ODD

**A4** ODD EVEN ODD

**A5** If $f(x) \equiv x\cos 2x + \sin 3x$
$f(-x) \equiv -x\cos(-2x) + \sin(-3x)$
$\equiv -x\cos 2x - \sin 3x$
$\equiv -(x\cos 2x + \sin 3x)$
$\equiv -f(x)$
$\therefore$ ODD

**A6** ODD EVEN ODD

**B1** EVEN so reflect in $y$ axis

**B2** a) Stretch SF 2 $\|$ $y$ axis
b) Translation $\begin{pmatrix}-1\\0\end{pmatrix}$
c) 'Compression' SF 2 $\|$ $x$ axis
d) 'Stretch' SF 2 $\|$ $x$ axis

**B3** a) $y = f(x-2)$ is $y = f(x)$ trans $\begin{pmatrix}2\\0\end{pmatrix}$

b) $y = \frac{1}{2}f(x+2)$ is $y = f(x)$ trans $\begin{pmatrix}-2\\0\end{pmatrix}$

stretch $\|$ $y$ axis SF $\frac{1}{2}$
c) 'Squash' SF 2 $\|$ $x$ axis
'Squash' SF 3 $\|$ $y$ axis

**B4** b) $f(x-1)+2$ is translation $\begin{pmatrix}1\\2\end{pmatrix}$

### Exercise 7.4

**A1** a) If $f(x) = 4x^2 - 13x + 3$ then
$f(3) = 36 - 39 + 3 = 0$
i.e. $(x-3)$ is a factor of $f(x)$
b) If $f(x) = x^3 - x^2 + 6x - 36$ then
$f(3) = 27 - 9 + 18 - 36 = 0$
i.e. $(x-3)$ is a factor of $f(x)$
c) If $f(x) = x^4 - 81$ then
$f(3) = 3^4 - 81 = 81 - 81 = 0$
i.e. $(x-3)$ is a factor of $f(x)$

**A2** $a = -1$

**A3** i) Remainder is $-1$ ii) Remainder is $-25$
iii) Remainder is $a^3 - 3a^2 + 2a - 1$

**A5** $f(x) \equiv (x-4)(x+4)(x+1)$

**A6** $x = -3$ or $x = \pm\frac{3}{2}$

**B1** ii) $p = 1, q = 0, r = -5$ iii) $x = 2, \pm\sqrt{5}$

**B2** $P(x) \equiv x^3 + 3x^2 + 10x - 24$
i) $P(-2) = -8 + 12 + 20 - 24 = 32 - 32$
$= 0$
$\therefore (x+2)$ is a factor of $P(x)$
ii) $P(x) \equiv (x+2)(x^2 + x - 12)$
$\equiv (x+2)(x+4)(x-3)$
iii) Inequality is $P(x) > 0$
$-4 < x < -2$ or $x > 3$

**B3** $a = -4, b = 1$

**B4** $f(x) \equiv x^3 - 8x^2 + 14x - 4$
i) $f(2) = 8 - 32 + 28 - 4 = 36 - 36 = 0$
$\therefore (x-2)$ is a factor of $f(x)$
ii) $f(x) \equiv (x-2)(x^2 - 6x + 2)$
$f(x) = 0$ when $x = 2$ or when
$x^2 - 6x + 2 = 0$
$x^2 - 6x + 9 = 7$
$(x-3)^2 = 7$
$x = 3 \pm \sqrt{7}$

**B5** i) $a = 1, b = 5, c = -1$
ii) $x = 2$ or $x = \dfrac{-5 \pm \sqrt{29}}{2}$
iii) $\dfrac{-5-\sqrt{29}}{2} < x < \dfrac{-5+\sqrt{29}}{2}$
or $x > 2$

### A level questions

**C1** a) $ff(x) = f(x^2 - 8) = (x^2 - 8)^2 - 8$
$= x^4 - 16x^2 + 64 - 8$
$= x^4 - 16x^2 + 56$
If $ff(x) = 56$ then $x^4 - 16x^2 = 0$
$x^2(x^2 - 16) = 0 \quad x = 0(\text{rep}), \pm 4$
b) $gf(x) = g(x^2 - 8) = |(x^2 - 8) - 2|$
$= |x^2 - 10|$
If $gf(x) = 6$ i.e. $|x^2 - 10| = 6$ then
$x^2 - 10 = \pm 6$ giving $x^2 = 16$ or $4$
i.e. $x = \pm 4, \pm 2$

**C3** a) If $g(x) \equiv 2x^3 - 9x^2 - 20x + 12$,
$g(2) = 16 - 36 - 40 + 12 \neq 0$
i.e. $x - 2$ is not a factor of $g(x)$
b) $g(x) \equiv (x+2)(2x^2 - 13x + 6)$
$\equiv (x+2)(2x-1)(x-6)$
$p = 2, q = -13, r = 6$
c) $g(x) \leqslant 0$ for $x \leqslant -2$ or $+\frac{1}{2} \leqslant x \leqslant 6$

**C4** $P(x) \equiv x^3 - 9x^2 + 14x + 24$
If $x = 4$,
$P(x) = 64 - 144 + 56 + 24$
$= 144 - 144 = 0$
i.e. $x = 4$ fits $P(x) = 0$ and is $\therefore$ a root
Now $P(x) \equiv (x-4)(x^2 - 5x - 6)$
$\equiv (x-4)(x-6)(x+1)$
Other roots of $P(x) = 0$ are $x = 6, -1$
If $f(x+4) = 0$ then $x + 4 = 4, 6, -1$
i.e. $x = 0, 2, -5$

**C5** a) i) $g(x) = f(x-1) = e^{x-1}$
ii) $h(x) = g(2x) = e^{2x-1}$
iii) $h^{-1}(x)$ given by $x = e^{2y-1}$
$2y - 1 = \ln x$
$y = \frac{1}{2}(1 + \ln x)$
$h^{-1}(x) = \frac{1}{2}(1 + \ln x)$
b) If $f^{-1} = h^{-1}$ then $\ln x = \frac{1}{2}(1 + \ln x)$
$2\ln x = 1 + \ln x$
$\ln x = 1$
$x = e$

**C6** i) As $x^2 - a^2 \equiv (x+a)(x-a)$ is a factor of
$P(x)$ then $P(-a) = 0$ and $P(a) = 0$
i.e. $-a^3 + a^2 - pa + q = 0$

and $a^3 + a^2 + pa + q = 0$
Add $2a^2 + 2q = 0 \quad q = -a^2$
Subt $2a^3 + 2pa = 0 \quad p = -a^2$
$\therefore p = q = ka^2$ where $k = -1$
ii) $P(x) \equiv x^3 + x^2 - a^2x - a^2$
$\equiv (x^2 - a^2)(x + 1)$ i.e. $r = 1$
iii) $P(x)$ has zeros at $\pm a, -1$
For $P(x) < 0$ then $x < -1$ or $-a < x < a$

**C7** If $f(x) = \dfrac{1}{1-x} + 4$ say $y = \dfrac{1}{1-x} + 4$

then $f^{-1}$ is given by $x = \dfrac{1}{1-y} + 4$

$x - 4 = \dfrac{1}{1-y} \quad 1 - y = \dfrac{1}{x-4}$

$y = 1 - \dfrac{1}{x-4}$

i.e. $f^{-1}(x) \equiv 1 - \dfrac{1}{x-4}$

Range $\quad f^{-1} \in \mathrm{R} \quad f^{-1} \neq 1$
Domain $\quad x \in \mathrm{R} \quad x \neq 4$

$y = f^{-1}(x)$ is $y = \dfrac{1}{x}$ trans $\begin{pmatrix} 4 \\ 0 \end{pmatrix}$ then reflected

in $y = 0$ and then trans $\begin{pmatrix} 0 \\ 1 \end{pmatrix}$

**C8** $f(x) = \begin{cases} x^2 & 0 \leqslant x \leqslant 2 \quad f(2) = 4 \\ \frac{1}{2}(x+6) & 2 \leqslant x \leqslant 6 \quad f(6) = 6 \end{cases}$

$f^{-1}(x)$

$= \begin{cases} +\sqrt{x} & 0 \leqslant x \leqslant 4 \quad \text{e.g. } f^{-1}(4) = 2 \\ 2x - 6 & 4 \leqslant x \leqslant 6 \quad f^{-1}(6) = 6 \end{cases}$

**C9** ii) $f(x-2) = \dfrac{3}{1 + (x-2)^2}$

$= \dfrac{3}{x^2 - 4x + 5}$

**C10** The graph of $y = f(x-2)$ is the graph of b) $y = f(x)$ 'shifted 2 units to the right' $(-2, 0)$ becomes $(0,0)$ and $(2, 0)$ becomes $(4, 0)$, etc

# Chapter 8

## Exercise 8.1

**A1** a) $y = 2x^2 + 7x + 3 \quad \dfrac{dy}{dx} = 4x + 7$

$\dfrac{d^2y}{dx^2} = 4$

b) $y = 9x^2 - 6x + 1$

$\dfrac{dy}{dx} = 18x - 6 = 6(3x - 1) \quad \dfrac{d^2y}{dx^2} = 18$

c) $y = 4 - 25x^2 \quad \dfrac{dy}{dx} = -50x$

$\dfrac{d^2y}{dx^2} = -50$

**A2** a) $f(x) = x^3 - 4x^2 + 9x + 1$
$f'(x) = 3x^2 - 8x + 9 \quad f''(x) = 6x - 8$

b) $f(x) = x^{-3} + x^3 \quad f'(x) = -\dfrac{3}{x^4} + 3x^2$

$f''(x) = \dfrac{12}{x^5} + 6x$

**A3** $y = x^{-1} + x^{-2} - x^{-3}$

$\dfrac{dy}{dx} = -1x^{-2} - 2x^{-3} + 3x^{-4}$

$= -\dfrac{1}{x^2} - \dfrac{2}{x^3} + \dfrac{3}{x^4}$

**A4** $f(x) = x^2 + 2 + x^{-2}$

$f'(x) = 2x - 2x^{-3} = 2x - \dfrac{2}{x^3}$

**A5** $y = x^3 - 6x^2 + 12x - 8$

$\dfrac{dy}{dx} = 3x^2 - 12x + 12 = 3(x^2 - 4x + 4)$

$= 3(x-2)^2$

**A6** a) $s = 4t^{-2} \quad \dfrac{ds}{dt} = -\dfrac{8}{t^3}$

b) $s = t^{\frac{3}{2}} \quad \dfrac{ds}{dt} = \dfrac{3\sqrt{t}}{2}$

**A7** $g(x) = x^{\frac{3}{2}} - x^{\frac{1}{2}} \quad g'(x) = \dfrac{3x - 1}{2\sqrt{x}}$

**A8** $v = 1 + 3t^{-1} + t^{-2} \quad \dfrac{dv}{dt} = -\dfrac{3t + 2}{t^3}$

**A9** $h(t) = t^2 - 4 + 4t^{-2}$ $h^1(t) = \frac{2}{t^3}(t^4 - 4)$

**A10** $y = x^8 - x^2$ $\frac{dy}{dx} = 8x^7 - 2x$

$\frac{d^2y}{dx^2} = 56x^6 - 2$ $\frac{d^3y}{dx^3} = 336x^5$

**B1** $y = 2x^6 + 3x^5$ $\frac{dy}{dx} = 12x^5 + 15x^4$

$\frac{d^2y}{dx^2} = 60x^3(x + 1)$

**B2** $y = x^{\frac{1}{2}} + x^{-\frac{1}{2}}$ $\frac{dy}{dx} = \frac{x-1}{2x\sqrt{x}}$ $\frac{d^2y}{dx^2} = \frac{3-x}{4x^2\sqrt{x}}$

**B3** $y = ax^{\frac{1}{2}} + bx^4$ $\frac{dy}{dx} = \frac{a}{2}x^{-\frac{1}{2}} + 4bx^3$

$\frac{d^2y}{dx^2} = -\frac{a}{4x^{\frac{3}{2}}} + 12bx^2$ $a = 6$ and $b = \frac{1}{2}$

**B4** $y = x^{\frac{5}{2}} + \frac{3x^{\frac{3}{2}}}{2} + x^{\frac{1}{2}}$

$\frac{dy}{dx} = \frac{1}{4\sqrt{x}}(10x^2 + 9x + 2)$

$a = 10$ $b = 2$ $c = 2 \therefore a + 2b + c = 30$

**B5** $f(x) = 4x + 12 + 9x^{-1}$ $f'(x) = 4 - \frac{9}{x^2}$

$f''(x) = \frac{18}{x^3}$

**B6** $z = 2t^{-5} + 3t^{-6}$ $\frac{dz}{dt} = -\frac{5t+9}{t^7}$

**B7** $g(x) = x + 4 + 4x^{-1}$

$g'(x) = 1 - \frac{4}{x^2} = \frac{(x+2)(x-2)}{x^2}$

**B8** $y = 4x^3 - x^4$ $\frac{dy}{dx} = 12x^2 - 4x^3 = 0$

when $x = 0$ (rep) or 3

$\frac{d^2y}{dx^2} = 24x - 12x^2 = 12$ when $x = 1$ (rep)

**B9** $f(x) = x^3 - 3x^2 + x - 3$
$f'(x) = 3x^2 - 6x + 1$ hence $f'(0) = 1$
$f''(x) = 6x - 6 = 6(x - 1)$ and $f''(0) = -6$

**B10** $f(x) = \frac{3x^2}{2} - 4x^{-1}$ $f'(x) = 3x + 4x^{-2}$

$f''(x) = 3 - \frac{8}{x^3}$ when $f''(x) = 4$ $x = -2$

## Exercise 8.2

**A1** $y = xe^x$ $\frac{dy}{dx} = e^x(x + 1)$

**A2** $y = \frac{x}{e^x}$ $\frac{dy}{dx} = \frac{1-x}{e^x}$ $\frac{dy}{dx} = 0$ when $x = 1$

**A3** $f(x) = \frac{x^2}{x+3}$ $f'(x) = \frac{x^2 + 6x}{(x+3)^2}$

**A4** a) $f(x) = x^{-1} - 3x^{-2}$ $f'(x) = \frac{6-x}{x^3}$

b) $f(x) = \frac{x-3}{x^2}$ $f'(x) = \frac{6-x}{x^3}$

**A5** a) $(x^2 + 2x + 3)e^x$ b) $\frac{(x^2 - 2x + 3)e^x}{(x^2 + 3)^2}$

c) $\frac{2x - x^2 - 3}{e^x}$

**A6** $g'(x) = \frac{(x-4)e^x}{x^5}$

$g'(x) = 0$ only when $x = 4$ as $e^x \neq 0$

**A7** $h'(x) = x^3e^x(x + 4)$
$h'(x) = 0$ when $x = 0, -4$

**A8** $y = x^4 \ln x$ $\frac{dy}{dx} = x^3 + 4x^3 \ln x$

$= x^3(1 + 4 \ln x)$

$\frac{dy}{dx} = 0$ only when $\ln x = -\frac{1}{4}$ i.e.

$x = e^{-\frac{1}{4}}$ $(x > 0)$

**A9** a) $\frac{dy}{dx} = x^2(16x - 9)$

b) $\frac{dy}{dx} = x^2(16x - 9)$

**B1** a) $\frac{dy}{dx} = x^2(1 + 3 \ln x)$ b) $\frac{dy}{dx} = \frac{1 - 3 \ln x}{x^4}$

**B2** a) $\frac{dy}{dx} = \frac{1}{x}$ b) $\frac{dy}{dx} = -\frac{1}{x}$

c) $\dfrac{dy}{dx} = \dfrac{5}{x}$

**B3** a) $\dfrac{dy}{dx} = x^4(5\ln x + 1)$

$\dfrac{dy}{dx} = 0$ when $x = e^{-\frac{1}{5}}$

b) $y' = x^2e^x(3 + x)$
$y' = 0$ when $x^2 = 0$ or $x = -3$
so $x = 0$ (rep) or $-3$

**B4** $\dfrac{dy}{dx} = \dfrac{18}{x} - 3x^2$ $\dfrac{dy}{dx} = 0$ when $x^3 = 6$

**B5** $f(x) = \dfrac{x^{\frac{1}{2}}}{x+3}$ $f'(x) = \dfrac{3 - x}{2(x+3)^2\sqrt{x}}$

$f'(x) = 0$ when $x = 3$

## Exercise 8.3

**A1** $y = (4x + 1)^5$ $\dfrac{dy}{dx} = 20(4x + 1)^4$

**A2** $y = e^{-3x}$ $\dfrac{dy}{dx} = -3e^{-3x}$

**A3** $y = \ln(5 - 3x)$ $\dfrac{dy}{dx} = -\dfrac{3}{5 - 3x}$

**A4** $f(x) = (1 - x^2)^{\frac{1}{2}}$ $f'(x) = \dfrac{-x}{\sqrt{1 - x^2}}$

**A5** $f(x) = (1 - x^2)^{-\frac{1}{2}}$

$f'(x) = \dfrac{x}{(1 - x^2)\sqrt{1 - x^2}}$

**A6** i) $y = (2x - 3)^4$ $\dfrac{dy}{dx} = 8(2x - 3)^3$

ii) $y = (2x - 3)^{-4}$ $\dfrac{dy}{dx} = -\dfrac{8}{(2x - 3)^5}$

**A7** i) $s = e^{4t-5}$ $\dfrac{ds}{dt} = 4e^{4t-5}$

ii) $s = \ln(4t - 5)$ $\dfrac{ds}{dt} = \dfrac{4}{4t - 5}$

**A8** i) $v = (2 - 3t)^3$ $\dfrac{dv}{dt} = -9(2 - 3t)^2$

ii) $v = (2 - 3t)^{-1}$ $\dfrac{dv}{dt} = \dfrac{3}{(2 - 3t)^2}$

**A9** $z = 3e^{5x}$ $\dfrac{dz}{dx} = 15e^{5x}$ $\dfrac{d^2z}{dx^2} = 75e^{5x}$

$5z = 15e^{5x}$ and $25z = 75e^{5x}$

**A10** $y = (4 - x^2)^{\frac{1}{2}}$ $\dfrac{dy}{dx} = -\dfrac{x}{(4 - x^2)^{\frac{1}{2}}}$

i.e. $\dfrac{dy}{dx} = -\dfrac{x}{y}$ i.e. $\dfrac{dy}{dx} + \dfrac{x}{y} = 0$

**B1** $f(x) = (2x + 5)^4$ $f'(x) = 8(2x + 5)^3$
$f'(0) = 1000$

**B2** $y = 3e^{-4x}$ $\dfrac{dy}{dx} = -12e^{-4x}$

$\dfrac{d^2y}{dx^2} = 48e^{-4x}$ $\therefore$ $\dfrac{d^2y}{dx^2} + 4\dfrac{dy}{dx} = 0$

**B3** $f(x) = 3(6x + 1)^{-5}$ $f'(x) = -\dfrac{90}{(6x + 1)^6}$

$f'(0) = -90$

**B4** $f(x) = x^2e^{5x}$ $\dfrac{d}{dx}(e^{5x}) = 5e^{5x}$

$f'(x) = x(5x + 2)e^{5x}$
$f'(x) = 0$ when $x = 0$ or $-\frac{2}{5}$

**B5** $f(x) = x^2e^{5x}$ $f'(x) = (5x^2 + 2x)e^{5x}$
$f''(x) = e^{5x}(25x^2 + 20x + 2)$
so $f''(x) + 2e^{5x} = e^{5x}(25x^2 + 20x + 4)$

Hence result.

**B6** $y = ae^{-bx}$ $\dfrac{dy}{dx} = -b(ae^{-bx}) = -by$

i.e. $\dfrac{dy}{dx} + by = 0$

**B7** $y = (1 - x)^{-1} - (1 + x)^{-1}$

$\dfrac{dy}{dx} = -1(1 - x)^{-2}(-1) - (-1)(1 + x)^{-2}(1)$

$\dfrac{dy}{dx} = \dfrac{1}{(1 - x)^2} + \dfrac{1}{(1 + x)^2}$,

the sum of two squares

Hence $\dfrac{dy}{dx}$ is always positive

**B8** a) $2e^{2t}$
b) $-2e^{-2t}$

$\dfrac{dx}{dt} = 6e^{2t} - 8e^{-2t}$

$$\frac{d^2x}{dt^2} = 12e^{2t} + 16e^{-2t} = 4x$$

**B9** i) $\frac{d}{dx}\ln(ax+b) = \frac{a}{ax+b}$

ii) $y = \ln(2x+1) - \ln(x-1)$

iii) $\frac{dy}{dx} = 2(2x+1)^{-1} - (x-1)^{-1}$

$\frac{d^2y}{dx^2} = -4(2x+1)^{-2} - (-1)(x-1)^{-2}(1)$

$= \frac{-4}{(2x+1)^2} + \frac{1}{(x-1)^2}$

**B10** i) $\frac{d}{dx}(2x-5)^4 = 8(2x-5)^3$

ii) $y = x(2x-5)^4$

$\frac{dy}{dx} = 5(2x-1)(2x-5)^3$

$\frac{dy}{dx} = 0$ when $x = \frac{1}{2}$ or $\frac{5}{2}$

**Exercise 8.4**

**A1** a) $2\cos 2x$ b) $-3\sin 3x$ c) $4\sec^2 4x$

**A2** a) $\frac{1}{4}\cos\frac{1}{4}x$ b) $\sec^2\left(x + \frac{\pi}{4}\right)$

c) $2\sin\left(\frac{\pi}{3} - 2x\right)$

**A3** a) $\frac{ds}{dt} = 8(1 + 4\sin t)\cos t$

b) $s = (1 - 4\cos t)^{-3}$

$\frac{ds}{dt} = \frac{-12\sin t}{(1 - 4\cos t)^4}$

**A4** a) $\cos x e^{\sin x}$ b) $-\sin x e^{\cos x}$ c) $\sec^2 x e^{\tan x}$

**A5** a) $f(t) = \ln(\sin t)$ $f'(t) = \cot t$

b) $f(t) = \ln(1 + \cos t)$

$f'(t) = -\frac{\sin t}{1 + \cos t}$

**A6** a) $3\cos 3x$ b) $-3\sin 3x$ c) $5\sec^2 5x$

**A7** a) $f(x) = \sin^3 x$ $f'(x) = 3\sin^2 x\cos x$

b) $f(x) = \cos^2 x$ $f'(x) = -2\cos x\sin x$

c) $f(x) = \tan^3 x$

$f'(x) = 3\tan^2 x\sec^2 x$

**A8** a) $x = e^{\sin 2t}$ $\frac{dx}{dt} = 2\cos 2te^{\sin 2t}$

b) $x = e^{-\cos 2t}$ $\frac{dx}{dt} = \sin te^{\cos t}$

**A9** a) $f(t) = \ln\left(\sin\frac{t}{2}\right)$ $f'(t) = \frac{1}{2}\cot\frac{t}{2}$

b) $f(t) = \ln(\cos 3t)$ $f'(t) = -3\tan 3t$

**A10** $f(x) = \sin^2 x$ $f'(x) = 2\sin x\cos x$

$g(x) = \cos^2 x$ $g'(x) = -2\cos x\sin x$

$\therefore \frac{d}{dx}[f(x) + g(x)] = 0$

**B1** $f'(x) = \cos x - \sin x$

$f'(x) = 0$ when $\sin x = \cos x$

$\tan x = 1$

i.e. $x = \frac{\pi}{4}, -\frac{3\pi}{4}$ if $|x| < \pi$

**B2** $\frac{d}{dx}\sin^3 2x = 6\sin^2 2x\cos 2x$

**B3** $y = e^{-x}\sin x$ $\frac{dy}{dx} = e^{-x}(\cos x - \sin x)$

When $e^{-x}(\cos x - \sin x) = 0$

$\cos x = \sin x$

$1 = \tan x$

$x = \frac{\pi}{4}$

**B4** $x = 2\sin t + 3\cos t$

$\frac{dx}{dt} = 2\cos t - 3\sin t$

$\frac{d^2x}{dt^2} = -(2\sin t + 3\cos t) = -x$

$\therefore \frac{d^2x}{dt^2} + x = 0$

**B5** $-2\sin 2t$ and $2\cos 2t$, $s = 3\cos 2t - 4\sin 2t$

$\frac{ds}{dt} = -6\sin 2t - 8\cos 2t$ $\frac{d^2s}{dt^2} = -4s$

**B6** $\frac{d}{dx}(\tan^2 3x) = 6\tan 3x\sec^2 3x$

**B7** $f'(t) = 2\cos t - 2\sin 2t$

$f'(t) = 0$ when $2\cos t - 4\sin t\cos t = 0$

$\cos t(1 - 2\sin t) = 0$

$t = \frac{\pi}{2}, \frac{3\pi}{2}, \frac{\pi}{6}, \frac{5\pi}{6}$

**B8** $y = \ln(\cos x) - \ln(\sin x)$

**B9** $\frac{d^2y}{dx^2} = \sec x \tan x$

**B10** i) $\frac{d}{dt}(e^{2t}) = 2e^{2t} \quad \frac{d}{dt}(\cos 2t) = -2\sin 2t$

ii) $f'(t) = 2e^{2t}(\cos 2t - \sin 2t)$

iv) If $0 < t < \frac{\pi}{2}$ only solution is $2t = \frac{\pi}{4}$

i.e. $t_1 = \frac{\pi}{8}$ so $f(t_1) = e^{\frac{\pi}{4}} \cos \frac{\pi}{4}$ = result

### Exercise 8.5

**A1** $\frac{dy}{dx} = -\frac{2}{9t^2}$

**A2** $\frac{dy}{dx} = \frac{4t+1}{t^2+1}$

**A3** $\frac{dy}{dx} = \frac{3}{2}\tan t$

**A4** a) $\frac{dy}{dx} = -\frac{x}{y}$ b) $\frac{dy}{dx} = \frac{1-x}{y+3}$

**A5** $\frac{dy}{dx} = \frac{2}{3t}$ When $t = -3$ $\frac{dy}{dx} = -\frac{2}{9}$

**A6** $\frac{dy}{dx} = 3\cot x$ At $t = \frac{\pi}{3}$ $\frac{dy}{dx} = \sqrt{3}$

**A7** $x^2 + y^2 = 25 \quad x = -4 \quad y > 0$ i.e. $y = +3$

$2x + 2y\frac{dy}{dx} = 0 \quad \frac{dy}{dx} = \frac{4}{3}$

**A8** $2x^2 + 3y^2 = 12 \quad 4x + 6y\frac{dy}{dx} = 0$

$\frac{dy}{dx} = -\frac{2x}{3y}$

**A9** a) $\frac{dy}{dx} = 2t$

b) $\frac{dy}{dx} = -\frac{t}{2}$

c) $\frac{dy}{dx} = -\frac{4}{3}\cot t$

**A10** $\frac{dy}{dx} = \frac{3-y}{x-2}$ or $\frac{y-3}{2-x}$

**B1** $\frac{dy}{dx} = 2 \cdot \frac{t^2-1}{t^2+1}$ when $t = 2$ $\frac{dy}{dx} = 1.2$

**B2** $2x + 2y\frac{dy}{dx} - 8 - 6\frac{dy}{dx} = 0$

when $x = 4$ and $y = -1$ $\frac{dy}{dx} = 0$

**B3** If $x = 2 - t$ then

$x^2 - 4x + 7 = (2-t)^2 - 4(2-t) + 7$
$= t^2 + 3 = y$

If $y = 7 \quad t = \pm 2 \quad \frac{dy}{dx} = \frac{2t}{-1} = -2t$

when $t = 2$ $\frac{dy}{dx} = -4$

when $t = -2$ $\frac{dy}{dx} = 4$

**B4** $z^3 + 3y^2 = z \quad \frac{d}{dy}(z^3) + 6y = \frac{dz}{dy}$

$\frac{d}{dz}(z^3)\frac{dz}{dy} + 6y = \frac{dz}{dy} \quad 3z^2\frac{dz}{dy} + 6y = \frac{dz}{dy}$

$\frac{dz}{dy}(1 - 3z^2) = 6y \quad \frac{dz}{dy} = \frac{6y}{1-3z^2}$

**B5** a) $\frac{dy}{dx} = \frac{3t}{2}$

b) $\left.\begin{array}{l} y^2 = (t^3)^2 = t^6 \\ x^3 = (t^2)^3 = t^6 \end{array}\right\} \therefore y^2 = x^3$

c) $2y\frac{dy}{dx} = 3x^2$

$\frac{dy}{dx} = \frac{3x^2}{2y} = \frac{3(t^2)^2}{2t^3} = \frac{3t^4}{2t^3} = \frac{3t}{2}$

**B6** $\frac{dy}{dx} = \frac{4t-3}{6t+2}$, $t = 1$, $x = 8$ and $y = 0$

**B7** $\frac{dy}{dx} = \frac{x+3}{4-y}$

When $\frac{dy}{dx} = 0$, $x = -3$, $y = 9$ or $-1$

**B8** $\dfrac{dy}{dx} = 3$

**B9** ii) $\dfrac{dy}{dx} = 2\cos t$ and $k = 2$

iii) $t = \dfrac{\pi}{3}, \dfrac{5\pi}{3}$

**B10** $x = \frac{1}{8}$ $y = \dfrac{3\sqrt{3}}{8}$

### Exercise 8.6

**A1** $\dfrac{4}{\sqrt{1 - 16x^2}}$

**A2** $\dfrac{3}{1 + 9x^2}$

**A3** $\dfrac{1}{\sqrt{4 - x^2}}$

**A4** $\dfrac{4}{16 + x^2}$

**A5** $\dfrac{3}{\sqrt{16 - 9x^2}}$

**A6** $\dfrac{15}{9 + 25x^2}$

**B1** $\dfrac{dz}{dx} = \dfrac{-1}{x^2}\dfrac{dy}{dx} = -\dfrac{1}{x^2 + 1}$

**B2** $\dfrac{x + 1}{1 + x^2}$, $x = -1$

**B3** $\dfrac{-x}{\sqrt{1 - x^2}}, \dfrac{1 - 2x^2}{\sqrt{1 - x^2}}$

**B4** i) $\dfrac{2x}{1 + x^4}$ ii) $\dfrac{2x}{\sqrt{1 - x^4}}$

### A level questions

**C1** When $x = 3$ $y = 2$ or $0$

$\dfrac{dy}{dx} = \dfrac{y - x}{3y - x}$

When $x = 3$ and $y = 2$

$\dfrac{dy}{dx} = -\dfrac{1}{3}$

**C2** $\dfrac{dy}{dx} = \dfrac{1}{(1 - x)^2}$

**C3** $\dfrac{dy}{dx} = \dfrac{1}{1 + \cos x} \times -\sin x = \dfrac{-\sin x}{1 + \cos x}$

Now as $y = \ln(1 + \cos x)$, $1 + \cos x = e^y$

$\therefore \dfrac{d^2y}{dx^2} = -\dfrac{1}{e^y} = -e^{-y}$ i.e. $\dfrac{d^2y}{dx^2} + e^{-y} = 0$

Also as $\dfrac{d^2y}{dx^2} = -e^{-y}$ and as $e^{-y} > 0$ for all $y$

then $\dfrac{d^2y}{dx^2}$ is always negative

**C4** a) $x = 3e^t \cos t$ $y = 3e^t \sin t$

$x^2 + y^2 = 9(e^t)^2\cos^2 t + 9(e^t)^2\sin^2 t$
$= 9(e^t)^2(\cos^2 t + \sin^2 t)$
$= 9(e^{2t})$ because $(e^t)^2 = e^{2t}$
and $\sin^2 t + \cos^2 t \equiv 1$

b) $\dfrac{dy}{dt} = 3e^t(\cos t + \sin t)$

c) $\left(\dfrac{dx}{dt}\right)^2 = 9e^{2t}(1 - 2\sin t\cos t)$

$\left(\dfrac{dy}{dt}\right)^2 = 9e^{2t}(1 + 2\cos t\sin t)$

$\therefore \left(\dfrac{dx}{dt}\right)^2 + \left(\dfrac{dy}{dt}\right)^2$
$= 9e^{2t}(1 - 2\sin t\cos t + 1 + 2\cos t\sin t)$
$= 2 \times 9e^{2t}$
$= 2(x^2 + y^2)$

**C5** a) i) $\dfrac{dy}{dt} = -6e^{-2t}$

ii) $3e^{-2t} = y - 5$

$\therefore \dfrac{dy}{dt} = -2(3e^{-2t}) = -2(y - 5) = 10 - 2y$

b) $f(x) = \sin(x^2 - 4)$
$f'(x) = 2x\cos(x^2 - 4)$ $f'(2) = 4$

c) $\dfrac{d}{dx}(\sqrt{x}) = \dfrac{1}{2\sqrt{x}}$

$g'(x) = e^{\sqrt{x}} \cdot \dfrac{1}{2\sqrt{x}} = g(x) \cdot \left(\dfrac{1}{2\sqrt{x}}\right)$

$\therefore \dfrac{g'(x)}{g(x)} = \dfrac{1}{2\sqrt{x}}$ i.e. $\dfrac{g(x)}{g'(x)} = 2\sqrt{x}$

**C6** a) When $x = 2$ $y = \pm 1$

b) When $y = 2 \quad x = \frac{1}{2} \quad \frac{d}{dx}(y^2x) = 0$

$$\frac{d}{dx}(y^2)(\cdot x) + (y^2 \cdot)(\cdot 1) = 0$$

$$2y\frac{dy}{dx}(\cdot x) + y^2 = 0 \qquad \frac{dy}{dx} = -\frac{y^2}{2yx} = -\frac{y}{2x}$$

when $y = -1 \quad x = 2$ and

so $\frac{dy}{dx} = -\frac{-1}{4} = \frac{1}{4}$

**C7** a) $\frac{dx}{dt} = 1 + \frac{1}{t^2} \quad \frac{dy}{dt} = 1 - \frac{1}{t^2}$

$$\frac{dy}{dx} = \frac{1 - \frac{1}{t^2}}{1 + \frac{1}{t^2}} = \frac{t^2 - 1}{t^2 + 1}$$

b) $y^2 - x^2 = 4 \quad \therefore 2y\frac{dy}{dx} - 2x = 0$

$$\frac{dy}{dx} = \frac{2x}{2y} = \frac{x}{y}$$

c) $\therefore \frac{dy}{dx} = \frac{t - \frac{1}{t}}{t + \frac{1}{t}} = \frac{t^2 - 1}{t^2 + 1}$

d) When $\frac{dy}{dx} = 0 \quad t^2 - 1 = 0$ i.e. $t = \pm 1$

e) When $\frac{dy}{dx} = \frac{1}{2} \quad \frac{t^2 - 1}{t^2 + 1} = \frac{1}{2}$

$2(t^2 - 1) = t^2 + 1 \quad 2t^2 - 2 = t^2 + 1$
$t^2 = 3 \quad t = \pm\sqrt{3}$

**C8** a) $\frac{dx}{dt} = -4\cos^3 t \sin t$

b) $\frac{dy}{dt} = 4\sin^3 t \cos t$

d) $t = \frac{\pi}{6}$ so $x = \frac{9}{16}, y = \frac{1}{16} \quad \frac{dy}{dx} = -\left(\frac{1}{\sqrt{3}}\right)^2$

$= -\frac{1}{3}$

$t = \frac{\pi}{4} \quad x = \frac{1}{4} \quad y = \frac{1}{4} \quad \frac{dy}{dx} = -1$

**C9** $g(x) = x^2e^{4x} \quad g'(x) = 2xe^{4x}(2x + 1)$
$g'(x) = 0$ only when $x = 0$ or $-\frac{1}{2}$ as $e^{4x} \neq 0$
i.e. $x_1 = 0, x_2 = -\frac{1}{2} \quad g(x_1) = 0$

$$g(x_2) = \tfrac{1}{4}\ e^{-2} = \frac{1}{4e^2}$$

**C10** $f(x) = \frac{3x - 6}{(x + 2)(x - 1)} = \frac{A}{x - 1} + \frac{B}{x + 2}$

where $3x - 6 \equiv A(x + 2) + B(x - 1)$
$x = -2, -12 = -3B \quad B = 4 \quad x = 1, -3 = 3A$
$A = -1$

$$\therefore f(x) = \frac{4}{x + 2} - \frac{1}{x - 1}$$
$$= 4(x + 2)^{-1} - (x - 1)^{-1}$$

$$f'(x) = -4(x + 2)^{-2} + (x - 1)^{-2}$$
$$= \frac{1}{(x - 1)^2} - \frac{4}{(x + 2)^2}$$

$a = 1, b = -4 \quad f'(0) = 0$

$f'(x) = 0$ when $\frac{1}{(x - 1)^2} = \frac{4}{(x + 2)^2}$

$(x + 2)^2 = 4(x - 1)^2$
$x^2 + 4x + 4 = 4x^2 - 8x + 4 \quad 0 = 3x^2 - 12x$
$0 = 3x(x - 4) \quad x = 0, 4$
So the other value of $x$ is $x = 4$

# Chapter 9

**Exercise 9.1**

**A1** $f'(x) = 2(2 - x) > 0$ if $x < 2$
$\therefore f$ is an increasing function
$g'(x) = 6(x + 1) > 0$ if $x > -1$
i.e. $g$ is an increasing function

**A2** a) $f' : x \to -e^{-\frac{1}{2}x}$ which is negative as $e^{-\frac{1}{2}x} > 0$ for all $x \in R$ c) $F' : x \to -\frac{1}{x}$

which is neg if $x > 0$
b) $g' : x \to -6 \sin 2x$

If $0 < x < \frac{\pi}{2}$ then $0 < 2x < \pi$

and $\sin 2x > 0 \quad \therefore g' < 0$ d) $G' : x \to -2x^{-\frac{3}{2}}$

Now $x^{-\frac{3}{2}} = \frac{1}{x\sqrt{x}} > 0$ for $x > 0 \quad \therefore G' < 0$

All 4 derivatives are negative over given domains $\therefore$ All 4 functions are decreasing

**A3** $3x^2 + 4x - 4 = (3x - 2)(x + 2) > 0$ when $x < -2$ or $x > \frac{2}{3}$
i) $y$ inc with $x$ when $x < -2$ or $x > \frac{2}{3}$ because

$\frac{dy}{dx} > 0$

ii) $y$ dec with $x$ for $-2 < x < \frac{2}{3}$ because

$\frac{dy}{dx} < 0$

**A4** a) $z = 3 - \frac{2}{x-2}$ b) $\frac{dz}{dx} = \frac{2}{(x-2)^2} > 0$

i.e. is inc function

**A5** a) $y = (x+2)x(x-2)$ is a cubic with zeros at $-2, 0, 2$ $y > 0$ if $-2 < x < 0$ or $x > 2$
$y < 0$ if $x < -2$ or $0 < x < 2$
b) $f'(x) = 4x(x+2)(x-2) = 4y$
$\therefore$ from a) $f(x)$ is a dec function when $y < 0$
i.e. $x < -2$ or $0 < x < 2$

**A6** $\frac{dy}{dx} \equiv e^{-x}(x+1)(1-x), e^{-x} > 0$

$\therefore$ the sign of $\frac{dy}{dx}$ is the same as the sign of

$(x+1)(1-x)$ This is positive for
$-1 < x < 1$ i.e. for $|x| < 1$

**A7** a) $f'(x) \equiv -\tan x$ b) $g'(x) \equiv e^{\tan x} \cdot \sec^2 x$

c) $h'(x) \equiv -\frac{1}{\tan x}$ As $0 < x < \frac{\pi}{2}$

$\tan x > 0$ $\therefore f'(x) < 0$ $\therefore f$ is decreasing
$e^{\tan x}$ and $\sec^2 x$ both positive
$\therefore g$ is increasing.
$\tan x > 0$
$\therefore h'(x) < 0$ $h$ is decreasing

**A8** a) i) $x(1 + 2\ln x)$ ii) $x^2(1 + 3\ln x)$
b) $f' > 0$ when $1 + 2\ln x > 0 \therefore x > e^{-\frac{1}{2}}$
$g' > 0$ when $1 + 3\ln x > 0 \therefore x > e^{-\frac{1}{3}}$ where
$a = -\frac{1}{3}$

**Exercise 9.2**

**A1** Tgt $y + 4x = 8$ Norm $4y = x + 15$
**A2** Tgt $9y + x = 15$ Norm $y = 9x + 28\frac{1}{3}$
**A3** Tgt $y = 6x + 6$ Norm $6y + x + 1 = 0$

**A4** Tgt $2y = x + \sqrt{3} - \frac{\pi}{3}$

Norm $y + 2x = \frac{2\pi}{3} + \frac{\sqrt{3}}{2}$

**A5** Tgt $y = e^2x - e^2$ Norm $ye^2 + x = 2 + e^4$
**A6** Tgt $y = 6x - 10$ Norm $6y + x = 51$
**A7** Tgt $y = x - 1$ Norm $y + x = 1$

**A8** Tgt $2y + 2x\sqrt{3} = 1 + \frac{\pi\sqrt{3}}{3}$

Norm $2y\sqrt{3} - 2x = \sqrt{3} - \frac{\pi}{3}$

**A9** $4y + x = 4$ and $4y + x = -4$
**A10** A(0, 3) B(−3, 0) AB $= 3\sqrt{2}$

**B1** $y = x^2$
$\frac{dy}{dx} = 2x$

At $x = 3$, $\frac{dy}{dx} = 6$

Tangent at (3, 9)
$y - 9 = 6(x - 3)$
$y = 6x - 9$

At $x = 1$, $\frac{dy}{dx} = 2$

Normal at (1, 1) is $y - 1 = -\frac{1}{2}(x - 1)$
$2y - 2 = -x + 1$
$2y + x = 3$
At intersection, $2(6x - 9) + x = 3$
$13x - 18 = 3$
$13x = 21$
$x = \frac{21}{13}$

$2y = 3 - \frac{21}{13} = \frac{18}{13}$
$y = \frac{9}{13}$
Point is $(\frac{21}{13}, \frac{9}{13})$

**B2** $y = x^2 - 2x$
$\frac{dy}{dx} = 2x - 2$

At (3, 3) $\frac{dy}{dx} = 4$

Tangent here is $y - 3 = 4(x - 3)$
$y = 4x - 9$

At (−3, 15) $\frac{dy}{dx} = -8$

Tangent here is $y - 15 = -8(x + 3)$
$y = -8x - 9$
At intersection $4x - 9 = -8x - 9$
$12x = 0$
$x = 0$
Therefore meet on $y$ axis at (0, −9)

**B3** $P(\frac{5}{4}, 0)$ Q(0, −15)
**B4** $a = 1$ $b = 2$ Tgt is $y = 2x + 3$
**B5** a) $a = 4$ $b = -1$ b) At P Tgt is $y = x + 2$
At Q Tgt is $y = x + 6$
c) Both are perp to PQ as '$m_1 \times m_2 = -1$'

**B6** At A $\dfrac{dy}{dx} = \dfrac{1}{2}$

i) Tgt is $2y = x + 4$
ii) Normal is $y + 2x = 12$
TN = 10 area of $\Delta$ATN = 20
mid pt of AT is (0, 2)

**B7** A(0, 3) $\dfrac{dy}{dx} = 2e^{2x} + 2e^{-2x}$

Tgt at A is $y - 3 = 4x$
$B(-\frac{3}{4}, 0)$ AB $= \frac{3}{4}\sqrt{17}$

**B8** i) Vertex (3, 1) ii) A(4, 0) (2, 2) (3, 1)

**B9** Tgt is $y = x + 1$ Norm is $y = -x + 3$
B is $(-1, 0)$ C is (3, 0) AB $= \sqrt{8}$
AC $= \sqrt{8}$

**B10** Tgt is $e^2y = x + e^2$ $C(-e^2, 0)$

### Exercise 9.3

**A1** i) $(-\frac{1}{3}, -\frac{4}{27})$ and $(-1, 0)$ ii) (2, 0)
iii) No stat pts

**A2** Min (2, 0) max $(\frac{4}{3}, \frac{4}{27})$

**A3** $x = \sqrt{2}$

**A4** Min pt is (2, 8)

**A5** $f'(x) \equiv 3(x-2)^2$ $f'(x) = 0$ when $x = 2$
Inflexion pt is (2, 4)

**A6** Max (0, 5) min (4, −27)
mid (2, −11) lies on the graph

**A7** Max value is $f(\ln 3) = 3(\ln 3 - 1)$

**A8** Min pt is $[\frac{1}{3}, f(\frac{1}{3})]$ $f(\frac{1}{3}) = 1 + \ln 3$

**A9** $\dfrac{dy}{dx} = -e^{-x} + 4e^x$ $\dfrac{d^2y}{dx^2} = e^{-x} + 4e^x$

$\dfrac{dy}{dx} = 0$ $e^x = \frac{1}{2}$ i.e. $x = \ln\frac{1}{2} = -\ln 2$

**A10** Max pt $\left(\dfrac{\pi}{2}, e^{\frac{\pi}{2}}\right)$

**B1** Dimensions are $\frac{35}{2}$ m by 35 m
Area is $\frac{1125}{2}$ $m^2$

**B2** Min when $x = 3$
Least possible area of metal is 27 $m^2$

**B3** a) Area $y = x(15 - x)$ max when $x = 7\frac{1}{2}$
max area is $\frac{227}{4}$ $cm^2$

b) $w = p - x$ $z = x(p - x)$ max at $x = \dfrac{p}{2}$

max area is $\frac{1}{4}p^2$ $cm^2$

**B4** a) Perimeter is $p = 2x + \dfrac{400}{x}$

min perim when $x = 10\sqrt{2}$ and
length $= 40\sqrt{2}$ b) $A = 200$

**B5** Max vol $\approx f(2.4274)$ $\therefore$ max vol is
262.68 $cm^3$ (2 dp) best $x$ was 2.4
% error is 1.1 (1 dp)

**B6** Max volume when $x = 3$ and $h = 3$
i.e. when tank is a cube

**B7** Min area when $x = 2$ and $y = 2$

**B8** a) Proof

b) $\dfrac{dz}{d\theta} = (1 + \cos\theta)\cos\theta + (-\sin\theta)\sin\theta$

$= (2\cos\theta - 1)(\cos\theta + 1)$ $\theta = \dfrac{\pi}{3}$

c) Max area $= \dfrac{3\sqrt{3}}{4}$ $cm^2$

**B9** a) Max when $x = 100$
i.e. 'straight' is 100 m 'bend' is 100 m
b) Extra is $20\pi$ m

**B10** a) Proof
b) Shortest dist $= \frac{3}{2}$ at $(2, \sqrt{2})$
i.e. B is pt on curve nearest A
c) Grad of tgt at B × grad of AB = −1
$\therefore$ Perp!

### Exercise 9.4

**A1** Tgt is $y = 4(4x - 5)$ $\lambda = 4$

**A2** Tgt is $4y = 3x - 50$ Normal is $3y + 4x = 0$

**A3** Proof

**A4** Tgt is $2y + 9x = -16$ B is $(-\frac{16}{9}, 0)$
$\dfrac{dy}{dx} = \dfrac{9x}{4y}$ C is (0, −8) Area $= \frac{64}{9}$

**A5** a) $\dfrac{dy}{dx} = \dfrac{2}{3t}$ $(t \neq 0)$

b) Tangent is $3py = 2x + p^3$

c) Q is $\left(-\dfrac{p^3}{8}, \dfrac{p^2}{4}\right)$

**B1** B is $(\frac{3}{22}, \frac{15}{22})$

**B2** a) A is (12, 16) B is (3, −2)
b) Tgt at A is $y = 2x - 8$ B lies on this line

**B3** a) $\dfrac{d}{dy}(\ln y)\dfrac{dy}{dx} = \dfrac{1}{y}\dfrac{dy}{dx}$

b) $\dfrac{dy}{dx} = y\ln 2 = 2^x \ln 2$

c) Tgt is $y = x\ln 2 + 1$

Normal is $y = -\dfrac{x}{\ln 2} + 1$

d) $A\left(-\dfrac{1}{\ln 2}, 0\right)$ $B(\ln 2, 0)$

**B4** a) $\dfrac{dy}{dx} = -\dfrac{1}{t^2}$

b) Tgt is $y = -4x + 8$
Norm is $4y = x + 15$ D is $(2, 0)$
E is $(-15, 0)$ DE is 17 area $\Delta ADE = 34$

**B5** a) $\dfrac{dy}{dx} = \dfrac{-6 \sin 2t}{-4 \sin t} = 3 \cos t$

b) Tgt at B is $y = 3x - 9$ c) D is $(3, 0)$
$OD = 3$ $DB = \sqrt{10} > 3$
D nearer 0 than B

**B6** b) $t = 3$ c) $k = 2$

### Exercise 9.5

**A1** $\ln(3 + x) = \ln 3 + \dfrac{x}{3} - \dfrac{x^2}{18} + \dots$

**A2** $e^x = 1 + x + \dfrac{x^2}{2!} + \dots$

$\cos x = 1 - \dfrac{x^2}{2!} + \dots$

$e^{2x} = 1 + 2x + 2x^2 + \dots$
$\cos 2x = 1 - 2x^2 + \dots$
$e^{2x} \cos 2x = (1 + 2x + 2x^2 + \dots)$
$(1 - 2x^2 + \dots)$
$= 1 + 2x + \dots$

**A3** a) $\sin^2 x = x^2 - \dfrac{x^4}{3} + \dots$

b) $\cos 2x = 1 - 2x^2 + \dfrac{2x^4}{3} + \dots$

**A4** a) If $f(x) = \ln(1 + x)$, $f'(x) = \dfrac{1}{1 + x}$, $f''(x)$

$= \dfrac{-1}{(1 + x)^2}$, $f'''(x) = \dfrac{2}{(1 + x)^3}$
$f(0) = \ln 1 = 0$, $f'(0) = 1$, $f''(0)$
$= -1$, $f'''(0) = 2$

$\ln(1 + x) = x - \dfrac{x^2}{2} + \dfrac{2x^3}{3} - \dots$

$= x - \dfrac{x^2}{2} + \dfrac{x^3}{3} - \dots$

b) $\ln(3 + x) = \ln 3 + \dfrac{x}{3} - \dfrac{x^2}{18} + \dots$

**A5** $e^{-2x} = 1 - 2x + 2x^2 - \dots$

**A6** a) $\ln(1 - x) = -x - \dfrac{x^2}{2} - \dfrac{x^3}{3} - \dots$

b) $\ln\left(\dfrac{1 + x}{1 - x}\right) = \ln(1 + x) - \ln(1 - x)$

$= 2\left(x + \dfrac{x^3}{3} + \dots\right)$

### A level questions

**C1** Tgt is $y = 12x + 16$ At B $y = x^3$ and
$y = 12x + 16$ i.e. $x^3 - 12x - 16 = 0$
$f(x) \equiv (x + 2)^2(x - 4)$
Roots are $x = -2$ (rep) and $x = 4$
Former is A $\therefore$ B is $(4, 64)$

**C2** One minimum $\left(\dfrac{\pi}{2}, 1\right)$

two maxima $\left(\dfrac{\pi}{6}, \dfrac{3}{2}\right)\left(\dfrac{5\pi}{6}, \dfrac{3}{2}\right)$

**C3** a) $\dfrac{dy}{dx} = -\dfrac{a}{x^2} + \dfrac{1}{x}$ $\dfrac{d^2y}{dx^2} = \dfrac{2a}{x^3} - \dfrac{1}{x^2}$

b) $y_{min} = 1 + \ln a$

c) Min always pos when $a$ exceeds $\dfrac{1}{e}$

**C4** $\dfrac{dy}{dx} = 2 \sin x \cos x > 0$ for $0 < x < \dfrac{\pi}{2}$

$\dfrac{dz}{dx} = -2 \sin x \cos x < 0$ in $\left(0, \dfrac{\pi}{2}\right)$

**C5** $F'(x) \equiv a - \dfrac{b}{x^2}$

If $a > 0$ and $b < 0$ $F'(x) > 0$ and so $F$ is increasing. $F'(x) \equiv 2 - \dfrac{8}{x^2}$

If $0 < x < 2$ i.e. $0 < x^2 < 4$
$\dfrac{8}{x^2} > 2$ and $F'(x) < 0$

**C6** a) $y = \dfrac{14 - 3x}{(x - 3)(x + 2)} = \dfrac{1}{x - 3} - \dfrac{4}{x + 2}$

b) When $x = 8$ $\dfrac{dy}{dx} = 0$ $\therefore$ stat. pt at $x = 8$

c) Max at $(\frac{4}{3}, -\frac{9}{5})$. Min at $(8, -\frac{1}{5})$

**C7** Dimensions are base 10 m by 20 m,

height = 5 m  Cost $y = 60x^2 + \dfrac{120000}{x}$

**C8** a) P(2, 2), Q(10, 6)
b) $\begin{cases}\text{At P tgt is } y = x \\ \text{At Q tgt is } 3y = x + 8\end{cases}$
c) R is (4, 4)
d) RM = 2, M(6, 4)

**C9** a) A is (16, 16)  B is (−4, 1)
AB is $4y = 3x + 16$
b) $\dfrac{dy}{dx} = t$
Product of grads is $2 \times -\frac{1}{2} = -1$
∴ lines are at rt ∠s
c) Tgt at A is $y = 2x - 16$
Tgt at B is $2y = -x - 2$
Intersection at (6, −4)

**C10** a) Proof  b) Error $= \frac{5}{8} - e^{-\frac{1}{2}} \approx .018$
c) $e^{-2x} = 1 - 2x + 2x^2 - \ldots$

## Chapter 10

### Exercise 10.1

**A1** a) $y = \dfrac{2x^3}{3} - \dfrac{3x^2}{2} + c$
b) $y = 3x^3 - 3x^2 + x + c$
c) $y = \frac{2}{3}x\sqrt{x} + 4\sqrt{x} + c$

**A2** a) $f(x) = \dfrac{4x^3}{3} - 6x^2 + 9x + c$
b) $f(x) = 2x^3 - \dfrac{5x^2}{2} - 4x + c$
c) $f(x) = \dfrac{x^5}{5} - \dfrac{x^4}{4} + c$

**A3** a) $y = \sin x + c$  b) $y = \frac{1}{2}\sin 2x + c$
c) $y = \tan x + c$

**A4** a) $f(x) = \dfrac{x^2}{2} + \ln|x| + c$
b) $f(x) = \ln|x| - \dfrac{x^2}{2} + c$

**A5** a) $y = \frac{1}{2}e^{2x} + c$  b) $y = e^x - \frac{1}{3}e^{-3x} + c$
c) $y = e^x + \frac{1}{3}e^{-3x} + c$

**A6** $s = 12t^3 - 12t^2 + 13t + c$

**A7** $\dfrac{t^3}{3} - \dfrac{3t^2}{4} + 4t + c$

**A8** $v = 3t + 2\ln|t| + c$

**A9** a) $\dfrac{5x^4}{4} - \dfrac{x^5}{5} + c$
b) $\dfrac{1}{x} - \dfrac{5}{2x^2} + c = \dfrac{2x - 5}{2x^2} + c$

**A10** a) $\dfrac{dy}{dx} = 2x^2 + 3x + c$
b) $y = \dfrac{2x^3}{3} + \dfrac{3x^2}{2} + cx + k$

**B1** a) $y = \dfrac{x^3}{3} + 2x - \dfrac{1}{x} + c$
b) $y = \dfrac{x^2}{2} + 2x + \ln|x| + c$

**B2** a) $y = \dfrac{x^3}{3} - \dfrac{4x^{\frac{3}{2}}}{3} + \ln|x| + c$
b) $y = 2x^2 - 24\sqrt{x} - \dfrac{9}{x} + c$

**B3** $y = x + 6\ln|x| - \dfrac{9}{x} + c$

**B4** $y = -\cos 2x - 2\cos\dfrac{x}{2} + c$

**B5** $y = x - \frac{1}{2}\cos 2x + c$

**B6** $y = \dfrac{x^3}{3} + \dfrac{3x^2}{2} - 2x + 5$

**B7** $x = 2\sin 2t - 3\cos 3t + 5$

**B8** a) $A = x^2 + 5x$  b) $A = x^2 + 5x + 6$

**B9** $y = x^3 - 2x^2 + x - 2 = (x^2 + 1)(x - 2)$

**B10** a) $s = 2t^2 + 4t$  b) $s = \dfrac{t^3}{3} + \dfrac{t^2}{2} + 4t$

### Exercise 10.2

**A1** a) 12  b) 12
**A2** a) 6  b) 6
**A3** a) 6.9  b) $4\frac{3}{4}$
**A4** a) 6  b) $\frac{2}{3}$
**A5** a) ln 3  b) −ln 3
**A6** $\frac{1}{2}(e^2 - 1)$
**A7** 1
**A8** a) 55  b) 34  c) 21
**A9** $I_1 = 63$  $I_2 = 63$
**A10** $I_1 = -\frac{81}{4}$  $I_2 = \frac{81}{4}$

**B1** b) 12.06 (2 dp), a) $2e^2 - e$

**B2** Derivative is $\dfrac{1}{\sqrt{1 + 2x}}$  $\sqrt{3} - 1$

**B3** Derivative is $-4\sin 4x$

**B4** Derivative is $\dfrac{-6}{(2x+1)^4}$ $\frac{13}{81}$

**B5** $-\frac{455}{2}$

**B6** 2

**B7** $\frac{26}{3}$

**B8** $\frac{7}{12}$

**B9** $\frac{16}{5}$

**B10** $\frac{3}{8}$

### Exercise 10.3

**A1** $\ln|2x+3|+c \quad 36\ln|2x+3|+c_1$
$\frac{1}{2}\ln|2x+3|+c_2 \quad \frac{3}{5}\ln|2x+3|+c_3$

**A2** $3\ln|1-x|+c$

**A3** $2\ln|x+3|+4\ln|1-x|+c$

**A4** $\ln|x^2+3x+4|+c$

**A5** $\frac{1}{3}\ln|3x-1|+3\ln|x-1|+c$

**A6** a) $2\ln\frac{7}{3}$ b) $-3\ln 4$

**A7** a) $5\ln 3$ b) $-3\ln 4$

**A8** $\frac{1}{2}\ln 2$

**A9** $\frac{1}{3}\ln 4$

**A10** $2\ln 4$ or $4\ln 2$

**B1** $\frac{1}{2}\ln 3$

**B2**
$$\int_0^1 \frac{x}{4-x^2}\,dx = -\tfrac{1}{2}\int_0^1 \frac{-2x}{4-x^2}\,dx$$
$$= -\tfrac{1}{2}\left[\ln|4-x^2|\right]_0^1$$
$$= -\tfrac{1}{2}(\ln 3 - \ln 4)$$
$$= \tfrac{1}{2}(\ln 4 - \ln 3)$$
$$= \tfrac{1}{2}\ln\tfrac{4}{3}$$

**B3** $\dfrac{2}{x} + \dfrac{3}{x+1}$, $a = 16, b = 3$

**B4** $\dfrac{1}{x^2+5x+6} \equiv \dfrac{1}{(x+2)(x+3)} \equiv \dfrac{1}{x+2} - \dfrac{1}{x+3}$

$$\therefore \int_0^1 \frac{1}{x^2+5x+6}\,dx$$
$$= \int_0^1 \left(\frac{1}{x+2} - \frac{1}{x+3}\right)dx$$
$$= \left[\ln(x+2) - \ln(x+3)\right]_0^1$$
$$= (\ln 3 - \ln 4) - (\ln 2 - \ln 3)$$
$$= 2\ln 3 - 3\ln 2$$
$$= \ln 9 - \ln 8$$
$$= \ln\tfrac{9}{8}$$

**B5** $a = 1 \quad a = \frac{3}{8}$

**B6** $A = 1, B = -1$

**B7** $\ln 3$

**B8** $\ln\frac{9}{5}, \frac{1}{2}\ln 5, \frac{1}{2}\ln\frac{81}{5}$

**B9** $\frac{1}{2}\ln\frac{81}{5}$

**B10** $2 + \ln 5$

### Exercise 10.4

**A1** $-\frac{1}{4}e^{-2x}(1+2x)+c$

**A2** $\frac{1}{4}x^2(2\ln x - 1)+c$

**A3** $-e^{-x}(1+x)+c$

**A4** $\dfrac{x^5}{25}(5\ln x - 1)+c$

**A5** $-x\cos x + \sin x + c$

**A6** $e^x(x+1)+c$

**A7** $e^{x+2}(x-1)+c$

**A8** 1

**A9** $\dfrac{\pi}{2} - 1$

**A10** $\frac{1}{9}(2e^3+1)$

**B1** $-\dfrac{x}{2}\cos 2x + \frac{1}{4}\sin 2x + c$

**B2** $\dfrac{x}{2}\sin 2x + \frac{1}{4}\cos 2x + c$

**B3** $\frac{1}{3}e^{3x}(3x-1)+c$

**B4** $e^x(x^2-2x+2)+c$

**B5** $\frac{1}{2}e^x(\sin x - \cos x)+c$

**B6** $e^2+1$

**B7** $\frac{1}{4}\left(1 - \dfrac{3}{e^2}\right)$

**B8** $\dfrac{\pi\sqrt{3}}{3} - \dfrac{\pi^2}{18} - 1$

**B9** $\frac{1}{10}(2x+1)(x-2)^4+c$

**B10** 24.3

### Exercise 10.5

**A1** $x - 3\ln|x+3|+c$

**A2** $\dfrac{x}{2} - \dfrac{3}{4}\ln|2x+3|+c$

**A3** $\frac{1}{18}(3x+1)^6+c$

**A4** $\frac{1}{3}(2x-1)^{\frac{3}{2}}+c$

**A5** $\sqrt{2x-1}+c$

**B1** 156.2

**B2** $\frac{7}{4}$

**B3** $\frac{1}{3}$

**B4** $1 - \dfrac{\sqrt{3}}{2}$

**B5** $\ln\left(\frac{3}{2}\right)$
**B6** $\frac{3}{8}$
**B7** 111.6
**B8** $\frac{3}{16}$
**B9** $\frac{98}{3}$
**B10** $\frac{1}{30}$
**B11** $\frac{112}{3000}$
**B12** $\frac{4}{3}$

### Exercise 10.6

**B1** $\frac{1}{2}$
**B2** $\frac{1}{2}\ln 2$
**B3** $\tan^2 x = \sec^2 x - 1,\quad 1 - \dfrac{\pi}{4}$
**B4** a) $\frac{1}{2}\ln 2$ b) $\ln 2$ c) $\ln 2$
**B5** a) $2\sin x\cos x$ b) $\frac{1}{2}\ln 2$
**B6** $\dfrac{\pi}{4}$
**B7** $\dfrac{\pi}{6}$
**B8** $\frac{1}{160}$ $\frac{21}{128}$
**B9** $\dfrac{dz}{dx} = \cos x - \sin x$ a) $\frac{1}{2}\ln 2$ b) 0
**B10** $\sin^2 x = \frac{1}{2}(1 - \cos 2x)$ $\dfrac{\pi}{4}, \dfrac{\pi}{2}, \dfrac{\pi}{4}$

### A level questions

**C1** a) $1 + \dfrac{4}{x^2 - 4}$ b) $\dfrac{1}{x-2} - \dfrac{1}{x+2}$

c) $1 + \ln\dfrac{2 \times 5}{6} = \ln e + \ln\dfrac{5}{3} = \ln\dfrac{5e}{3}$

**C2** i) $-\dfrac{1}{\sin^2 x} = -\operatorname{cosec}^2 x$

ii) $-\dfrac{\sqrt{3}}{3} + \sqrt{3} = \dfrac{2}{3}\sqrt{3}$

**C3** a) $\cos 2x = \cos^2 x - \sin^2 x$
$\sin 2x = 2\sin x\cos x$

b) $\cos 3x = \cos(2x + x)$
$= \cos 2x\cos x - \sin 2x\sin x$
$= (\cos^2 x - \sin^2 x)\cos x - 2\sin x\cos x\sin x$
$= \cos^3 x - 3\sin^2 x\cos x$
$= \cos^3 x - 3(1 - \cos^2 x)\cos x$ because $\sin^2 x = 1 - \cos^2 x$
$= \cos^3 x - 3\cos x + 3\cos^3 x$
$= 4\cos^3 x - 3\cos x$

c) $I = \displaystyle\int_0^{\pi/6} (4\cos^3 x - 3\cos x)\sin x\,dx$

Put $z = \cos x$ so that '$dz = -\sin x\,dx$'

$I = \displaystyle\int_1^{\sqrt{3}/2} (3z - 4z^3)\,dz = \tfrac{1}{16}$

**C4** If $x = \sin z$ then '$dx = \cos z\,dz$'
Also $\sqrt{1 - x^2} = \sqrt{1 - \sin^2 z} = \cos z$

$I = \displaystyle\int_0^{\pi/6} \sin^2 z\,dz = \dfrac{2\pi - 3\sqrt{3}}{24}$

**C5** $\dfrac{d}{dx}(\cos^2 x) = 2\cos x \times -\sin x$
$= -2\sin x\cos x$

$\displaystyle\int_{\pi/6}^{\pi/4} \dfrac{\sin x\cos x}{1 - \cos^2 x}\,dx = -\tfrac{1}{2}\left[\ln|1 - \cos^2 x|\right]_{\frac{\pi}{6}}^{\frac{\pi}{4}}$
$= \frac{1}{2}\ln\frac{1}{2}$

**C6** a) $2\sin x\cos x$

b) $\displaystyle\int_0^{\pi/4} x\sin x\cos x\,dx = \tfrac{1}{2}\int_0^{\pi/4} x\sin 2x\,dx = \tfrac{1}{4}$

**C7** a) $\dfrac{2}{x}\ln x$

By subst $y = (\ln x)^2 = z^2$ where $z = \ln x$

b) $\displaystyle\int_1^{e^2} \dfrac{1}{x}\ln x\,dx = \left[\tfrac{1}{2}(\ln x)^2\right]_1^{e^2} = 2$

c) $-2$

**C8** a) $a = -4$ $b = 36$
b) $a = 24$ $b = -10$

**C9** a) $\cos 2x = 2\cos^2 x - 1$
b) $\frac{1}{2}(x + \frac{1}{2}\sin 2x) + c$

c) $\displaystyle\int_0^{\pi/2} x\cos^2 x\,dx$
$= \left[x \cdot \tfrac{1}{2}(x + \tfrac{1}{2}\sin 2x)\right]_0^{\frac{\pi}{2}}$
$\displaystyle -\int_0^{\pi/2} \tfrac{1}{2}(x + \tfrac{1}{2}\sin 2x)\,dx = \tfrac{1}{16}(\pi^2 - 4)$

(here '$u$' $= x$ $\dfrac{\text{'}dv\text{'}}{dx} = \cos^2 x$
which gives '$v$' $= \frac{1}{2}(x + \frac{1}{2}\sin 2x)$ from (b))

**C10** a) $\dfrac{dy}{dx} = \dfrac{2ax}{ax^2 + b}$

b) If $\dfrac{2x^3 + 20x}{x^4 + 2x^2 - 8} \equiv \dfrac{Ax}{x^2 - 2} - \dfrac{Bx}{x^2 + 4}$

then, as $(x^2 - 2)(x^2 + 4) = x^4 + 2x^2 - 8$

$$2x^3 + 20x \equiv Ax(x^2 + 4) - Bx(x^2 - 2)$$
$$\equiv (A - B)x^3 + (4A + 2B)x$$
$A = 4$ and $B = 2$

c) $2\int_2^3 \dfrac{x^3 + 10x}{x^4 + 2x^2 - 8}\,dx$

$= \int_2^3 \left(\dfrac{4x}{x^2 - 2} - \dfrac{2x}{x^2 + 4}\right) dx$

$= [2\ln|x^2 - 2| - \ln(x^2 + 4)]_2^3 = \ln\left(\frac{98}{13}\right)$

## Chapter 11

### Exercise 11.1

**A1** a) $16\frac{2}{3}$ b) $\frac{8}{9}$ c) 84
d) $8\ln 2$ e) $3\sqrt{3}$

**A2** a) $16\frac{2}{3}$ b) $\frac{19}{3}$ c) $2\pi$

**A3** $x = 0$ or 4. $10\frac{2}{3}$

**A4** a) $17\frac{1}{3}$ b) 4 c) $13\frac{1}{3}$

**A5** (0, 0), (5, 25) $21\frac{2}{3}$

**A6** a) 1 b) $\alpha = \dfrac{\pi}{3}$

**A7** a) 6 b) $\frac{3}{4}$

**A8** a) $A(\frac{3}{2}, \frac{9}{2})$ $(\frac{3}{2}, -\frac{9}{4})$ b) $\frac{27}{2}$

**A9** Cubic is 'upper' $2\frac{2}{3}$

**A10** a) $A(-3, 0)$ $B(3, 0)$ b) 36 c) 6

**B1** 1 : 7

**B2** $\frac{1}{3}$

**B3** a) $1 + \ln x$ b) $x\ln x - x + c$

c) Area $= \int_2^4 \ln x\,dx$

$= [x\ln x - x]_2^4$
$= 4\ln 4 - 4 - (2\ln 2 - 2)$
$= 4\ln 2^2 - 4 - 2\ln 2 + 2$
$= 4 \times 2\ln 2 - 2\ln 2 - 2$
$= 6\ln 2 - 2$

d) $\frac{1}{2}(1 - \ln 2)$

**B4** $A_2 : A_1 = 3 : 2$ i.e. $A_2 = \frac{3}{2}A_1$ $A_2 = 19.2$

**B5** $\int_0^2 e^x dx = e^2 - 1$

a) $y = e^x - 1$ is $y = e^x$ translated $\begin{pmatrix} 0 \\ -1 \end{pmatrix}$

b) $y = e^{x-2}$ is $y = e^x$ translated $\begin{pmatrix} 2 \\ 0 \end{pmatrix}$

$\int_0^2 (e^x - 1)dx = e^2 - 3$ $\int_2^4 e^{x-2}dx = e^2 - 1$

**B6** a) Area = 312 b) Area = 156
c) Ratio = 2 : 1

**B7** $E: x = 2\cos\theta,\ y = \sin\theta$

$\dfrac{dx}{d\theta} = -2\sin\theta$

$\dfrac{dy}{d\theta} = \cos\theta$

Area $= \int_{x_B}^{x_A} y\,dx = \int_{\theta_B}^{\theta_A} \sin\theta \cdot (-2\sin\theta)\,d\theta$

$= \int_{\frac{\pi}{2}}^{0} -2\sin^2\theta\,d\theta$

Now $\cos 2\theta \equiv 1 - 2\sin^2\theta$
$\therefore -2\sin^2\theta \equiv \cos 2\theta - 1$

$\therefore$ Area $= \int_{\frac{\pi}{2}}^{0} (\cos 2\theta - 1)d\theta = [\frac{1}{2}\sin 2\theta - \theta]_{\pi/2}^{0}$

$= (0 - 0) - \left(0 - \dfrac{\pi}{2}\right) = \dfrac{\pi}{2}$

**B8** a) A is (4, 0) B(0, −1) C(0, 4)
b) Area = $18\frac{2}{3}$

**B9** a) Int at (0, 0), (4, 4)
b) $y = x^2 - 3x = x(x - 3)$ has zeros 0, 3.
$y = 5x - x^2 = x(5 - x)$ has zeros 0, 5.

c) $\int_0^4 [(5x - x^2) - (x^2 - 3x)]dx = 21\frac{1}{3}$ or

$\int_0^4 (5x - x^2)dx - \int_3^4 (x^2 - 3x)dx$

$- \int_0^3 (x^2 - 3x)dx = 21\frac{1}{3}$

**B10** B is (2, 1) A is $(\frac{1}{2}, 4)$ Shaded area is

$\frac{15}{4} - \int_{1/2}^{2} \dfrac{2}{x}dx = \frac{15}{4} - 4\ln 2$

### Exercise 11.2

**A1** a) $42\pi$ b) $\frac{109}{6}\pi$ c) $\dfrac{31\pi}{5}$

d) $\dfrac{58\pi}{5}$ e) $\dfrac{\pi}{2e^2}(8e + e^2 - 1)$

**A2** a) $42\pi$ b) $\dfrac{31\pi}{80}$ c) $\dfrac{\pi}{2}(e^4 - 1)$

**A3** a) $\cos(x + x) = \cos x\cos x - \sin x\sin x$
$= \cos^2 x - \sin^2 x$
$\cos 2x = (1 - \sin^2 x) - \sin^2 x$
$= 1 - 2\sin^2 x$
$\therefore 2\sin^2 x = 1 - \cos 2x$

b) $V = \pi\int_0^{\pi} 4\sin^2 x\,dx = 2\pi\int_0^{\pi}(1-\cos 2x)dx$

$= 2\pi\,[x - \frac{1}{2}\sin x]_0^{\pi}$
$= 2\pi\{(\pi - \frac{1}{2}\sin 2\pi) - (0 - \frac{1}{2}\sin 0)\}$
$= 2\pi(\pi - 0 - 0 + 0) = 2\pi^2$

**A4** Graph meets $x$ axis where $x^2 = 1$, i.e. $x = \pm 1$

$$V = \pi\int_{-1}^{1}(x^2-1)^2\,dx = \pi\int_{-1}^{1}(x^4 - 2x^2 + 1)dx$$

$$= \pi\left[\frac{x^5}{5} - \frac{2x^3}{3} + x\right]_{-1}^{1}$$

$$= \pi\left\{\left(\frac{1}{5} - \frac{2}{3} + 1\right) - \left(-\frac{1}{5} + \frac{2}{3} - 1\right)\right\}$$

$$= \frac{16\pi}{15}$$

If $\frac{4}{3}\pi r^3 = \frac{16\pi}{15}$

$r^3 = \frac{4}{5}$ i.e. $r = \sqrt[3]{\frac{4}{5}}$ $\therefore$ radius is $\left(\frac{4}{5}\right)^{\frac{1}{3}}$

**A5** $12\pi$

**B1** b) 2 c) $\pi\left(1 + \frac{\pi}{2}\right)$

**B2** $V = \int_2^4 \frac{4}{(2x-3)^2}dx = 4\pi\int_2^4(2x-3)^{-2}dx$

$$= -2\pi\left[\frac{1}{2x-3}\right]_2^4$$

$$= -2\pi\left(\frac{1}{5} - 1\right)$$

$$= -2\pi \times \frac{-4}{5} = \frac{8\pi}{5}$$

**B3** Hint: $\pi\int_0^2 t^4 .\, 3t^2\,dt = V$

**B4** $240\pi$ Hint: $V = \pi\int_1^2 64t^3\,dt$

**B5** a) 1.0 (1 dp) b) 6.4 (1 dp)

c) On graph $\frac{dy}{dx} = \frac{1}{2}x^{-\frac{1}{2}} - \frac{1}{2}x^{-\frac{3}{2}}$

At $x = 1$ this is $\frac{1}{2} - \frac{1}{2} = 0$ $\therefore$ at A, gradient is zero hence A is a stationary pt

Now $\frac{d^2y}{dx^2} = -\frac{1}{4}x^{-\frac{3}{2}} + \frac{3}{4}x^{-\frac{5}{2}} = -\frac{1}{4} + \frac{3}{4} > 0$ at A which confirms A as a minimum point

## Exercise 11.3

**A1** a) $y = \frac{x^2}{2} + c$ b) $y = Ae^x$

c) $y = \ln|x| + c$ d) $y^2 = 2x + k$

**A2** a) $y = Ae^{\frac{x^2}{2}}$ b) $y^2 = x^2 + k$ c) $y = kx$

**A3** $y = e^{x^2+3x-4} - 2$

**A4** $x^2 + 2y^2 + 3x - 3y + 1 = 0$

**A5** $\sin y = \frac{3}{2} - e^{-x}$

**A6** $-\frac{1}{x} + 1 + \ln 2 = \frac{1}{2}\ln(y^2 + 4)$

**A7** $3e^{-2y} = 2e^{-3x} + 1$

**A8** $v = 2e^2$

**A9** $t = \frac{1}{k}\ln 5$

**A10** i) 4 ii) 0

**B1** $t = 10$

**B2** $y\frac{dy}{dx} = -2e^{2x-y} = -2e^{2x} \times e^{-y}$

So $-e^{2x} = ye^y - \int e^y\,dy$

$= ye^y - e^y + c$
$e^{2x} = e^y - ye^y - c$ $(0, 0)$ $\therefore c = 0$
$e^{2x} = e^y(1-y)$
$\therefore \ln(e^{2x}) = \ln[e^y(1-y)]$
$= \ln e^y + \ln(1-y)$ $(y < 1)$
$2x = y + \ln(1-y)$
$x = \frac{1}{2}[y + \ln(1-y)]$

**B3** a) $\frac{1}{2+x} + \frac{1}{2-x}$

b) $\int\frac{1}{y}dy = 2\int\left(\frac{1}{2+x} + \frac{1}{2-x}\right)dx$

$\ln y = 2[\ln(2+x) - \ln(2-x)] + c$

$c = 0$ $\therefore \ln y = \ln\left(\frac{2+x}{2-x}\right)^2$ or

$y = \left(\frac{2+x}{2-x}\right)^2$

c) When $x = -1$ $y = \frac{1}{9}$

**B4** $\int \frac{1}{v}\,\mathrm{d}v = \int \frac{2}{t+3}\,\mathrm{d}t$

when $x = 78$ $t = 3$
$\ln v = 2\ln(t+3) + c = \ln(t+3)^2 + c$
$c = 0$
$\therefore v = (t+3)^2$

**B5** $\int 3s^{\frac{1}{2}}\mathrm{d}s = 4\int \mathrm{d}t$ $\quad 2s^{\frac{3}{2}} = 4t + c;\ c = 2$

a) When $t = 13$ $\quad s = 9$
b) When $s = 25$ $\quad t = 62$

**B6** a) $\frac{\mathrm{d}}{\mathrm{d}x}(x^2 - 9)^{\frac{1}{2}} = \frac{x}{\sqrt{x^2 - 9}}$

$\int \frac{x}{\sqrt{x^2-9}}\,\mathrm{d}x = \sqrt{x^2 - 9} + c$

b) $\sqrt{x^2 - 9}\,\frac{\mathrm{d}y}{\mathrm{d}x} = 2x\sqrt{y}$

$\int y^{-\frac{1}{2}}\mathrm{d}y = 2\int \frac{x}{\sqrt{x^2-9}}\,\mathrm{d}x$

$\sqrt{y} = \sqrt{x^2 - 9} + c \quad c = -1$
$\therefore \sqrt{y} = \sqrt{x^2 - 9} - 1.$
When $x = 3\sqrt{5}$ $\quad y = 25$

**B7** a) $\int \frac{1}{y^2}\,\mathrm{d}y = \int \frac{1}{x^2}\,\mathrm{d}x \quad -\frac{1}{y} = -\frac{1}{x} + c$

$c = 1 \therefore -\frac{1}{y} = 1 - \frac{1}{x} = \frac{x-1}{x}$

$\frac{1}{y} = \frac{1-x}{x}$

$y = \frac{x}{1-x}$

b) $\int y^2\mathrm{d}y = \int x^2\mathrm{d}x \quad y^3 = x^3 + 3c = x^3 + A.$

Hence result.

**B8** $\int v\,\mathrm{d}v = k\int x\,\mathrm{d}x$ gives $v^2 = kx^2 + c$

$x = 0,\ v = 4$ gives $c = 16$
$x = 3,\ v = 5$ gives $k = 1$
When $v = 8$, using $v^2 = x^2 + 16$
then $x^2 = 48$
i.e. $x$ is nearly 7

**Exercise 11.4**

**B1** Grad of tgt at $P(x, y)$ is $\frac{\mathrm{d}y}{\mathrm{d}x}$

Grad AP $= \frac{y}{x+1}$ Grad BP $= \frac{y}{x-1}$

If grad of normal is $n$ $\quad n = \frac{y^2}{x^2 - 1}$

$\frac{y^2}{x^2-1}\,\frac{\mathrm{d}y}{\mathrm{d}x} = -1$ which is $\frac{\mathrm{d}y}{\mathrm{d}x} = \frac{1-x^2}{y^2}$

$\int y^2\mathrm{d}y = \int (1 - x^2)\,\mathrm{d}x$

$y^3 = 3x - x^3 + 1$ is required equation

**B2** Curve has equation $(y-1)^2 = x$ or
$y = 1 + \sqrt{x}$ When $x = 16$
$1 + \sqrt{x} = 1 + 4 = 5 \therefore (16, 5)$ lies on curve

**B3** $\frac{\mathrm{d}P}{\mathrm{d}t} = kP$ where $k$ is a positive constant

$\int \frac{1}{P}\,\mathrm{d}P = k\int \mathrm{d}t \quad \ln P = kt + c$

Take $t = 0$ as 1975 $\quad \ln 500 = c$
$P = 560$ when $t = 10$
$k = \frac{1}{10}\ln\frac{560}{500},\ P \approx 627$

**B4** $\frac{\mathrm{d}x}{\mathrm{d}t} = kx, \quad \int \frac{1}{x}\,\mathrm{d}x = \int k\,\mathrm{d}t, \quad x = Ae^{kt}, \quad k = \ln\frac{3}{2}$

$A = \frac{1600}{3}, \quad x = \frac{1600}{3}\left(\frac{3}{2}\right)^t$
Initial population is about 530 and pop. after 2 days is around 1200
(Here $e^k = \frac{4050}{2700}$ i.e. $k = \ln\frac{4050}{2700} \approx 0.4055$)

**B5** Cooling $\therefore \frac{\mathrm{d}\theta}{\mathrm{d}t} < 0$

So $\frac{\mathrm{d}\theta}{\mathrm{d}t} = -k(\theta - 18)$

where $k$ is a positive constant

$\int \frac{1}{\theta - 18}\,\mathrm{d}\theta = -\int k\,\mathrm{d}t$

$\ln(\theta - 18) = -kt + c,\ c = \ln 60 = \ln 60,$
$\theta \approx 43.3 \quad k = \frac{1}{10}\ln\frac{4}{3} \quad t \approx 55.9$ It takes about 56 mins

**B6** $\frac{\mathrm{d}m}{\mathrm{d}t} = -km$ ($k$ positive const)

$\int \frac{1}{m}\,\mathrm{d}m = \int -k\,\mathrm{d}t \quad \ln m = -kt + c$

$m = Ae^{-kt}$ where $A = e^c$ a pos. const

$k = \frac{\ln 2}{1500}$ or $k \approx 0.000462$

To nearest gm, remnant should be 63 after 1000 yrs and 40 after 2000 yrs

**B7** $\dfrac{dy}{dx} \times \dfrac{y-2}{x-1} = -1$

$\int (y-2)\,dy = \int (1-x)\,dx$

$y^2 - 4y = 2x - x^2 + c \quad c = 20$ Curve has equ $x^2 + y^2 - 2x - 4y - 20 = 0$

**B8** $\dfrac{dx}{dt} = -kx$ where $k$ is a pos. const

$\int \dfrac{1}{x}\,dx = -\int k\,dt, \quad \ln x = -kt + c$

$c = \ln 15000 \quad x = 15000e^{-kt} \quad e^{-24k} = \frac{2}{3}$

a) When $t = 60 \quad x = 15000e^{-60k}$
$15000(e^{-24k})^{\frac{5}{2}} \approx 5443$
Likely value is about £5400

b) When $x = 7500 \quad t = \dfrac{24 \ln 2}{\ln 1.5} \approx 41.03$

Half its cost when new after about $3\frac{1}{2}$ years

## A level questions

**C1** a) $\cos 2x \equiv \cos(x + x) \equiv 2\cos^2 x - 1$

b) $y_1 = 1 \quad y_2 = \frac{1}{2}$ mid pt of AC is $\left(\dfrac{\pi}{4}, \dfrac{1}{2}\right)$

which is B ∴ A, B, C are collinear

c) Area $= \displaystyle\int_0^{\pi/2} \cos^2 x\,dx = \tfrac{1}{4}\pi$

area of Δ is $\frac{1}{2} \times OC \times OA = \dfrac{\pi}{4}$

**C2** $P(\frac{1}{3}, 3\frac{1}{3}) \quad Q(3, 3\frac{1}{3})$
a) $y_P = y_Q = \frac{10}{3}$ PQ ∥ $x$ axis (equal $y$ coords)

b) Area 'under curve' is $A_1 = \displaystyle\int_{1/3}^{3} \left(x + \frac{1}{x}\right)dx$
$= \frac{40}{9} + 2\ln 3$
Shaded area is 'rectangle − $A_1$'
$= \frac{80}{9} - A_1$, hence result

c) When $x = 1, y = 2, \dfrac{dy}{dx} = 0$ and

$\dfrac{d^2y}{dx^2} > 0$ which establishes minimum at

A(1, 2)

**C3** a) $I = \displaystyle\int_{-3}^{0} (u+3)u^2\,du = \frac{27}{4}$

b) Area A $= \displaystyle\int_{-3}^{0} (x^3 + 3x^2)\,dx = \frac{27}{4}$

c) The graph of $y = x(x-3)^2$ is the graph of $y = (x+3)x^2$

translated $\begin{pmatrix} 3 \\ 0 \end{pmatrix}$

Areas *must* therefore be identical

**C4** a) $e^{2x} + e^{-2x} + 2$ b) A(0, 2) is a minimum

c) $V = \pi \displaystyle\int_0^{\ln 2} (e^x + e^{-x})^2\,dx$

$= \pi \displaystyle\int_0^{\ln 2} (e^{2x} + e^{-2x} + 2)\,dx$

$= \pi(\frac{15}{8} + 2\ln 2)$

**C5** $V = \pi \displaystyle\int_{\pi/6}^{\pi/3} (\tan x)^2\,dx = \pi \int_{\pi/6}^{\pi/3} \tan^2 x\,dx$

$= \pi \displaystyle\int_{\pi/6}^{\pi/3} (\sec^2 x - 1)\,dx = [\tan x - x]_{\pi/6}^{\pi/3}$

= result

**C6** Area A = 2 area B = 2 Vols are

respectively $\pi\displaystyle\int_0^1 25x^3\,dx$ and $\pi\displaystyle\int_0^1 49x^5\,dx$

Ratio is $\dfrac{25\pi}{4} : \dfrac{49\pi}{6} = 75 : 98$

**C7** $\dfrac{dz}{dt} = -k\sqrt{z} \quad \displaystyle\int \frac{1}{\sqrt{z}}\,dz = \int -k\,dt$

$2\sqrt{z} = -kt + c \quad c = 40 \quad k = \frac{8}{5}$
a) When $z = 49 \quad t = \frac{65}{4}$
b) When $t = 15 \quad z = 64$

**C8** a) $-xe^{-x} - e^{-x} + c$

b) $\int \cos 2y\,dy = \frac{1}{2}\sin 2y + c'$

If $(\cos^2 y - \sin^2 y)\dfrac{dy}{dx} = \dfrac{x}{e^x}$

then $\int \cos 2y\,dy = \int xe^{-x}\,dx$

$\frac{1}{2}\sin 2y = -xe^{-x} - e^{-x} + k$

**C9** $\dfrac{dm}{dt} = -km \quad \displaystyle\int \frac{1}{m}\,dm = \int -k\,dt$

$\ln m = -kt + c$
$c = \ln m_0$ ∴ $\ln m - \ln m_0 = -kt$
so $m = m_0 e^{-kt}$
a) When $t = 10 \quad m = \frac{1}{4}m_0$

b) When $m = \frac{m_0}{3}$, $\frac{1}{3} = e^{-kt}$

i.e. $e^{kt} = 3$ or $kt = \ln 3$
But $e^{5k} = 2$ i.e. $5k = \ln 2$

$\therefore \frac{kt}{5k} = \frac{\ln 3}{\ln 2}$ i.e. $\frac{t}{5} = \frac{\ln 3}{\ln 2}$ or $t = \frac{5 \ln 3}{\ln 2}$

**C10** $\frac{dT}{dt} = k(20 - T)$ where $k > 0$ and const.

$\int \frac{1}{20 - T} dt = \int k dt$, $c = -\ln 16$

$-\ln (20 - T) = kt + c$

$c = \ln 16 \quad T = 20 - 16e^{-kt}$
Temp is $13\frac{1}{4}$°C after $1\frac{1}{2}$ hrs
At 15° in just over 2 hrs (≈ 121.3 mins)

# Chapter 12

### Exercise 12.1

**A1** a) Max area = 2.35 × 4.25 cm²
min area = 2.25 × 4.15 cm²
diff = 0.65 cm²
b) Max perim = 2(2.35 + 4.25) cm
min perim = 2(2.25 + 4.15) cm
diff = 0.4 cm

**A2** a) Greatest possible area = $420.25\pi$ cm²
b) Least poss circumf = $39\pi$ cm

**A3** a) Min volume = 37595 mm³
b) Max SA = 7142 mm²

**A4** Total min = 79.2 gm total max = 80.8 gm

**A5** Max is approx 20.12° min is approx 18.83°

**A6** a) Max abs error is 0.05 cm and max relative error is ≈ .0139
b) % error ≈ 1.17

**A7** Maximum relative error = 0.030 (2 sfs)
max % error = 3.0 (2 sfs)

**A8** $V_{max} \approx 64.3485$ $V_{min} \approx 63.3727$
max rel error = 0.0076 (2 sf).
max % rel error = 0.76 (2 sfs)

### Exercise 12.2

**A1** $f(2) = -2 < 0$ $f(3) = 13 > 0$
root in (2, 3) $f(2.5) = 4.5 > 0$
$f$ changes sign in (2, 2.5)
root is nearer 2 than 3

**A2** $g(2) = -1 < 0$ $g(3) = 1 > 0$
∴ root $\alpha$ in (2, 3)
$g(4) = -3 < 0$
∴ root $\gamma$ in (3, 4)

**A3** Root is $x = 3.4$ (1 dp)

**A4** N = 1. Root is 1.5 to 1 dp

**A5** Root is 2.8 (1 dp)

**A6** a) $f(x) \equiv 2x - \tan x$, $-\frac{\pi}{2} < x < \frac{\pi}{2}$

($f$ is continuous)
$f(1) \approx 0.44$, $f(1.5) \approx -11.1$ } sign change, so there is a root in (1, 1.5)
b) $f(-x) \equiv 2(-x) - \tan(-x)$
$\equiv -2x - (-\tan x)$
$\equiv -(2x - \tan x)$
$\equiv -f(x)$ ∴ $f$ is an odd function
c) Root is −1.2 (1 dp)

**A7** i) Root is 0.3 to 1 dp
ii) Root is 2.1 to 1 dp

**A8** a) Sign changes in (0, 1) and (3, 4) ∴ a root in each of these intervals
Roots are $x = 0.6$ (1 dp) and $x = 4.0$ (1 dp)
b) $f(-x) \equiv (-x)^4 - 16(-x)^2 + 5$
$\equiv x^4 - 16x^2 + 5 \equiv f(x)$
∴ EVEN function
c) Neg roots are −0.6 and −4.0 each corr. to 1 dp—symmetry about $y$ axis
d) a = 8, b = 59 Roots are ±0.565, ±3.960, each corr. to 3 dps

### Exercise 12.3

**A1** Root seems to be 0.30 (2 dp)

**A2** It seems that $30^{\frac{1}{5}} = 1.97$ (2 dp), probably 1.974 (3 dp)

**A3** $x_2 \approx 1.8708$ $x_3 \approx 1.964$ $x_4 \approx 1.8998$
Solution seems to be 1.9 (1 dp), $x_{10} \approx 1.904$ which is probably OK to 3 dp

**A4** Root is probably 1.9 to 1 dp

**A5** sol ≈ 0.45

**A6** 2.21 (2 dp)

### Exercise 12.4

**A1** a) $\int_1^5 \ln x \, dx \approx 3.983$

b) $\int_1^5 \ln x \, dx = 5 \ln 5 - 4 \approx 4.047$

c) % error 1.6 approx. (underestimate)

**A2** a) Area ≈ 0.977 b) Area = 1
c) % error ≈ 2.3

**A3** $\int_2^6 \frac{1}{\ln x} dx \approx 3.253$ (overestimate)

Integral will be around 3.2

**A4** $I = \int_0^2 e^x\sqrt{x}\,dx \approx 7.22$ (overestimate)

**A5** Area $= \int_0^1 e^{-x^2}dx \approx .74298 = 0.743$ (3 dp)

**A6** a) $\int_0^\pi 2\sin^2 x\,dx = \pi$

b) $\int_0^\pi (1 - \cos 2x)\,dx = \pi$

**A7** $I \approx 3.1454$ % error $\approx 0.121$

**Exercise 12.5**

**A1** i) Grad $\approx -0.086$

ii) Grad as above as $y = 6 + 2^{-x}$ is a translation $\begin{pmatrix}0\\6\end{pmatrix}$ of $y = 2^{-x}$

**A2** a) $\frac{dV}{dt} \approx 15.23$

A good estimate is probably 15.2

b) i) $\approx -15.2$ as graph is reflection in $t$ axis

ii) $\approx -15.2$ as graph is part (a) given vertical 'lift'

**A3** $f'(1.4) \approx -1.06$

**A4** $\frac{dy}{dx} \approx 2.285$ using $x = .695$ and $.705$

**A5** $\frac{dN}{dt} \approx 730$ when $t = 2$ using $t = 2$, $t = 2.01$

**A6** $\frac{dM}{dt} \approx -1.457$ using $t = 5$ and $t = 5.1$

**A level questions**

**C1** a) $v_{max}$ is given by $\frac{1}{v} = \frac{1}{9.5} - \frac{1}{15.5}$

$v_{max} \approx 24.54$ (2 dp)

b) % error $\approx 19.3$

**C2** a) $p = 2r + r\theta$ $\theta = \frac{p}{r} - 2$

b) $1.43 < \theta < 1.86$, each to 2 dp

**C3** a) $\int_0^{1.2} e^{\frac{x}{3}}dx \approx 1.4767$ (overestimate)

Reasonable estimate would seem to be 1.47

b) $\int_0^{1.2} e^{\frac{x}{3}}dx = 3(e^{0.4} - 1) \approx 1.4755$

**C4** a) Area $\approx 5.625$ b) 5.410 (3 dp)

c) 0.21 (dp)

**C5** a) If 'curve' joining (0, 2) to (1, 1) were 'straight' area of trapezium formed would be $\frac{1}{2}(2 + 1) \times 1 = 1.5$

b) $\int_0^1 \frac{2}{1 + x^2}dx \approx 1.567$ This is 1.57 (2 dp)

c) % error $\approx .051$

**C6** Rate of deprec. $\frac{dV}{dt} \approx -2990$

When $t = 3$ $\frac{dV}{dt} \approx -1712$ After 6 months value is dropping at about £3000 pa but after 3 yrs, it's dropping at about £1700 pa. A nearly new car loses value more quickly.

**C7** a) $f(x)$ changes sign in (1, 2) and is continuous i.e. $f(x) = 0$ has a root in this interval

b) $f'(x) \equiv 2x - 3x^2$. Root $\approx 1.73$ (First approx 1.5) So 1.7 should be a better approximation

c) Strong evidence that the root is 1.70 to 2 dp

**C8** b) Strong evidence that the root is 1.9 to 1 dp (1.895 is correct to 3 dp!)

**C9** c) $\alpha = 1.0$ (1 dp)

d) $\frac{dy}{dx} = 0$ when $2x\cos 2x + \sin 2x = 0$

i.e. when $2x + \tan 2x = 0$

$a = \alpha = 1.0$ (1 dp) and

$b \approx 1.0 \sin 2.0 \approx 0.909 = 0.9$ to 1 sf

**C10** a) Sector AOB $= \frac{1}{2}r^2\theta$ $\Delta$ AOB $= \frac{1}{2}r^2 \sin\theta$

b) $f(\theta) = 3\sin\theta - 2\theta$ is a continuous function.

$\left.\begin{array}{l} f(1.4) \approx 0.16 \\ f(1.5) \approx -0.008 \end{array}\right\}$ sign change.

So there is a root to $f(\theta) = 0$ in (1.4, 1.5).

c) $\left.\begin{array}{l} f(1.4) \approx 0.16 \\ f(1.5) \approx -0.008 \end{array}\right\}$ sign change

$\therefore f(\theta) = 0$ has a root in (1.4, 1.5)

d) Solution of $f(\theta) = 0$ is $\theta = 1.496$ to 3 dp

# INDEX